CREATIVE STRATEGIES FOR TEACHING AMERICAN HISTORY

Blackline Masters with Answer Key

For permission to reprint copyrighted material, grateful acknowledgment is made to the following source:

California State Department of Education: Goal and Curriculum Strand titles from chart, "History–Social Science K–12 Goals and Curriculum Strands," developed by the History–Social Science Curriculum Framework and Criteria Committee. Copyright © 1988 by the California State Department of Education.

Printed in the United States of America
ISBN 0-03-047637-2

0 1 2 3 4 5 6   164   7 6 5 4 3 2 1

CONTENTS

Introduction

Creative Strategies for Teaching American History provides the teacher with 80 teaching strategies, ranging in time from the period of exploration and colonization of America to the present. The teaching strategies include reproducible resource materials and worksheets for students, as well as detailed instructions to the teacher. Strategies integrate primary and secondary source readings, illustrations and photographs, and maps.

The teaching strategies cover a wide range of topics and activities. Students may plan a wagon-train journey, find information on African American leaders who lived during the Reconstruction period, and complete a community survey. Students will read primary sources by authors such as Harriet Beecher Stowe, Helen Hunt Jackson, Mark Twain, Alexis de Tocqueville, Randolph B. Marcy, General William F. Butler, Charles Dickens, Martin Luther King, Jr., and many others. Primary source documents include the Mennonite Resolutions, the Stamp Act Resolutions, and the Black Codes of Louisiana and Mississippi. Secondary sources provide insight into topics such as life in Spanish California, the political campaign of 1840, and Wilson's neutrality policy during World War I.

Creative Strategies for Teaching American History helps students meet **three specific curriculum goals.** Supporting the curriculum goals are curriculum strands, or basic learnings. On pages ix-xi you will find a chart that explains the goals and strands that are addressed by each strategy.

The **first curriculum goal** helps students develop knowledge and cultural understanding. In meeting this goal students will be able to incorporate what they have learned in history with the other humanities, geography, and the social sciences. Literacy strands that support this goal are historical literacy, ethical literacy, cultural literacy, geographic literacy, economic literacy, and sociopolitical literacy. A key part of this goal is the development of historical and ethical empathy for the past. Another important part of the goal is for students to understand the diverse cultures that have helped shape American society and to respect the many various groups in America today.

The **second curriculum goal** helps students develop democratic understanding and civic values. In meeting this goal students will be able to understand the national identity of our country as well as their individual identities as Americans. The curriculum strands that support this goal include national identity, constitutional heritage, and civic values, rights, and responsibilities.

The **third curriculum goal** helps students develop participation skills, critical thinking skills, and basic study skills. In meeting this goal students will be able to complete learning activities that help them master basic study skills and critical thinking skills. Students will also take part in many group activities that help them master skills for successful social participation.

Most of the teaching strategies in *Creative Strategies for Teaching American History* involve cooperative learning. In cooperative learning, small groups of students of different ability levels work together to solve problems and complete assigned tasks. The major goal of cooperative learning is to create an environment in which students work toward a common goal. Simply putting students in groups and asking them to complete the cooperative assignments, however, will not guarantee successful learning. The following aspects of cooperative learning should be included in order for cooperative learning to succeed in your classroom.

Positive Interdependence: Students must feel that they need each other to complete each assignment. Establish positive interdependence by requiring the group to turn in one assignment that they have worked on together. Also, tell students that answers must reflect ideas from every group member.

Individual Accountability: Stress to students that they will be held personally responsible for learning and for helping their group. Circulate around the classroom while the groups are working and quiz individuals to see if they can explain the answers their group has completed so far. If they cannot, ask group members to review until each student can answer correctly. Reward groups when everyone shows that they can explain answers. Also, give each group member a role to play such as reader, recorder, or quizzer.

Face-to-Face Interaction: Maximize learning by making sure students orally exchange ideas, information, and explanations.

Cooperative Skill Teaching: Help students to take responsibility for interacting with their group by insisting on standards of group behavior. Discuss with students the behaviors you expect to see, display those behaviors prominently, remind students to use them while in groups, and use a check list to document their use. Behaviors might include: *Everyone contribute, Listen carefully, Ask others to explain, Praise good ideas*, and *Disagree with ideas, not people.*

Processing Group Effectiveness: Groups will improve only if students take the time to evaluate their group's progress and formulate a plan for improvement. At the end of each cooperative learning assignment, have groups list what they are doing well and how they can improve. Also, have students tell other group members something positive they do that helps the group. Such statements will help all students feel valuable to the group and will help build self-esteem.

By incorporating the following teaching strategies into your teaching of American history, you will enable students to attain the three curriculum goals and to learn how to successfully interact in a cooperative group situation. The teaching strategies provide a creative, informative, and motivational method of instilling in your students historical knowledge and empathy and an understanding of individual and social ethics.

Editorial Rationale for Source Material

The following sources were excerpted to focus on a particular topic. Sources not listed below had no editorial changes.

Page 15
Source: *The Book of the General Lawes and Liberties of 1648*
Editing Rationale: Excerpted to focus on the idea that many colonial laws were taken directly from the Bible.

Page 15
Source: *Frame of Government for Pennsylvania* by William Penn
Editing Rationale: Excerpted to focus on Penn's definition of good government.

Page 15
Source: Reply by John Tyler, Speaker of the House of Burgesses, to Thomas Jefferson, upon Jefferson's refusal to take office
Editing Rationale: Excerpted to focus on the importance of participation in government.

Page 16
Source: Letter by Robert Carter to a London agent supervising the education of Carter's sons
Editing Rationale: Excerpted to focus on the moderate religious views of a Virginia colonist.

Page 16
Source: *Cambridge Platform*, a Puritan statement on church discipline and organization
Editing Rationale: Excerpted to focus on the strict religious views of Puritans in Massachusetts.

Page 16
Source: Journal entry of George Fox, founder of the Quaker movement, dated 1664
Editing Rationale: Excerpted to focus on the Quaker's view of pacifism.

Page 19
Source: Resolutions of the Mennonite Community of Germantown, Pennsylvania, February 18, 1688
Editing Rationale: Excerpted to exclude irrelevant material.

Page 27
Source: Resolutions from the Stamp Act Congress, October 19, 1765
Editing Rationale: Title not given in order for students to conjecture about what the resolutions might be.

Page 31
Source: "What is an American?" by Michel-Guillaume Jean de Crèvecoeur, from *Letters from an American Farmer*, first published in London in 1782
Editing Rationale: Excerpted to focus on Crèvecoeur's views concerning the circumstances that changed British subjects into Americans.

Page 47
Source: *The Female Review* by Herman Mann, revised with Deborah Sampson Gannett, from *Weathering the Storm: Women of the American Revolution* by Elizabeth Evans (Paragon House, 1975)
Editing Rationale: Excerpted to focus on Deborah Sampson Gannett's experiences in the Revolutionary War.

Page 48
Source: An address delivered by Deborah Sampson Gannett, from *Weathering the Storm: Women of the American Revolution*, by Elizabeth Evans (Paragon House, 1975)
Editing Rationale: Excerpted to focus on Gannett's reasons for fighting in the Revolutionary War.

Page 94
Source: Reactions to Horatio Greenough's statue of George Washington, compiled from *Letters of Horatio Greenough*, edited by Frances B. Greenough, published in Boston in 1887; and *Horatio Greenough: The First American Sculptor*, by Nathalia Wright (University of Pennsylvania Press, 1963)
Editing Rationale: Excerpted to focus on various reactions to the statue.

Page 97
Source: Writings of Madison and Jefferson on the subject of freedom of religion
Editing Rationale: Excerpted to focus on Madison and Jefferson's view on freedom of religion.

Page 103
Source: "On the Education of Women" by John Winthrop, from *The History of New England from 1630 to 1649*, edited by James Savage (Little, Brown and Company, 1853)

Editing Rationale: Excerpted to focus on Winthrop's views concerning the education of women in the colonies.

Page 119
Source: *The Prairie Traveler* by Randolph B. Marcy, published by the authority of the War Department in 1859
Editing Rationale: Excerpted to focus on the best routes and the preparations and provisions needed for a wagon-train journey.

Page 123
Source: *The World Rushed In* by J.S. Holliday (Simon & Schuster, 1981)
Editing Rationale: Excerpted to focus on preparations and provisions needed for a wagon-train journey.

Page 124
Source: "How to Make the Trek", from *Route and Distances to Oregon and California* by J.M. Shively (W. Greer, 1846)
Editing Rationale: Excerpted to focus on preparations and provisions needed for a wagon-train journey.

Page 128
Source: *The Heroic Triad* by Paul Horgan (World Publishing, 1970)
Editing Rationale: Excerpted to focus on Spanish American culture.

Page 130
Source: *Two Years Before the Mast* by Richard Henry Dana, published in 1840
Editing Rationale: Excerpted to focus on Dana's experiences in California and also to point out some of his prejudices.

Page 131
Source: *California Pastoral* by Hubert Howe Bancroft (The History Company, 1888)
Editing Rationale: Excerpted to focus on Spanish culture in California.

Page 135
Source: "Why the Americans Are Often So Restless in the Midst of Their Prosperity," from *Democracy in American* by Alexis de Tocqueville, edited by J.P. Mayer (Doubleday, 1969)
Editing Rationale: Excerpted to focus on Tocqueville's ideas as an explanation of the westward movment in the first half of the nineteenth century.

Page 138
Source: *Westward the Women* by Nancy Wilson Ross (Ballantine, 1944)
Editing Rationale: Excerpted to focus on pioneer women's work.

Page 139
Source: *Conversations with Pioneer Women* by Fred Lockley
Editing Rationale: Excerpted to focus on pioneer women's work and on the positive and negative effects of constant hard work on personal development. Brackets added to identify each woman. For example, [from interview with Marill R. Washburn Bailey].

Page 149
Source: *The Vineyard of Liberty* by James MacGregor Burns (Knopf, 1982)
Editing Rationale: Excerpted to focus on the election of 1840 and to exclude derogatory language.

Page 156
Source: *American Notes and Pictures from Italy* by Charles Dickens, published in 1850
Editing Rationale: Excerpted to focus on Dicken's view of the American people.

Page 158
Source: Comment on the purpose of education by Horace Bushnell, from *Views of Christian Nurture, and of Subjects Adjacent Thereto* (Edwin Hunt, 1848)
Editing Rationale: Excerpted to focus on Bushnell's ideas of the purpose of a Christian education for children.

Page 158
Source: Comment on the purpose of education by Thomas Jefferson, from the Report of the Commissioners for the University of Virginia, 1818
Editing Rationale: Excerpted to focus on Jefferson's views concerning education as a means of preparing people for good citizenship.

Page 158
Source: Comment on the purpose of education by Francis Wayland, from *The Education Demanded by the People of the United States* (Phillips, Sampson, and Company, 1855)
Editing Rationale: Excerpted to focus on Wayland's views that education should be available to all classes of people.

Page 173
Source: *The Mind of the South* by W.J. Cash (Vintage Books, 1960)
Editing Rationale: Excerpted to focus on Irishman's portrait and to exclude profanity and derogatory references.

Page 197
Source: *Uncle Tom's Cabin* by Harriet Beecher Stowe (Houghton Mifflin, 1851)
Editing Rationale: Excerpted to focus on theme of slave-catching and to exclude derogatory references.

Page 207
Source: Speech by Abraham Lincoln, given at Peoria, Illinois, in 1854
Editing Rationale: Excerpted to focus on Lincoln's views concerning his opposition to the Kansas–Nebraska Act.

Page 207
Source: Letter from Abraham Lincoln to Joshua Speed, dated August 24, 1855
Editing Rationale: Excerpted to focus on Lincoln's views concerning his opposition to the Know-Nothings. Brackets included to acknowledge misspelling of *hypocrisy* (hypocracy [*sic*].)

Page 208
Source: Speech by Abraham Lincoln, given at Springfield, Illinois, in 1857
Editing Rationale: Excerpted to focus on Lincoln's views concerning the Dred Scott decision.

Page 223
Source: "We Are Willing to Fight" by Major General Benjamin F. Butler, in *A Civil War Treasury of Tales, Legends and Folklore*, edited by B.A. Botkin (Random House, 1960)
Editing Rationale: Excerpted to focus on General Butler's recruitment of black regiments and on the insights he gained from speaking with an African American officer.

Page 231
Source: Three Tales of Heroism: Lieutenant Lemuel L. Crocker, in *A Civil War Treasury of Tales, Legends and Folklore*, edited by B.A. Botkin (Random House, 1960)
Editing Rationale: Excerpted to focus on Crocker's act of bravery.

Page 232
Source: Three Tales of Heroism: Robert Smalls, in *A Civil War Treasury of Tales, Legends and Folklore,* edited by B.A. Botkin (Random House, 1960)
Editing Rationale: Excerpted to focus on Robert Smalls's act of bravery.

Page 233
Source: Three Tales of Heroism: Emma Samson, in *A Civil War Treasury of Tales, Legends and Folklore,* edited by B.A. Botkin (Random House, 1960)
Editing Rationale: Excerpted to focus on Emma Samson's act of bravery.

Page 253
Source: "Letter from a Freedman to His Old Master" by Jourdan Anderson, in *The Freedman's Book,* edited by Lydia Maria Child, published in 1865
Editing Rationale: Excerpted to focus on the situation of freedmen.

Page 257
Source: "Black Code of Mississippi," from *Laws of Mississippi*, 1865
Editing Rationale: Excerpted to focus on rights and freedoms denied freed blacks under the Black Codes.

Page 257
Source: "Black Code of Louisiana," from *Acts of the General Assembly of Louisiana Regulating Labor, Extra Session,* 1865
Editing Rationale: Excerpted to focus on rights and freedoms denied freed blacks under the Black Codes.

Page 283
Source: Chief Joseph's surrender speech and the argument for keeping his people in the Wallowa Valley, published in *The North American Review,* in April 1879
Editing Rationale: Excerpted to focus on Chief Joseph's reasons for surrendering and for wanting to keep his people in the Wallowa Valley.

Page 284
Source: Newspaper article concerning Chief Joseph's death, published in the Wilbur newspaper, September 26, 1904
Editing Rationale: Excerpted to focus on the cause of Chief Joseph's death.

Page 293
Source: *Ramona* by Helen Hunt Jackson, (Roberts Brothers, 1884)

Editing Rationale: Excerpted to focus on the plight of Spanish Californians who were losing their lands.

Page 293
Source: *Barrio Boy* by Ernesto Galarza (University of Notre Dame Press, 1971)
Editing Rationale: Excerpted to focus on problems faced by Mexicans during the Mexican Revolution and on the experiences of Mexican immigrants in California.

Page 309
Source: "The United States of Lyncherdom," from *In Europe and Elsewhere* by Mark Twain
Editing Rationale: Excerpted to focus on Twain's views concerning lynching and lynch mobs.

Page 309
Source: "Why the Lynching Bee Failed," from Chapter 22 in *Huckleberry Finn* by Mark Twain
Editing Rationale: Excerpted to focus on Twain's views concerning lynching and lynch mobs.

Pages 322 and 323
Source: Witness statements concerning the Triangle Shirtwaist Factory Fire, from *The Triangle Fire* by Leon Stein (J.B. Lippincott Company, 1962)
Editing Rationale: Excerpted to focus on specific evidence upon which students will conduct their trial. Bracketed material provides necessary location details. For example, "I tried to open the [Washington Place stairway] door but I couldn't."

Page 331
Source: Speech to Congress by Robert La Follette, from the *Congressional Record,* 65th Cong. 1st sess., April 4, 1917
Editing Rationale: Excerpted to focus on La Follette's opinion of the United States neutrality policy.

Page 332
Source: *Was War Necessary* by Melvin Small (Sage Publications, 1980)
Editing Rationale: Excerpted to focus on Small's views concerning the neutral conduct of the United States between 1914 and 1917.

Page 341
Source: *Stride Toward Freedom* by Martin Luther King, Jr. (Thomas Y. Crowell, 1967)
Editing Rationale: Excerpted to focus on the Montgomery, Alabama, bus boycott and on the concept of "massive noncooperation."

Acknowledgments

For permission to reprint copyrighted material, grateful acknowledgment is made to the following sources:

Claro Music Corporation: "Liberation, Now!," words by Betty Friedan and Jacquelyn Reinach, music by Jacquelyn Reinach and Jo Rene. Copyright © 1970 by Claro Music Corporation. International Copyright Secured. All Rights Reserved.

Fall River Music, Inc.: "Where Have All the Flowers Gone?" by Pete Seeger, Verses 4 & 5 by Joe Hickson. Copyright © 1961 by Fall River Music, Inc.

Gypsy Boy Music, Inc.: "Now That the Buffalo's Gone" by Buffy Sainte-Marie. Copyright © 1965 by Gypsy Boy Music, Inc.

Harper & Row, Publishers, Inc.: From *Stride Toward Freedom* by Martin Luther King, Jr. Copyright © 1958 by Martin Luther King, Jr. From "Why the Americans are Often So Restless in the Midst of Their Prosperity" from *Democracy in America* by Alexis de Tocqueville, translated by George Lawrence, edited by J.P. Mayer. Copyright © 1969 by J.P. Mayer. Copyright © 1966 in the English translation by Harper and Row, Publishers, Inc. From "The United States of Lyncherdom" from *Europe and Elsewhere* by Mark Twain.

Alfred A. Knopf, Inc: From "Whigs: The Business of Politics" from *The Vineyard of Liberty* by James MacGregor Burns. Copyright © 1981 by James MacGregor Burns. From *The Mind of the South* by W.J. Cash. Copyright © 1941 by Alfred A. Knopf, Inc.

J.B. Lippincott Company: From *The Triangle Fire* by Leon Stein. Copyright © 1962 by Leon Stein.

Ludlow Music Inc.: "The Sioux Indians," collected, adapted, and arranged by John A. Lomax and Alan Lomax. TRO, Copyright 1938 and renewed © 1966 by Ludlow Music, Inc., New York, NY. "We Shall Overcome," new words and music adaption by Zilphia Horton, Frank Hamilton, Guy Carawan, and Pete Seeger. Copyright © 1960 and 1963 by Ludlow Music, Inc. All Rights Reserved.

Paragon House Publishers: From *Weathering the Storm: Women of the American Revolution* by Elizabeth Evans, Copyright © 1975 by Elizabeth Evans.

Praeger Publishers: From "Richard Henry Dana's Califronia" from *A Documentary History of the Mexican American* edited by Wayne Moquin with Charles Van Doren. Copyright © 1971 by Praeger Publishers, Inc.

Prentice-Hall, Inc.: "The Old Settler's Song" and "Sweet Betsy from Pike" from "Songs of the American Pioneers" from *A Folk Song History of America: America Through Its Songs* by Samuel L. Forcucci. Copyright © 1984 by Prentice-Hall, Inc.

Rainy Day Press: From *Conversations with Pioneer Women* by Fred Lockley, compiled and edited by Mike Helm. Copyright © 1981 by Rainy Day Press.

Random House, Inc.: From "We are Willing to Fight" by Major General Benjamin F. Butler, from "Crocker's Errand of Mercy" from *History of the Corn Exchange Regiment, 118th Pennsylvania Volunteers*, from "The Captain of the Planter" from *House Report No 3305, Forty-Ninth Congress, Second Session*, and from "Emma Sansom's Ride with Forrest" by Emma Sansom; from *A Civil War Treasury of Tales, Legends and Folklore*, edited by B. A. Botkin. Copyright © 1960 by B. A. Botkin. From *Westward the Women* by Nancy Wilson Ross. Copyright 1944 by Nancy Wilson Ross.

Sage Publishing, Inc.: From "A Neutral's Lot is Not a Happy One" from *Was War Necessary? National Security and U.S. Entry into War* by Melvin Small. Copyright © 1980 Sage Publications, Inc.

Simon & Schuster, Inc.: From "Fitting for a Start" from *The World Rushed In: The California Gold Rush Experience* by J.S. Holliday. Copyright © 1981 by J. S. Holliday. "Beans, Bacon & Gravy" from *Carry It On! A History in Song and Picture of the Working Men and Women of America* by Pete Seeger and Bob Reiser. Copyright © 1985 by Pete Seeger and Bob Reiser.

Social Science Education Consortium, Inc.: "The District School in the Early 1800s" from *A Humanities Approach to Early National U. S. History: Activities and Resources for the Junior High School Teacher*, edited by James R. Giese and Lynn Parisi. Copyright © 1986 by Social Science Education Consortium, Inc.

University of Notre Dame: From *Barrio Boy* by Ernesto Galarza. Copyright © 1971 by University of Notre Dame Press, Notre Dame, IN.

White House Historical Association: "Abigail Smith Adams, 1744–1818" from *The First Ladies* by Margaret Brown Klapthor. Copyright © 1975, 1979, 1981, 1983, 1985 by White House Historical Association, Washington, D.C.

World Publishing Company: From "Conquering Spaniards & Their Mexican Sons" from *The Heroic Triad* by Paul Horgan. Copyright © 1954, 1955, 1970 by Paul Horgan.

Photo Credits

Curriculum Goals and Strands

Strategy	KCU						DUCV			SASP		
	HL	EL	CL	GL	ECL	SPL	NI	CH	CVRR	PS	CTS	BSS
Exploration and Discovery—A Game of Latitude and Longitude	✓	✓		✓			✓	✓			✓	✓
Indians of North America	✓	✓	✓	✓		✓	✓			✓	✓	✓
God and Government	✓	✓	✓			✓	✓	✓	✓	✓	✓	✓
The Problem of Slavery	✓	✓		✓	✓		✓		✓	✓	✓	✓
A Tavern at the Crossroads—American Currents, 1740	✓	✓	✓		✓	✓	✓			✓	✓	✓
"From Many, One"—The Colonies Move Toward Union	✓	✓			✓	✓	✓	✓	✓	✓	✓	✓
"The American, This New Man"	✓		✓	✓	✓	✓	✓		✓		✓	✓
"No Taxation Without Representation"	✓				✓	✓	✓	✓	✓	✓	✓	✓
The Declaration Of Independence	✓	✓				✓	✓	✓		✓	✓	✓
Who's Who in the Revolutionary War	✓						✓			✓		✓
An Unlikely Soldier	✓	✓					✓			✓	✓	✓
Diplomacy and the Treaty of Paris (1783)	✓					✓	✓			✓	✓	✓
The Need for a Constitution	✓	✓		✓	✓	✓	✓	✓	✓	✓	✓	✓
The Constitutional Convention—The Key Was Compromise	✓	✓		✓	✓	✓	✓	✓	✓	✓	✓	✓
What Is in the Articles?	✓					✓	✓	✓		✓	✓	✓
The Debate over Ratification	✓						✓	✓	✓	✓	✓	✓
The History Behind the Bill of Rights	✓	✓					✓	✓	✓	✓	✓	✓
Amending the Constitution	✓	✓			✓		✓	✓	✓	✓	✓	✓
The Constitution and Judicial Review	✓	✓					✓	✓			✓	✓

Key to Abbreviations

KCU   **Knowledge and Cultural Understanding**
HL   Historical Literacy
EL   Ethical Literacy
CL   Cultural Literacy
GL   Geographic Literacy
ECL   Economic Literacy
SPL   Sociopolitical Literacy

DUCV   **Democratic Understanding and Civic Values**
NI   National Identity
CH   Constitutional Heritage
CVRR   Civic Values, Rights, and Responsibilities

SASP   **Skills Attainment and Social Participation**
PS   Participation Skills
CTS   Critical Thinking Skills
BSS   Basic Study Skills

Curriculum Goals and Strands

Strategy	KCU						DUCV			SASP		
	HL	EL	CL	GL	ECL	SPL	NI	CH	CVRR	PS	CTS	BSS
The Controversial Statue of George Washington	✓		✓				✓				✓	✓
The Bill of Rights—Freedom of Religion	✓	✓				✓	✓	✓		✓	✓	✓
The Connection Between Education and Democracy	✓		✓			✓	✓		✓		✓	✓
The Louisiana Purchase—Jefferson's Difficult Decision	✓	✓		✓			✓	✓		✓	✓	✓
"The Legend of Sleepy Hollow" by Washington Irving	✓		✓	✓			✓			✓	✓	✓
Planning a Wagon-Train Journey	✓	✓		✓					✓	✓	✓	
Life in Spanish California	✓	✓	✓	✓			✓			✓	✓	✓
Alexis de Tocqueville on the Restless Americans	✓	✓	✓			✓	✓			✓	✓	✓
The Work of Pioneer Women	✓	✓	✓	✓			✓		✓		✓	✓
Folk Songs of the Forty-Niners	✓		✓				✓			✓	✓	✓
A New Kind of Political Campaign	✓	✓	✓			✓	✓			✓	✓	✓
Effects of the Telegraph	✓		✓	✓	✓		✓			✓	✓	
Charles Dickens Describes the American People	✓	✓	✓		✓	✓	✓			✓	✓	✓
The Purpose of Education	✓	✓	✓				✓			✓	✓	✓
"Bloomerism"—Feminism Meets Fashion	✓	✓	✓				✓				✓	✓
Ideal Communities	✓	✓	✓		✓	✓	✓			✓	✓	✓
An Imaginary Panel Discussion	✓	✓	✓	✓		✓	✓		✓	✓	✓	✓
Imaginative Recreation of Lives of Southern Farmers	✓		✓	✓		✓	✓				✓	✓
The Mississippi River and the South	✓			✓	✓		✓			✓	✓	✓
The Constitutional Rights of Free African Americans	✓	✓				✓	✓	✓	✓	✓	✓	✓
The Cotton and Slave Economy of the South	✓	✓			✓		✓				✓	✓
The Impact of Slavery on the Southern Economy	✓	✓			✓	✓	✓			✓	✓	✓
Spirituals as an Art Form Expressing the Inner Life of a People	✓		✓				✓				✓	✓
Workers on the Underground Railroad	✓	✓	✓	✓			✓		✓	✓	✓	✓
Images of the South on the Eve of the Civil War	✓	✓	✓		✓	✓	✓			✓		✓
The Fugitive Slave Act	✓	✓				✓	✓	✓	✓	✓		✓
The Battle for Kansas	✓	✓		✓		✓	✓	✓	✓	✓	✓	✓
Abe Lincoln, in His Own Words	✓	✓	✓		✓	✓	✓			✓	✓	✓
John Brown on Trial	✓	✓		✓		✓	✓		✓	✓	✓	✓
A Chain of Events—The Path to Civil War	✓					✓	✓	✓	✓	✓		✓
Why Did the South Secede?	✓	✓		✓			✓				✓	✓
African American Soldiers	✓			✓			✓	✓		✓	✓	✓
How Legend Can Disprove History	✓		✓	✓			✓			✓	✓	✓
Faces of Heroism	✓	✓	✓	✓			✓			✓	✓	✓

Curriculum Goals and Strands

Strategy	KCU						DUCV			SASP		
	HL	EL	CL	GL	ECL	SPL	NI	CH	CVRR	PS	CTS	BSS
Behind the Scenes—Faces Among the Blue and Gray	✓	✓	✓	✓		✓	✓		✓		✓	✓
Images of War in Paintings, Drawings, and Photographs	✓	✓	✓		✓		✓			✓	✓	✓
"This Reminds Me of a Little Joke"—Views of Lincoln	✓		✓				✓		✓		✓	✓
A New Birth of Freedom	✓	✓					✓	✓		✓	✓	✓
The (Cotton) Empire Strikes Back	✓	✓			✓	✓	✓	✓	✓	✓	✓	✓
Leaders of the Reconstructed South	✓					✓	✓	✓	✓	✓	✓	✓
Andrew Johnson Versus the Radicals	✓	✓					✓	✓	✓	✓	✓	✓
Causes of Immigration, 1820–1914	✓	✓		✓	✓		✓			✓	✓	✓
Transcontinental Railroad Newspaper	✓	✓	✓	✓	✓		✓			✓	✓	✓
Chief Joseph—Writing a Biopoem	✓	✓	✓				✓			✓	✓	
John D. Rockefeller—Business Practices in the Gilded Age	✓	✓			✓	✓	✓			✓	✓	
Our Multicultural Background—Mexican Americans	✓		✓				✓			✓	✓	✓
The Spanish–American War	✓	✓	✓	✓		✓	✓			✓	✓	✓
Literature as a Reflection of Societal Concerns	✓	✓	✓			✓	✓	✓	✓	✓		
United States Policy in the Caribbean	✓			✓			✓			✓	✓	✓
Annexation of the Philippines—Conflicting Points of View	✓	✓					✓		✓	✓	✓	
Mother Jones	✓	✓				✓	✓			✓	✓	
The Westward Movement and the Closing of the Frontier	✓			✓			✓			✓	✓	✓
The Triangle Shirtwaist Factory Fire	✓	✓				✓	✓		✓	✓	✓	
Education During the Progressive Era	✓	✓	✓				✓		✓	✓	✓	✓
Neutrality and World War I	✓	✓		✓			✓			✓	✓	✓
The WPA's Federal Art Project	✓	✓	✓				✓		✓	✓		
The USO (United Service Organizations, Inc.)	✓		✓				✓			✓		✓
The Montgomery, Alabama, Bus Boycott	✓	✓	✓				✓		✓	✓	✓	✓
Protest Songs of the Twentieth Century	✓	✓	✓		✓		✓			✓	✓	✓
Watergate and Executive Privilege	✓	✓				✓	✓	✓	✓	✓	✓	✓
Community Awareness		✓		✓	✓	✓	✓		✓	✓	✓	✓

Creative Strategies for Teaching American History

Exploration and Colonization

TOPIC: GEOGRAPHY—Exploration and Discovery—A Game of Latitude and Longitude
TIME: One class period
TIME PERIOD: After study of European discovery and exploration of North America

BACKGROUND

In this teaching strategy students will review the sequence and circumstances of the European discovery of America, associating with precise geographical detail the discoveries of the various explorers. The teaching strategy is presented in the form of a game in which students must use map and globe skills to identify locations by their latitude and longitude. Students are given facts about a particular discovery and are asked to identify the modern name for a place visited on the voyage, or they are given the place name and are asked to find the location. Through this teaching strategy students will associate historical events with their geographical counterparts. Students will be able to explain how geographic facts were causal factors in the course of discovery and settlement of America.

MATERIALS

1. Copies of the game worksheet for each student
2. Detailed globes and/or maps of the world and North America, indicating latitude and longitude in detail. Each group should have access to one globe or map.

SUGGESTED PROCEDURE

1. Review with the class the complexity of social, political, and economic circumstances and motivations that prompted the European discovery and exploration of America.
2. Discuss the methods and technology available to sixteenth-century navigators in finding their way across the ocean.
   a. Have students review the circumstances of Christopher Columbus's first voyage. Make sure students realize that the objection raised to Columbus's plan was not that the earth was flat but that the distance westward from Europe to Asia was far greater than Columbus imagined. Ask students: What would have happened to Columbus's crew on their voyage to Asia if there had not been a "New World" in between? (They probably would have perished.)
   b. Have students discuss and compare the early European explorers of America with the modern and future exploration of space.
   c. Ask students: What method did mariners use to record the location of the places they discovered so that others could find their way to the same places? (latitude and an estimate of longitude) On a wall map, review the concepts of latitude and longitude. Have a student find the latitude and longitude of your town or city. Ask students: How were sailors in the sixteenth century able to determine the latitude and longitude of their position? (Latitude was determined by the position of the stars. Sailors had no way to accurately determine longitude until the invention of the chronometer in the eighteenth century.)
3. Tell students that they are going to play a game in which they will answer questions about the European discovery and exploration of North America by using latitude and longitude. Tell them that they will be allowed to use maps and globes to find answers to the questions, but they will not be allowed to refer to their textbooks. Ask students the following question as an example of how the game works: "Columbus's first landfall in the New World was an island located at 24 degrees north latitude and between 74 and 75 degrees west longitude. By what name is this island known today?" (San Salvador) Have students locate the island on the wall map using the coordinates.
4. Organize students into groups of four and distribute copies of the game worksheet to each student. Provide each group with a detailed globe or world map. Allow the groups the rest of the class period to play the game. Decide on some system of awards for speed and/or accuracy in completing the game worksheet.

Answers to Game Worksheet (Pages 5–6)

1. Ceram
2. Puerto Rico
3. Venezuela
4. Approximately 46° N, 60° W
5. Approximately 6° S, 35° W
6. Mexico
7. Approximately 7° 30′ N, 79° 30′ W
8. Veracruz
9. Mactan Island
10. Quebec
11. The Grand Canyon
12. Topeka, Kansas
13. San Diego, California
14. Approximately 30° N, 81° W
15. San Francisco, California
16. Approximately 36° N, 75° 40′ W
17. Santa Fe, New Mexico
18. The Hudson and the Mohawk; Albany, New York
19. Niagara Falls
20. Chicago, Illinois

EXPLORATION AND DISCOVERY
A Game of Latitude and Longitude

Directions: Use a detailed world map or globe to find the answers to the following questions. Write the answer on the space provided.

_____ 1. One of the "Spice Islands" for which Columbus and other explorers were searching is located at 2° 45′ S, 130° E. (Two degrees, 45 minutes south latitude, 130 degrees east longitude.) By what name do we know this island?

_____ 2. On November 19, 1492, Columbus was sailing past an island near 18° N, 66° 45′ W. The people he found there called the island Borinquén. By what name do we know it?

_____ 3. Columbus did not discover the mainland of the Americas until his third voyage, when in 1498 he anchored near 8° 65′ N, 61° 52′ W. In the territory of what modern country was his anchorage located?

_____ 4. John Cabot, commander of the first English expedition to the New World, probably made his first landfall at Cape Breton Island, off the coast of Canada. What would he have recorded in his logbook as the latitude and longitude of his discovery?

_____ 5. Brazilians today speak Portuguese because the Portuguese explorer Pedro Cabral first landed on the northeastern "bulge" of that country, near the present-day city of Natal, in 1500. What is the latitude and longitude of his discovery?

_____ 6. The first map that used the name *America* was published in 1507. It showed Zipangu (Japan) at about 20° N, 100° W. What country actually *is* located there?

_____ 7. Vasco Nuñez de Balboa was the first European to sight the Pacific Ocean, in 1513. He saw it from the town in Panama that now bears his name. What was the latitude and longitude of the spot?

_____ 8. Hernán Cortés' first landfall in Mexico in 1519 was at 19° 15′ N, 96° W. What modern city is on that spot?

_____ 9. Ferdinand Magellan was killed in 1521 near an island located at about 10° 20′ N, 124° E. What is the name of the island?

_____10. The French explorer Jacques Cartier spent the winter of 1535–1536 at a Huron Indian village near 47° N, 71° W. We know this site today by its Huron name, which means "Narrowing of the River." What is its name?

_____11. On Coronado's search for the fabled golden cities of Cibola, some of his soldiers discovered a genuine marvel located near 36° N, 112° W. What was it?

_____ **12.** Coronado's expedition may have penetrated as far as the site of this present state capital at 39° N, 95° 45′ W.

_____ **13.** In 1542 the Spanish explorer Juan Cabrillo entered a bay at about 33° N, 117° W, which he named San Miguel. By what name do we know that city today?

_____ **14.** The earliest permanent European settlement in what became the United States was the Spanish town of St. Augustine, Florida, founded in 1565. How would a navigator describe its location?

_____ **15.** Sir Francis Drake put into a bay at about 38° N, 122° 30′ W, on his round-the-world voyage in 1578. What important city is just southeast of "Drake's Bay"?

_____ **16.** English colonists led by Sir Walter Raleigh attempted to establish a settlement on Roanoke Island in 1585. Where would English navigators have pointed their ships to find this settlement?

_____ **17.** The oldest state capital in the United States was founded in 1610 at 35° N, 106° W. What is the name of this city?

_____ **18.** Dutch settlers established the trading center of Fort Orange in 1624, at 42° 45′ N, 73° 45′ W. What two rivers meet at this location? By what name do we know this city today?

_____ **19.** French priests and fur traders traveling inland by canoe through North America in the seventeenth century had to go around this natural barrier at 43° N, 79° W.

_____ **20.** Once past this barrier, explorers could travel by water all the way to the Mississippi River, except for one place where they were forced to carry their canoes overland at about 41° 45′ N, 87° 30 W. What city arose on that site?

TOPIC: Indians of North America

TIME: Two class periods, with research and writing time. Allow one to two weeks between class periods for this teaching strategy.

TIME PERIOD: At the beginning of the instructional sequence on America's colonial heritage. The instructional sequence should be timed so that the second part of the lesson is introduced after students have learned about the relations between the Indians and the English colonists in America.

BACKGROUND

America's history begins with the Indians. To understand fully all subsequent history, it is necessary for students to be familiar with Native American culture, its conditioning by the geography and ecology of North America, and the ways in which the earliest European invaders interacted with this culture. In this teaching strategy students will compile and compare some basic facts about representative Indian peoples of North America. They will then consider the clash of cultures between the Native Americans and the European settlers. Students will be able to recognize that despite the wholesale destruction of the native culture by the newcomers, aspects of the Indians' civilization were adapted by the newcomers and are recognizable in modern American culture. Students will also gain some perspective and be able to express their views on the ethical issues arising out of the European conquest of America.

MATERIALS

1. Copies of the "Native Americans Worksheet"
2. Copies of the four illustrations for each group

SUGGESTED PROCEDURE

1. Write the words *American Indian* on the chalkboard. Ask students to describe images suggested by that phrase. Write the students' descriptions on the chalkboard. Very likely there will be some negative stereotypes among them. Focus on some of these negative stereotypes. Ask students to explain where their images of American Indians come from. Have them comment as to whether they can trust such sources. Then ask students the following questions:

   a. Suppose people from another planet were to land in our community and visit for a few weeks. Suppose they returned to their own planet and were asked to describe the people of Earth. What words do you suppose they would use to describe us? Write students' suggestions on the chalkboard.

   b. Now suppose that Earth had something valuable that was wanted by the aliens. Suppose the aliens were running out of room on their planet and some of them decided that [your state] would be a good place for them to settle. How would this situation change the way they thought about us? Allow the class to discuss this question.

2. Write the word *civilization* on the chalkboard. Ask students to suggest definitions. Then ask: What is the difference between a civilization and a culture? (If students have trouble with this distinction, tell them that our word civilization comes from a Latin word meaning "city.") Ask students whether there are any reasons why complex government, economic, and social systems can be said to be "better" than simple ones, or whether a culture that is centered around city life can be said to be "better" than a culture that is not. Guide the discussion toward the concepts of value judgments and value systems. Ask students to suggest how these concepts apply to the first contacts between Europeans and Native Americans. Ask how they apply to the imaginary first contacts between human beings and extraterrestrials.

3. Ask students to consider whether all Native American peoples were considered "uncivilized" by European standards. If students are unaware of the "high culture" of the Indians, give them background information about the native cultures of the Andes, Central America, and Mexico. Use a wall map to show that Indian trade networks before European contact extended from the northeast to the Great Lakes to Mexico. Tell students that archaeologists have found the remains of what may have been an Indian "capital" in southern Illinois (Cahokia, near the present city of Alton), a city that was home to about 35,000 people around the

year 1200. (By comparison, only two cities in Christian Europe at that time, Constantinople and Paris, were larger.) Remind students that in the Old World, native civilizations developed in only a few locations and spread to other parts of Europe, Asia, and Africa over a period of several thousand years.

4. Tell students that for the next week (to two weeks, as you determine), they will be conducting research projects on some of the American Indian groups encountered by the early European explorers and settlers in North America. Organize the class into groups of four. Distribute copies of the "Native Americans Worksheet" to each student. Ask students why we use the term *Native Americans* to refer to the people commonly called "Indians." (*Indians* is an erroneous term, deriving from Columbus's mistaken assumption that he had reached the East Indies.)

5. Tell the class that each group is to choose one of the Native American groups listed on the worksheet for its research project. Point out that all the groups on the list lived in regions that became part of the United States (as distinct from the cultures of Mexico and Central and South America). Students are to use reference works and other materials available in the classroom and in school and public libraries as sources. Allow students the rest of the class period to choose topics and to plan their research. Do not allow more than two groups to report on any one of the Indian cultures. Allow each group to agree among its members how to divide responsibilities for the project. If time permits allow students an additional class period for guided work on their projects; otherwise, allow them to complete the projects as homework.

6. Resume the lesson in one to two weeks. By this time students will have read additional material on the first two centuries of Native American and European cultural contact. Have students assemble in their groups. Allow each group five minutes to present its report to the class. Have group members use a wall map to show geographic information. Discuss the reports with the class. Have the class generalize about the patterns of cultural confrontation and assimilation between Native Americans and Europeans.

7. Distribute copies of the two illustrations to each group. Ask if students can identify what is illustrated in each picture. Tell them that one of the illustrations was drawn by a European visiting an Indian settlement, whereas the other one is a fanciful illustration of a specific event. Ask students to determine which is which. Have students comment on what is fanciful and what is factual about the illustrations. Ask students what the illustrations suggest about the artists' attitudes toward the Indians.

8. To close the activity, have students discuss whether they think the European discovery and settlement of America could have been accomplished without the disruption and destruction of Native American culture.

Native Americans Worksheet

Directions: Use this worksheet to help guide your research project.

1. Choose a Native American group for your research project from among the names on this list:

Wampanoag	Powhatan	Iroquois
Muskogee (Creek)	Leni-Lenape (Delaware)	Ojibwa (Chippewa)
Chumash	Pawnee	Huron
Apache	Choctaw	Zuñi

   Other (a Native American group that lived in your area when Europeans first arrived)

2. Show on the map where this group lived when its first meeting with Europeans occurred and where the members of the group live now.

3. Research the natural environment of the region where this group lived, its way of life, and how the environment conditioned its way of life. Use the space below to write your notes.

   _____

   _____

   _____

   _____

   _____

   _____

4. Research the history of this group's interactions with Europeans to 1763. Explain how its way of life was changed by contact with European explorers and settlers. Describe aspects of the group's culture such as clothing, housing, food, transportation, and language that were adopted by European explorers and settlers. Use the space below to write your notes.

_____

_____

_____

_____

_____

_____

_____

5. Research how this group lives now. If it no longer exists as a group, explain why. Use the space below to write your notes.

_____

_____

_____

_____

_____

_____

_____

PETER MINUIT AND WALTER VAN TWILLER
1626–1637

THE PURCHASE OF MANHATTAN ISLAND.

TOPIC: God and Government
TIME: One to two class periods
TIME PERIOD: During study of the the founding and the development of institutions in England's American colonies

BACKGROUND

The institutions of government and society that developed in the 13 colonies were to a great extent based on the Judeo–Christian religious tradition. But while the early English settlers in America were all at least nominally Christian, there were great differences among individuals. There was also a lack of consensus among the colonies about the practice and institution of religion and the proper relationship between religion and government. In this teaching strategy students will apply their knowledge of the history and settlement of the colonies to a series of excerpts from law codes, religious treatises, and other colonial expressions of ideas on religion and government. Students will use the ideas put forth in the selections to draw conclusions about the origins of American democratic institutions and church–state relations. As they continue their study of history, students will be able to explain the religious foundations of specific American institutions and ideals as well as the limits American democracy places on the application of religious doctrine in civil law.

MATERIALS

1. Copies of the reading "Three Colonial views of Government"
2. Copies of the reading "Three Colonial Views of Religion"

SUGGESTED PROCEDURE

1. Review with the class the circumstances leading to the founding of the 13 colonies. Elicit from students that there was a great diversity of motives among the founders and settlers of the respective colonies.
2. Distribute a copy of the reading selection "Three Colonial Views of Government" to each student. Have students read the three selections aloud. Discuss each selection as it is read to make sure students understand the concepts being expressed.
   a. Regarding the first selection, ask if anyone can explain the references *Rom. 13.1.* and *Rom. 13.5*. (They are Biblical citations from the New Testament book of Romans.) Tell students that in the King James version of the Bible, Romans 13:1 reads, "Let every soul be subject unto the higher power. For there is no power but of God: the powers that be are ordained of God." Romans 13:5 reads, "Wherefore *ye* must needs be subject, not only for wrath, but also for conscience' sake."
   b. Regarding the second selection, ask students what the author means by the reference to the "Jewish and Roman states." (The author refers to the Jewish kingdom of the Old Testament and to the Roman empire, which flourished under good rulers but suffered and eventually fell under bad rulers.)
   c. Ask students to identify from which colony they think each of the selections might have come. Have them give reasons for their conjectures, based on their knowledge of the differences between the colonies.
3. After students have discussed the reasons for their conjectures, reveal the sources. Selection 1 is from the first law code of Massachusetts, *The Book of the General Lawes and Liberties of 1648,* which served as the basis of later legislation in Massachusetts and other New England colonies. Tell students that many of these laws were taken directly from the Bible, such as "Thou shalt not suffer a witch to live," and "Whosoever curseth his father or mother shall surely be put to death." Selection 2 is from William Penn's *Frame of Government for Pennsylvania* of 1682. Selection 3 is from a statement of John Tyler, Speaker of the Virginia House of Burgesses, in 1782. (It is an admonition addressed to Thomas Jefferson, who wished to refuse his seat in the House after having been elected to it.)
4. Discuss how each selection reflects the laws and customs of the colony in which it was written. Review with students the facts concerning who had the right to vote and hold office in these three colonies. (in Massachusetts, only "freemen," those who were members of the Church; in Pennsylvania, only property owners; in Virginia, only those with large landholdings) Discuss whether these requirements constituted

"democracy" as we would understand it today. (Students should recognize that in all of these colonies only white males had the franchise. They should also be aware that in a colony where land was cheap, most Pennsylvanians were in fact property owners.) Ask students: Which of the three ideas is closest to "democracy" as we understand it today?

5. Distribute a copy of the reading selection "Three Colonial Views of Religion" to each student. Have students read the three excerpts aloud. Discuss each selection as it is read to make sure students understand the concepts expressed. Tell students that each of these selections either was written in, or expresses ideas that were popularly held in, one of the same colonies as the first three selections. Have them match each pair of selections by colony and explain their reasoning.

6. After students have discussed their ideas and reasons, reveal the matches and sources. (1–B, from the *Cambridge Platform* of 1648, a Puritan statement on church discipline and organization; 2–C, from a journal entry of George Fox, founder of the Quaker movement, dated 1664; 3–A, from a letter by Virginia planter Robert Carter) Then ask students the following questions:
   a. How does each pair of selections suggest the colony's idea of the appropriate relationship between government and religion?
   b. Which colony's idea comes closest to the way in which most Americans today view this question? (Most students will agree that the Robert Carter selection from Virginia best expresses the idea of "separation of church and state." Tell the class that in Virginia at that time the Church of England (what we know as the Episcopal church in America) was established. It was the official church supported by the government, and everyone in Virginia had to pay a tax to it whether or not they were members. Discuss the apparent contradiction between this fact and the Robert Carter selection. Guide students toward the understanding that Americans' ideas about the relationship between government and religion were to undergo a great many changes.

7. Organize the class into groups of four and proceed in the following manner:
   a. Ask students: Imagine that three Americans from colonial times, a wealthy planter from Virginia, a Quaker shopkeeper from Pennsylvania, and a Puritan farmer from Massachusetts, all traveled by time machine to the America of today. What would each of them think about our system of government? What would each of them think about the relationship between government and religion in America today? Discuss these questions for several minutes.
   b. Have each group write a dialogue about these questions that might take place among the three hypothetical colonials. If time permits, allow the class an extra class period to discuss and write their dialogues. Have each group present its dialogue to the class. Use these dialogues as the basis of a class discussion.

Three Colonial Views of Government

Excerpted

1.

That distinction which is put between the Lawes of God and the lawes of men, becomes a snare to many as it is mis-applyed in the ordering of their obedience to civil Authoritie; for when the Authoritie is of God and in that way of an Ordinance *Rom. 13.1.* and when the administration of it is according to deductions, and rules gathered from the word of God, and the clear light of nature in civil nations, surely there is no humane law that tendeth to common good (according to those principles) but the same is mediately a law of God, and in that way of an Ordinance which all are to submit unto and that for conscience sake. *Rom. 13.5.*

2.

I know what is said by the several admirers of monarchy, aristocracy and democracy . . . when men discourse on the subject. But I chuse to solve the controversy with this small distinction, and it belongs to all three: Any government is free to the people under it (whatever be the frame) where the laws rule, and the people are a party to those laws, and more than this is tyranny, oligarchy, or confusion.

But lastly, when all is said, there is hardly one frame of government in the world so ill designed by its first founders that, in good hands, would not do well enough; and story tells us, the best, in ill ones, can do nothing that is great or good; witness the Jewish and Roman states. Governments, like clocks, go from the motion men give them; and as governments are made and moved by men, so by them they are ruined too. Wherefore governments rather depend upon men, than men upon governments. Let men be good, and government cannot be bad; if it be ill, they will cure it. But, if men be bad, let the government be never so good, they will endeavour to warp and spoil it to their turn.

3.

Good and able Men had better govern than be govern'd, since 'tis possible, indeed highly probable, that if the able and good withdraw themselves from Society, the venal and ignorant will succeed.

Three Colonial Views of Religion

Excerpted

A.

Let others take what courses they please in the bringing up of their posterity. I resolve the principles of our holy religion shall be distilled into mine betimes; as I am of the Church of England way, so I desire they should be. But the high-flown up top notions and the great stress that is laid upon ceremonies, any farther than decency and conformity, are what I cannot come into the reason of. Practical godliness is the substance—these are but the shell.

B.

The parts of Government are prescribed in the word, because the Lord Jesus Christ the King and Law-giver of his Church, is no less faithfull in the house of God then was Moses, who from the Lord delivered a form & pattern of Government to the Children of Israel in the old Testament: And the holy Scriptures are now also soe perfect, as they are able to make the man of God perfect & thoroughly furnished unto every good work, and therefore doubtless to the well ordering of the house of God.

C.

We are heirs of the gospel of peace, which is the power of God. . . . For Christ said, 'His kingdom was not of this world, if it were his servants would fight.' Therefore he bid Peter, put up his sword; for, said he, 'he that taketh the sword shall perish by the sword.' Here is the faith and patience of the saints, to bear and suffer all things, knowing vengeance is the Lord's, and he will repay it to them that hurt his people and wrong the innocent; therefore cannot we avenge but suffer for his name's sake. . . . The doctrine of Christ, who never sinned, is to 'love one another,' and those who are in this doctrine hurt no man, in which we are, in Christ, who is our life.

TOPIC: The Problem of Slavery
TIME: One class period
TIME PERIOD: After students have read about the establishment of the Quaker
colony in Pennsylvania and about the origins of the African slave trade

BACKGROUND

The most glaring contradiction in the American system and in America's image of itself—racism—had its
origins in the colonial period. By 1690 African slavery was firmly established in all the English colonies in
America, and some colonists were already agitating for its abolition. In this teaching strategy students will
review the origins of slavery in the colonies, its role in the economy, and how the circumstances of the
institution differed between northern and southern regions. The distinction between slavery and indentured
servitude will be considered, as well as the concept that the economic dependence on slavery and racist
justification for it fed off one another. Finally, students will read an early statement of protest against slavery
and consider how it might have been received in seventeenth-century America. Through this teaching strategy
students will be able to explain how the seeds of America's longest-continuing moral and political conflict
were sown in the earliest decades of American history.

MATERIALS

Copies of the Mennonite resolutions against slavery

SUGGESTED PROCEDURE

1. Review with the class the origins of the African slave trade and slavery in the American colonies. Make
   sure that students can define and/or explain the significance of the following words and concepts:

slavery	slave trade	African slave hunters
Middle Passage	plantation	cash crop

2. Discuss with the class the following questions relating to slavery and the African slave trade:
   a. Why did Europeans believe that they were justified in enslaving Africans?
   b. How were slaves captured in Africa, and how were they brought to America?
   c. Why did slavery take root more strongly in the South than in the North? What were some of the
      differences between the two sections in the way slaves were treated? What was the role of northerners
      in maintaining the African slave trade?
   d. What was indentured servitude, and how did it differ from slavery? How did people become
      indentured servants? Why did slavery gradually replace indentured servitude in the colonies?
   e. Why would it have become more and more difficult to end "the peculiar institution" the longer it was
      established? (Extend the discussion of this question. Guide students in understanding that slavery
      became a vested interest both to merchants who profited from the slave trade and to planters who
      depended on slave labor to profitably raise and sell their crops. Ask students what would happen to a
      Virginia tobacco planter who decided to free his slaves and run his plantation with hired agricultural
      labor.)
3. Ask students if they can guess which group among the white population of the colonies would have been
   most opposed to slavery and the slave trade, or where the first protests against slavery might have
   originated. (Some students may guess the Quakers because of what they have learned about that groups'
   philosophies. These students will be surprised when they read the resolutions!)
4. Distribute copies of the reading selection to each student. Ask if students can identify the Mennonite
   community. (A group of German farmers who had fled religious persecution and were granted permission
   by William Penn to settle in Pennsylvania.) Have students read the Mennonite resolutions aloud. Then
   proceed in the following manner:
   a. Ask students: Against whom was the protest directed? (Encourage students to comment on the fact that
      it was directed against Quakers involved in the slave trade.)

b. Have students summarize the reasons given by Mennonites for their opposition to slavery. (Make sure that students recognize the religious motivation for the protest, and the comparison drawn between the Mennonites having been persecuted in Europe for their "conscience" (i.e., religion) and the Africans being enslaved for their color.) Ask students: What do the Mennonites have to say about European reaction to the fact of Quakers owning and trading in slaves? What is the point made in the next-to-last paragraph about Quaker masters and mistresses opposing slaves who fight for their freedom?

c. Ask students to speculate about how the Mennonite resolutions might have been received by the Quakers to whom they were addressed.

5. Organize the class into groups of four. Have them write a brief reply to the Mennonite resolutions as it might have been written by any two of the following people:

   a. A Quaker merchant in Philadelphia who owns slave ships

   b. The owner of a tobacco plantation in Maryland

   c. An indentured servant in Maryland who is about to go free

   d. An African recently brought to America on a slave ship

   e. A former slave, born in America, who has bought his freedom

6. Allow students to discuss the assignment and to compare notes with members of their group, but have students complete their work individually.

Resolutions of the Mennonite Community of Germantown, Pennsylvania

February 18, 1688

Excerpted

This is to the monthly meeting held at Richard Worrell's:

These are the reasons we are against the traffic of men-body, as followeth: Is there any that would be done or handled at this manner? viz., to be sold or made a slave for all the time of his life? How fearful and faint-hearted are many at sea, when they see a strange vessel, being afraid it should be a Turk, and they should be taken, and sold as slaves into Turkey. Now, what is *this* better done, than Turks do? Yea, rather it is worse for them, which say they are Christians; for we hear that such negers are brought hither against their will and consent, and that many of them are stolen. Now, though they are black, we cannot conceive there is more liberty to have them slaves, as it is to have white ones. There is a saying, that we should do to all men as we will be done ourselves; making no difference of what colour they are. And those who steal or rob men, and those who buy or purchase them, are they not all alike? Here is liberty of conscience, which is right and reasonable; here ought to be likewise liberty of the body, except of evil-doers, which is another case. But to bring men hither, or to rob and sell them against their will, we stand against. In Europe there are many oppressed for conscience-sake; and here there are those oppressed which are of a black colour. . . . Ah! do consider well this thing, you who do it, if you would be done at this manner—and if it is done according to Christianity! . . . This makes an ill report in all those countries of Europe, where they hear . . . that the Quakers do here handel men as they handel there the cattle. And for that reason some have no mind or inclination to come hither. And who shall maintain this your cause, or plead for it? Truly, we cannot do so, except you shall inform us better hereof, viz., that Christians have liberty to practice these things. Pray, what thing in the world can be done worse towards us, that if men should rob or steal us away, and sell us for slaves to strange countries; separating husbands from their wives and children. Being now this is not done in the manner we would be done at; therefore, we contradict, and are against this traffic of men-body. And we who profess that it is not lawful to steal, must, likewise, avoid to purchase such things as are stolen, but rather help to stop this robbing and stealing, if possible. And such men ought to be delivered out of the hands of robbers and set free as in Europe. Then is Pennsylvania to have a good report, instead, it hath now a bad one, for this sake, in other countries; Especially whereas the Europeans are desirous to know in what manner *the Quakers* do rule in *their* province; and most of them do look upon us with an envious eye. But if this is done well, what shall we say is done evil?

If once these slaves (which they say are so wicked and stubborn men,) should join themselves—fight for their freedom . . . will these masters and mistresses take the sword at hand and war against these poor slaves, like, as we are able to believe, some will not refuse to do so? Or, have these poor negers not as much right to fight for their freedom, as you have to keep them slaves?

Now consider well this thing, if it is good or bad. And in case you find it to be good to handel these blacks in this manner, we desire and require you hereby lovingly, that you may inform us herein, which at this time never was done, viz., that Christians have such a liberty to do so. To the end we shall be satisfied on this point, and satisfy likewise our good friends and acquaintances in our native country, to whom it is a terror, or fearful thing, that men should be handelled so in Pennsylvania.

TOPIC: A Tavern at the Crossroads—American Currents, 1740

TIME: Two class periods, with homework. The class periods may be separated by several days.

TIME PERIOD: After students have read background material on life in colonial America, preferably after they have some familiarity with the colonial wars and the ideas of the Great Awakening

BACKGROUND

One aspect of colonial history that students often find difficult to grasp is the relative isolation in which people lived. With transportation restricted to horse-borne traffic over poor roads or to water travel, mobility was restricted; with few newspapers and no electronic communications, information about "the outside world" was limited. It was therefore a memorable experience to meet a traveler from the next county, and wayfarers from other colonies were often treated as exotic foreigners. Yet despite such circumstances, the colonists in the mid-1700s were developing a web of social and cultural contacts and a political consciousness that in another generation would make them citizens of the United States of America.

In this teaching strategy students will examine the culture, attitudes, and regional differences among the American colonists at mid-century by portraying characters at a crossroads tavern in Maryland. Students will select their characters from a list of thumbnail sketches, develop their characters in greater depth through research and discussion, participate in a discussion that might have taken place in the common room of a rural tavern, and describe and comment on it in a journal entry. The teaching strategy provides students with a view of the culture, economy, political issues, and regional concerns of the colonial period as it gives them insights into the common concerns and underlying unity of the emerging American nation.

MATERIALS

Copies of "A Tavern at the Crossroads" worksheet

SUGGESTED PROCEDURE

1. Ask the class to imagine that they live on a farm in the colony of New York in 1740. Ask: How often do you get to meet people from outside your county? Allow students to speculate on possible answers. Then ask: How often do you get to meet people from other colonies? Who are the people from other colonies that you are most likely to meet? After students discuss these questions, ask: How is your way of life similar to and different from that of people who live in New York City? How is it the same as and different from people living on the New York frontier? New Hampshire or North Carolina? Allow students to discuss the similarities and differences. Then ask: Where do you get your information about people in other colonies, or even about people in other parts of New York? How do you feel about these people?

2. Tell students that they are going to try to understand how people in various parts of the American colonies lived, thought, and believed by imagining themselves to be travelers in a tavern at a crossroads in Maryland in the year 1740. Then ask students the following questions:

   a. Why was Maryland a likely place for people from all over the colonies to meet? (It was in the center of British America.)

   b. How was a tavern in colonial America different from the way in which we understand the meaning of the word *tavern* today? (A tavern was more of a hotel and restaurant than a "bar." Taverns were located on rural roads and highways and offered meals and beds for travelers and stabling for their horses.)

3. Distribute copies of the worksheet to each student. Have students look over the list of characters. Tell them that they will choose a character from the list and research information that will make the character seem true to life. They will meet with other students who have chosen the same character and compare notes on what such a person might be like. Then they will take on the role of that character and have a conversation with other people whom they might meet in the tavern. Tell students that they may make up

their own character instead of using one from the list, but if they do so, they will lose the advantage of being able to develop the character with other students.

4. Allow students five minutes to look over the list and decide on a character. Tell them to select a first, second, and third choice. Most boys will choose male characters and most girls female characters but suggest that they may choose anyone who interests them regardless of gender. Have students assemble in groups depending on their first choice of characters. Then redistribute the groups for balance. Try not to have any fewer than two or any more than five people portray any single character. Ask students in the more crowded groups to volunteer to take on second- or third-choice characters to even out the groups.

5. Have a student read aloud the second part of the worksheet instructions. Allow students the rest of the class period to discuss the character with their groups and to begin their research. They may use their textbooks and any other sources available in their school and public libraries. Not everyone in their group has to imagine the character in the same way, but they should be authentic as to the thoughts, beliefs, and attitudes of a person from a particular place and should represent a particular way of life. Allow students to continue their research as homework. If time permits, allow them to meet in their groups for part of a subsequent class period to compare their research notes and to further discuss their characters.

6. On the designated day organize the class into groups so that no group has any more than one person portraying the same character. It is desirable, but not necessary, to have each of the 12 characters represented in each group. Do not worry if in a particular group, for example, there is a Mr. Harris but no Mrs. Harris. Keep the groups relatively equal in size. Remind students again that they are meeting in the common room of a tavern where they will all be spending the night. Have them imagine what the place looks like: what materials it was built with, what the furniture is like, what are they eating for supper, and so on. Have members of each group speak freely with one another "in character." Each character should tell the others something about where he or she comes from and what his or her life is like. Have them comment on each other's stories and attitudes. Have them consider the things about which certain people would agree and disagree. Also have them consider what thoughts people would choose to keep private. Allow students the entire class period for their conversations. Circulate among the groups to keep the conversations moving.

7. Then tell the class: Now everyone at the tavern has gone off to their rooms for the night. But all the travelers keep journals, and before they go to sleep they want to write about the interesting people they met, the things they talked about, and how they felt about them. Have students write the journal entries as homework, still in the role of their chosen characters. If some students observe that some of the characters might not know how to write, have them put down what those characters would have written if they could. Remind students that the two black people and the Indian might have been denied beds at the tavern and have been made to sleep in the stable.

A Tavern at the Crossroads

Directions: Select your character from this list, or choose your own character. If you choose your own character, make sure that he or she represents a person who was likely to be found in America in 1740.

Levi Fletcher is a 23-year-old Congregationalist minister from western Massachusetts. Last year he heard Jonathan Edwards preach a sermon, and he was caught up in the "Great Awakening." Since then he has been traveling throughout the colonies speaking at outdoor religious meetings, leaving his young wife and her brother to manage the family farm and fruit orchard.

Larissa Day owns a large tobacco plantation with 100 slaves in King William County, Virginia. She is 35 years old, has four children, and has been running the plantation since her husband died six years ago. Some of her ancestors were among the first to arrive at Jamestown. One of her grandfathers fought in Bacon's Rebellion.

Sarah Day, 19 years old, is Larissa's personal maid. She was born in Africa and was brought to Virginia on a slave ship when she was seven. She worked in the fields until she was 14, when Mrs. Day brought her into her house as a personal servant. Sarah cannot read or write, but she has become a skilled dressmaker.

Simon Saint-Jacques is a wealthy merchant from Newport, Rhode Island, and is 48 years old. His parents came to America from France to escape the Catholic persecution of Protestants. His father was a poor fisherman, but Simon owns 14 ships and has grown rich on trade with England, the West Indies, and Africa.

Mary Perkins Saint-Jacques, 26 years old, is Simon's wife. Born in England, she came to America as an indentured servant at the age of 16. She worked for Simon's family as a maid. Simon's first wife, Abigail, taught her how to read and write. After Abigail died in childbirth, Simon married Mary.

Katrin van Weert is an orphan from the upper Hudson Valley of New York. Her parents were killed and their farm was burned in an Indian raid when she was seven. Since then she has been living with an aunt and uncle on their farm, but she has never gotten along with them. Now she is 16 years old, and they have thrown her out.

Matthew Travis, 21 years old, grew up on the South Carolina frontier. One of his grandfathers came from England; one of his grandmothers was a Cherokee Indian. His family has cleared a small farm in the woods, but they earn their living mostly by hunting, trapping, and trading in furs.

Jonathan Harris, 32 years old, is a printer, bookseller, and brewer in Philadelphia, Pennsylvania. His parents were New Englanders of Puritan families. He is interested in science; his most prized possession is a brass telescope made in England. He plays the violin well, and his wife accompanies him on the harpsichord.

Rebecca Harris, 29 years old, is Jonathan's wife. She is a Quaker whose grandfather came from England with William Penn. She plans to open a school of music in Philadelphia when her children are grown. She learned nursing skills as a girl and is often called upon to help women who are having babies.

Jupiter Harris, 35 years old, was once a slave belonging to Jonathan Harris' family. He bought his freedom five years ago, but he still works for the Harrises, helping to run Jonathan's brewery and earning extra money as a blacksmith. His parents were both born in Africa and brought to America on a slave ship.

Heart-of-Oak is a Shawnee from the Ohio River valley. He is on his way to Williamsburg, Virginia, to protest to the House of Burgesses on behalf of his people that white trappers have invaded their hunting grounds, in violation of their treaty. He learned to speak English from white traders, but he has never been out of the forest before. He is 40 years old.

Ellen MacGillis is 75 years old and she has seen it all. She came to Maryland from Scotland as a bride of 23. She and her first husband were Catholics seeking religious freedom in America. She has farmed all her life, outlived three husbands, and borne 16 children, seven of whom survived. She is traveling alone to visit her daughter's family, who live on a frontier farm.

Take notes on your character. Make up more details concerning his or her life. Be sure that you only make up details that are historically plausible. Some things you might consider include: What is the reason for your character's journey, if not stated above? How does your character feel about the place where he or she lives or is going to? How does your character spend a typical day? What does he or she like to do for fun? What does he or she think about freedom, religion, government, trade, frontier settlements, the rights of Indians, slavery, the possibilities of war with France, people from other colonies? What hopes and expectations does your character have for the future? Write your notes on the lines below. Use another sheet of paper if you need more room.

_____

_____

_____

_____

_____

_____

_____

_____

_____

_____

_____

_____

TOPIC: "From Many, One"—The Colonies Move Toward Union
TIME: One class period
TIME PERIOD: During study of the Stamp Act and its aftermath

BACKGROUND

In 1754 Benjamin Franklin proposed a plan of union to the 13 colonies. There were no takers. Yet 11 years later delegates from nine of the colonies were meeting "in Congress" to protest an act of the Parliament of Great Britain—the Stamp Act. This action was the colonies' first act of unity, a harbinger of the break with England that was to follow in the next decade. In this teaching strategy students will read the Declarations written to King George III by the colonial delegation in protest of the Stamp Act. From the reading students will infer the rights and liberties that the colonists were asserting. They will discuss the origin of these rights and liberties in the British Parliamentary system. Finally, students will prepare a table of events from the Albany Plan of Union to the Stamp Act Resolution 11 years later to demonstrate the series of cause-and-effect relationships among the events leading toward the unification of the colonies. Students will be able to recognize in this series of events the progression of the American political consciousness from that of 13 individual colonies toward a union of independent states.

MATERIALS

1. Copies of the handout "Resolutions of ???"
2. 11" x 14" fan-fold computer paper (if available), or cellophane tape

SUGGESTED PROCEDURE

1. Distribute copies of the "Resolutions of ???" handouts. Do not tell students at first to what the resolutions refer. Tell them that they were drafted by delegates from nine colonies meeting in New York City in 1765 and that delegates from the other colonies were invited but did not come. Tell students to figure out to what the Resolutions refer by reading them. Have students read the document aloud. Ask students: To whom was the document addressed? (the king of England) For what were the colonists asking? (repeal of the Stamp Act)
2. Review with the class the circumstances of the Stamp Act and the colonists' reaction to it. Have students comment on the general tone of the document: was it in any way an angry, rude, or defiant document? How did the colonists expect the document to be received in England?
3. Review the document in the following manner:
   a. Have a student reread Article II of the resolutions aloud. Ask students: What were some of the "inherent rights and liberties" the colonists were asserting? Have them cite specific rights and liberties from the document. (the right to choose representatives, the right to be taxed only by the consent of the people or their representatives, the right of trial by jury, the right to petition rulers) Explain that these rights and others, such as the right not to testify against one's self in court and the right not to have one's property searched without cause, were secured in England over a period of more than five centuries.
   b. Have students reread Articles VII and VIII. Ask students: What acts of Parliament threatened the colonists' right of trial by jury? Ask them to explain the reference to the courts of Admiralty. Review the circumstances of the Sugar Act of 1764 and the colonists' reaction to it.
   c. Have students explain the colonists' objections to duties on British manufactured goods in Articles IX–XI. Ask: What are the colonists saying will happen if they have to pay these new taxes? Do you think the colonists had a valid point or were they just trying to find an excuse to avoid the taxes?
4. Review with the class the circumstances of the Albany Plan of Union of 1754. Ask students: Who proposed the plan? What was the result? Ask them for their views concerning why no colony was willing to take united action with any of the others in 1754, and yet nine of them came together to agree to the Stamp Act Resolutions 11 years later. What happened during that time to make Virginians, Pennsylvanians, New Yorkers, and so on begin to think of themselves as Americans? Allow students to

suggest possible reasons for this change in attitude. Write their suggestions on the chalkboard. Guide them toward the realization that the motion of the colonists toward unity had no single cause.

5. Organize the class into groups of four. Tell the class that each group will make a chart that shows the cause-and-effect relationships among the events leading to the Stamp Act Resolutions. Tell students to use the events listed on the chalkboard as a starting point for the activity but to fill out the list with other events that complete the chain of cause-and-effect relationships. Instruct the students to use the flowchart format to show the relationship between events. Explain that they are to use boxes to set off the terms that identify the events and to draw an arrow from the box that identifies a cause to the box that identifies its effect. Tell them that they may use events other than those listed. Remind them that a cause may have more than one effect and an effect may have more than one cause. Draw a sample flowchart on the chalkboard to show students how their charts might look. Tell students that next to each arrow showing a cause-and-effect relationship they should write a sentence or two explaining why one event was the cause of the other.

6. Ask two students to demonstrate the procedure at the chalkboard by writing three events in consecutive boxes such that event B is an effect of event A and a cause of event C.

7. Tell students in each group to work out and discuss a rough form for their chart before producing the final version. Advise them that they may need to attach two or more sheets of paper together to create enough space for their charts. Provide cellophane tape for this purpose, or use 11″ x 14″ fan-fold computer paper if available. Allow students the rest of the class period to work on their charts.

Resolutions of ???
(1765)
Title changed

The members of this Congress, sincerely devoted with the warmest sentiments of affection and duty to His Majesty's person and Government, inviolably attached to the present happy establishment of the Protestant succession, and with minds deeply impressed by a sense of the present and impending misfortunes of the British colonies on this continent, having considered as maturely as time will permit the circumstances of the said colonies, esteem it our indispensible duty to make the following declarations of our humble opinion respecting the most essential rights and liberties of the colonists, and of the grievances under which they labour, by reason of several late Acts of Parliament.

I.   That His Majesty's subjects in these colonies owe the same allegiance to the Crown of Great Britain that is owing to his subjects born within the realm, and all due subordination to the Parliament of Great Britain.

II.   That His Majesty's liege subjects in these colonies are intitled to all the inherent rights and liberties of his natural born subjects within the kingdom of Great Britain.

III.   That it is inseparably essential to the freedom of a people, and the undoubted right of Englishmen, that no taxes be imposed on them but with their own consent, given personally or by their representatives.

IV.   That the people of these colonies are not, and from their local circumstances cannot be, represented in the House of Commons in Great Britain.

V.   That the only representatives of the people of these colonies are persons chosen therein by themselves, and that no taxes ever have been, or can be constitutionally imposed on them, but by their respective legislatures.

VI.   That all supplies to the Crown being free gifts of the people, it is unreasonable and inconsistent with the principles and spirit of the British Constitution, for the people of Great Britain to grant to His Majesty the property of the colonists.

VII.   That trial by jury is the inherent and invaluable right of every British subject in these colonies.

VIII.   That the late act of Parliament, entitled *An act for granting and applying certain stamp duties, and other duties, in the British colonies and plantations in America, etc.,* by imposing taxes on the inhabitants of these colonies; and the said Act, and several other Acts, by extending the jurisdiction of the courts of Admiralty beyond its ancient limits, have a manifest tendency to subvert the rights and liberties of the colonists.

IX.   That the duties imposed by several late Acts of Parliament, from the peculiar circumstances of these colonies, will be extremely burthensome and grievous; and from the scarcity of specie, the payment of them absolutely impracticable.

X.   That as the profits of the trade of these colonies ultimately center in Great Britain, to pay for the manufactures which they are obliged to take from thence, they eventually contribute very largely to all supplies granted there to the Crown.

XI.   That the restrictions imposed by several late Acts of Parliament on the trade of these colonies will render them unable to purchase the manufactures of Great Britain.

XII.   That the increase, prosperity, and happiness of these colonies depend on the full and free enjoyments of their rights and liberties, and an intercourse with Great Britain mutually affectionate and advantageous.

XIII.   That it is the right of the British subjects in these colonies to petition the King or either House of Parliament.

Lastly, That it is the indispensible duty of these colonies to the best of sovereigns, the mother country, and themselves, to endeavour by a loyal and dutiful address to His Majesty, and humble applications to both Houses of Parliament, to procure the repeal of the Act for granting and applying certain stamp duties, of all clauses or any other Acts of Parliament, whereby the jurisdiction of the Admiralty is extended as aforesaid, and of the other late Acts for the restriction of American commerce.

TOPIC: "The American, This New Man"
TIME: One class period, with homework
TIME PERIOD: At the end of the instructional sequence on colonial America

BACKGROUND

In 1607 the first English settlers in America landed at Jamestown. One hundred and seventy years later Americans were in rebellion against England. In this teaching strategy students will consider the circumstances that changed British subjects into Americans. They will read and discuss excerpts from *Letters from an American Farmer,* written at the end of the colonial period by Michel-Guillaume Jean de Crèvecoeur, a French settler in New York. Students will gain a perspective concerning how Americans had come to regard themselves as a new nation, self-consciously separated from the traditions and concerns of Europe. Students will consider his famous question, "What, then, is the American, this new man?" as modern Americans looking back on our nation at its beginnings and from the point of view of the original settlers and their plans and purposes. As a summation of the instructional sequence on the colonial period, students will write essays on the process by which the settlers and their descendants created a new, distinctly American civilization in the New World.

MATERIALS

Copies of the exerpts from *Letters from an American Farmer*

SUGGESTED PROCEDURE

1. Ask the class: Suppose you were a farmer living in the colony of New York in 1700, and a visitor from England asked you to describe who you were and what your country was. How would you answer? Try to elicit a variety of student responses. Students should recognize that colonists would have identified themselves as English—or as Dutch; French; members of a particular African people, free or slave; Protestant or Catholic; and so on; and as residents of New York. They probably would not have called themselves "American." Then ask: Suppose you were that same farmer's grandson or granddaughter in the 1770s, and a visitor from Europe asked you to explain how you, as an American, were different from a European. How would you answer? Again, encourage a variety of responses.

2. Tell the class that they are going to read a selection from a short book called *Letters from an American Farmer* to get an idea of how at least one American at the end of the colonial period would have answered that question. Explain that the book was written by Michel-Guillaume Jean de Crèvecoeur, a French immigrant who traveled throughout much of North America and settled in New York in 1759. Distribute a copy of the reading selection to each student. Have students read the selection silently or aloud. Then ask the following questions:

   a. What do you think Crèvecoeur meant when he talked about "Americans?" Who did he exclude? (He speaks only of the free white population, he is essentially concerned only with men, and he does not consider the displaced Indians.) How would his perspective differ from ours in that respect?

   b. What does Crèvecoeur say is the origin of American liberty? (national genius) What does he say about the economy of America? (America is a country of farmers, working for themselves; whoever comes to America will find employment; industriousness will be rewarded.) What does he have to say about regional differences? (Each region has its own government, way of farming, habits, and circumstances.) Have students summarize his ideas about what makes America different from Europe.

   c. What do you think Crèvecoeur might say about America today?

3. Write the following question on the chalkboard: What changed Europeans into Americans? Discuss the question with the class. Remind them that the first European settlers came to America with specific dreams and plans but that the reality of circumstances they found in the New World led them to create a new civilization. Tell the class that some historians believe that the change from European to American was slow and gradual, whereas others believe that the really important changes happened within the first generation of American settlement. Ask the class for their opinions on this disagreement.

4. Have students write essays in which they answer the question, "What changed Europeans into Americans?" Have them follow these five steps in writing their essays:

Step 1: Prewriting

Organize the class into groups of four. Have students spend the rest of the class period discussing the question with their groups, taking notes on various points that will be made in their essays, and deciding how their essays will be structured. They may consult their textbooks and/or other available references.

Step 2: Writing a First Draft

Using their prewriting notes as a guide, students should write a first draft of their essays as homework.

Step 3: Revising

Students should exchange essays with a partner, critique the essays, and suggest ways to make them stronger. Redundant, repetitive, or irrelevant sections may be cut. New material may be added to strengthen or enhance a point.

Step 4: Proofreading

Students should proofread their essays for errors in spelling, punctuation, grammar, or usage.

Step 5: Writing a Final Copy

Have students write a final copy of their essays on clean paper.

Excerpts from "What is an American?"

From *Letters from an American Farmer,* by Michel-Guillaume Jean de Crèvecoeur, published in 1782

I wish I could be acquainted with the feelings and thoughts of an enlightened Englishman, when he first lands on this continent. He must greatly rejoice that he lived at a time to see this fair country discovered and settled; he must necessarily feel a share of national pride, when he views the chain of settlements which embellishes these extended shores. When he says to himself, this is the work of my countrymen, who, when convulsed by factions, afflicted by a variety of miseries and wants, restless and impatient, took refuge here. They brought along with them their national genius, to which they principally owe what liberty they enjoy, and what substance they possess. Here he sees the industry of his native country displayed in a new manner, and traces in their works the embryos of all of the arts, sciences, and ingenuity which flourish in Europe. . . . What a train of pleasing ideas this fair spectacle must suggest. . . . The difficulty consists in the manner of viewing so extensive a scene. He is arrived on a new continent; a modern society offers itself to his contemplation, different from what he had hitherto seen. It is not composed, as in Europe, of great lords who possess every thing, and of a herd of people who have nothing. Here are no aristocratical families, no courts, no kings, no bishops, no ecclesiastical dominion, no invisible power giving to a few a very visible one; no great manufacturers employing thousands, no great refinements of luxury. We are a people of cultivators, scattered over an immense territory, communicating with each other by means of good roads and navigable rivers, united by the silken bands of mild government, all respecting the laws, without dreading their power, because they are equitable. We are all animated with the spirit of an industry which is unfettered and unrestrained, because each person works for himself. If he travels through our rural districts he views not the hostile castle and the haughty mansion, contrasted with the clay-built hut and miserable cabbin, where cattle and men help to keep each other warm, and dwell in meanness, smoke, and indigence. There, on a Sunday, he sees a congregation of respectable farmers and their wives, all clad in neat homespun, well mounted, or riding in their own humble waggons. There is not among them an esquire, saving the unlettered magistrate. There he sees a parson as simple as his flock, a farmer who does not riot on the labour of others. We have no princes, for whom we toil, starve, and bleed: we are the most perfect society now existing in the world.

The next wish of this traveler will be to know whence came all these people. They are a mixture of English, Scotch, Irish, French, Dutch, Germans, and Swedes. From this promiscuous breed, that race now called Americans have arisen.

In this great American asylum, the poor of Europe have by some means met together, and in consequence of various causes; to what purpose should they ask one another what countrymen they are? Alas, two thirds of them had no country. Can a wretch who wanders about, who works and starves . . . can that man call England or any other kingdom his country? Formerly, they were not numbered in any civil list of their country, except in those of the poor; here they rank as citizens. By what invisible power has this surprising metamorphosis been performed? By that of the laws and that of their industry. . . . From whence proceed these laws? From our government. Whence the government? It is derived from the original genius and strong desire of the people ratified and confirmed by the crown.

What, then, is the American, this new man? He is either a European, or the descendant of a European; hence that strange mixture of blood, which you will find in no other country. . . . He is an American, who leaving behind him all his ancient prejudices and manners receives new ones from the mode of life he has embraced, the new government he obeys, and the new rank he holds. Here individuals of all nations are melted into a new race of men, whose labors and posterity will one day cause great changes in the world. . . . Here the rewards of his industry follow with equal steps the progress of his labour; his labour is founded on the basis of nature, *self-interest;* can it want a stronger allurement?. . .

British America is divided into many provinces, forming a large association, scattered along a coast 1500 miles extent and about 200 wide. This society I would fain examine, at least such as it appears in the middle provinces; if it does not afford that variety of tinges and gradations which may be observed in Europe, we have colours peculiar to ourselves. . . .

Those who live near the sea feed more on fish than on flesh, and often encounter that boisterous element. This renders them more bold and enterprising; this leads them to neglect the confined occupations of the land. They see and converse with a variety of people. . . . The sea inspires them with a love of traffic, a desire of transporting produce from one place to another; and leads them to a variety of resources which supply the place of labour. Those who inhabit the middle settlements, by far the most numerous, must be very different; the simple cultivation of the earth purifies them. . . . Europe has no such class of men; the early knowledge they acquire, the early bargains they make, give them a degree of sagacity. As freemen they will be litigious; pride and obstinacy are often the cause of law suits; the nature of our laws and our government may be another. As citizens it is easy to imagine that they will carefully read the newspapers, enter into every political disquisition, freely blame or censure governors and others. As farmers they will be careful and anxious to get as much as they can, because what they get is their own. As northern men they will love the cheerful cup. As Christians, religion curbs them not in their opinions; the general indulgence leaves everyone to think for them-

selves in spiritual matters; the laws inspect our actions, our thoughts are left to God.

Now we arrive near the great woods, near the last inhabited districts; there men seem to be placed still farther beyond the reach of government, which in some measure leaves them to themselves. How can it prevade every corner; as they were driven there by misfortunes, necessity of beginnings, desire of acquiring large tracts of land, idleness, frequent want of economy, ancient debts; the re-union of such people does not afford a very pleasing spectacle. When discord, want of unity and friendship; when either drunkenness or idleness prevail in such remote districts; contention, inactivity, and wretchedness must ensue. . . . They are often in a perfect state of war. . . . There men appear to be no better than carnivorous animals of a superior rank, living on the flesh of wild animals when they can catch them, and when they are not able, they subsist on grain. He who would wish to see America in its proper light, and have a true idea of its feeble beginnings and barbarous rudiments, must visit our extended line of frontiers where the last settlers dwell, and where he may see the first labours of settlement. . . . They are a kind of forlorn hope, preceding by ten or twelve years the most respectable army of veterans which come after them. . . . In all societies there are off-casts; this impure part serves as our precursors or pioneers; my father himself was one of that class; but he came upon honest principles, and was therefore one of the few who held fast; by good conduct and temperance, he transmitted to me his fair inheritance, when not above one in fourteen of his contemporaries had the same good fortune. . . .

Exclusive of those general characteristics, each province has its own, founded on the government, climate, mode of husbandry, customs, and peculiarity of circumstances. Europeans submit insensibly to these great powers, and become, in the course of a few generations, not only Americans in general, but either Pennsylvanians, Virginians, or provincials by some other name.

There is no wonder that this country has so many charms, and presents to Europeans so many temptations to remain in it. . . . There is room for every body in America. Whatever be his talents or inclinations, if they are moderate, he may satisfy them. I do not mean that every one who comes will grow rich in a little time; no, but he may procure an easy, decent maintenance by his industry. Instead of starving he will be fed; instead of being idle he will have employment; and these are riches enough for such men who come over here. The rich stay in Europe; it is only the middling and the poor that emigrate. Would you wish to travel in independent idleness, from north to south, you will find easy access, and the most cheerful reception at every house; society without ostentation, good cheer without pride, and every decent diversion which the country affords, with little expense.

An European, when he first arrives, seems limited in his intentions, as well as in his views; but he very suddenly alters his scale; two hundred miles formerly appeared a very great distance, it is not but a trifle; he no sooner breathes our air than he forms schemes, and embarks in designs he never would have thought of in his own country. There the plenitude of of society confines many useful ideas, and often extinguishes the most laudable schemes which here ripen into maturity. Thus Europeans become Americans.

After a foreigner from any part of Europe is arrived, and become a citizen, let him devoutly listen to the voice of our great parent, which says to him, "Welcome to my shores, distressed European; bless the hour in which thou didst see my verdant shores, my navigable rivers, and my green mountains!—If thou will be honest, sober, and industrious, I have greater rewards to confer on thee—ease and independence. I will give thee fields to feed and clothe thee; a comfortable fireside to sit by, and tell thy children by what means thou hast prospered; and a decent bed to repose on. I shall endow thee beside with the immunities of a freeman. If thou wilt carefully educate thy children, teach them gratitude to God, and reverence to that government, that philanthropic government, which has collected so many men here and made them happy. I will also provide for thy progeny; and to every good man this ought to be the most holy, the most powerful, the most earnest wish he can possibly form, as well as the most consolatory prospect when he dies. Go thou and work and till; thou shalt prosper, provided thou be just, grateful and industrious."

Creative Strategies for Teaching American History

The Emerging Nation
1765–1783

TOPIC: "No Taxation Without Representation"
TIME: Two class periods
TIME PERIOD: During study of the events leading to American independence

BACKGROUND

For much of the colonial period Britain had paid little attention to the colonies. The colonies were far away, and Britain was often engaged in European wars. The colonists were able to disobey laws passed by Parliament that they did not like. When the French and Indian War ended in 1763, however, the situation changed. Britain needed money to pay off war debts and saw no reason that the colonies should not help raise the money. In this teaching strategy students will work in home groups and in expert groups to gain an empathetic understanding of the events that led to the colonists' desire for independence.

MATERIALS

1. Pencils and paper for the entire class
2. Markers to be used as "money" (circles the size of quarters cut out of paper; five markers for each student)
3. Envelopes for markers (one envelope for each student)

SUGGESTED PROCEDURE

1. Before class begins, list on the chalkboard the following items: Quartering Act, Stamp Act, Declaratory Act, Townshend Acts, Boston Massacre, Boston Tea Party, Intolerable Acts. As students enter the classroom, give each student an envelope containing five markers. Tell students that their assignment is to identify each of the items written on the chalkboard. Then tell students that you have decided that they may not use their own pencils and paper for the assignment—they must buy the materials from you or fail the assignment. Tell them that it is for their own good—that you will use the "money" to buy something for the class but that students will not have any say in what you buy. Ask students to pay you one marker for a pencil and two markers for a sheet of paper. Have a volunteer help you collect the markers. Now tell students they may begin the assignment. Shortly after they have begun, ask the students to stop. Tell them that you have decided that you do not have enough "money." Tell them that they will now have to pay a tax on the paper. Have several students act as "stamp masters" to collect two markers in tax from each student. After the class has settled down, ask them for their reactions to this exercise. Ask them how the exercise compares to the situation experienced by the colonists.
2. Organize students into home groups of seven. Have group members number off from one through seven. Assign to each number one of the items listed on the board. Have students move to their numbered, or expert, groups. Tell students that they should use the rest of the class period to learn as much as they can about their group's topic. They may use any resources that are available. (If possible, make arrangements for the class to use the library.) Have each expert group prepare two test questions about their assigned topic. One student from each group should write down his or her group's test questions. Tell the groups that they must have their test questions ready by the end of the class period. Explain that all students will be responsible for teaching their home groups everything they have learned about their assigned topic. Caution expert groups to prepare well—each home group will be tested on the test questions created by each expert group. Collect the test questions at the end of the class period and prepare an informal test using the questions.
3. At the beginning of the next class period, have students meet in their home groups for about 30 minutes. Each group member should teach the home group about his or her expert topic. (They should not, however, give away the test questions.) Encourage students to take notes.
4. Distribute the informal test and have students individually complete the test. Use the test scores as an evaluation of the activity.

TOPIC: The Declaration of Independence
TIME: Two class periods
TIME PERIOD: During study of the Declaration of Independence

BACKGROUND

By 1776 a peaceful solution to the colonists' problems with Britain seemed unlikely. By June of that year nearly all of the members of the Second Continental Congress were ready to act. Richard Henry Lee of Virginia proposed a resolution for independence on June 7. But before passing this resolution, Congress appointed a committee to prepare a statement explaining why independence from Britain was necessary. The members of this committee were Robert Livingston of New York, Roger Sherman of Connecticut, Benjamin Franklin of Pennsylvania, John Adams of Massachusetts, and the youngest delegate, 33-year-old Thomas Jefferson of Virginia. Jefferson wrote the first draft of the Declaration in a little more than two weeks. The other members of the committee polished the language of the document and made a few changes. On July 2, 1776, voting by states, the delegates resolved to declare their independence. Then, on July 4, they officially approved the Declaration of Independence.

Although the Declaration may be somewhat difficult for students to read, it contains basic theories of government that all students should know. This teaching strategy breaks the document into manageable sections, enabling students to understand one of the most important documents in our nation's history.

MATERIALS

1. Copies of the Declaration of Independence, broken into six equal sections. Use the document in the textbook and decide how you want to divide it.
2. Copies of the Declaration of Independence Summary Sheets

SUGGESTED PROCEDURE

1. Organize students into six groups. Give each group one section of the Declaration of Independence. Tell students that it is their group's responsibility to become experts on their section of the Declaration. After groups have learned their section of the document, they will teach it to the rest of the class. Allow the groups the rest of the class period to complete the following steps:
   a. One student should act as a "vocabulary specialist" to record unfamiliar words and concepts, although all members of the group will help with the definitions. Students may use the dictionary, the textbook glossary, and any annotations in the textbook.
   b. Students should refer to the textbook for any historical references in their section of the Declaration.
   c. After students think that they understand their section of the Declaration, they will rewrite the section in modern language. Students should divide up the section they have rewritten and assign each group member an equal number of sentences from the rewritten version. Group members will read (in order) their sentences to the rest of the class.
   Note: For a more sophisticated approach, you might organize the class into five groups and assign each group to find evidence in the document that the Declaration is (a) a revolutionary charter, (b) a scientific paper, (c) a moral paper, (d) a propaganda piece, or (e) a national symbol.
2. At the beginning of the next class period, distribute the Declaration of Independence Summary Sheets. Each student will be responsible for listening to each group's version of their section of the Declaration and then writing a two or three sentence summary of that section. Students will also include a summary of their own group's section.
3. Call on the groups in the order in which their sections appear in the Declaration. Ask each group to stand in front of the class and have group members read aloud their modern versions of the Declaration. Allow time after each group for students to fill in their summary sheets.

Declaration of Independence
Summary Sheet

Summary of Section 1:

_____

_____

_____

Summary of Section 2:

_____

_____

_____

Summary of Section 3:

_____

_____

_____

Summary of Section 4:

_____

_____

_____

Summary of Section 5:

_____

_____

_____

Summary of Section 6:

_____

_____

_____

TOPIC: Who's Who in the Revolutionary War
TIME: One class period, with homework
TIME PERIOD: Before students are tested on the Revolutionary War

BACKGROUND

Following the progress of the Revolutionary War can be exciting but confusing. For example, two Clintons fought in the war: one Clinton (George) fought on the side of the Patriots; the other Clinton (Sir Henry) was a British general. Most students are familiar with names such as George Washington, John Adams, Samuel Adams, and Benjamin Franklin. But most students cannot tell you how these individuals participated in the prelude to or in the battles of the Revolutionary War.

This teaching strategy is designed to bring alive the many personalities involved in the Revolutionary War. It will help students assimilate the names and events of the Revolutionary War era. The teaching strategy will be especially helpful in preparing students to be tested on this part of history.

MATERIALS

1. One copy of the worksheet "Who's Who in the Revolutionary War" for each student
2. Slips of paper with one name from the list written on each slip

SUGGESTED PROCEDURE

1. At the end of the class period during which students are finishing their study of the Revolutionary War, ask them to name as many people involved in the Revolutionary War as they remember from reading the textbook. Write the names on the chalkboard as students list them.
2. Distribute copies of the "Who's Who" in the Revolutionary War worksheet. Students will probably be surprised at how many names are on the list. Tell students that during the next class period they are going to play a game. To prepare for the game they should, as homework, write down a few facts about each person on their lists. They should use their textbooks and any other resources available to them, such as encyclopedias and biographical dictionaries. Caution students that it will be to their benefit to do a thorough job. Do not give them any further instructions about the game.
3. At the beginning of the next class period, give each student a slip of paper with the name of one person from the list written on it, and tell them not to show the name to anyone else. Instruct students that the class is going to play a "Who Am I?" game. Explain the following rules:
   a. One student at a time will come up in front of the class and "be" the person on his or her slip of paper. He or she should give one or two minimal clues about the person he or she is portraying. ("I fought on the side of the Patriots," "I did not fight in the war," "I am not an officer," "I fought at the Battle of Trenton," and so on.)
   b. The student will call on one classmate at a time to ask a question that will help the class determine the identity of the historical figure being portrayed. A student may not ask more than one question for each historical figure. Limit the questions in some way, either by a limit on the number of questions (five) or by a limit on the amount of time (90 seconds). Assign a student to record the number of questions it takes to identify each person as well as the student who correctly identifies the person.
   c. Students should ask questions that can be answered by "yes" or "no." Students must keep the questions in the time context. For example, students could not ask "George Washington" if he was ever president.
   d. Students may use their worksheets to help them answer and formulate questions.
4. Have the student recorder tabulate which characters took the least and the most questions to identify. He or she should also determine which student in the class was able to identify the most characters. Tell students that everyone is a winner—they will all be able to perform better on the test covering the material on the Revolutionary War.
   Note: If you have more students than names (32), you might want to include battles of the Revolutionary War.

Who's Who in the Revolutionary War

1. George III: _____

_____

2. Frederick, Lord North: _____

_____

3. Thomas Hutchison: _____

_____

4. Samuel Adams: _____

_____

5. Benjamin Franklin: _____

_____

6. Thomas Gage: _____

_____

7. Samuel Prescott: _____

_____

8. John Pitcairn: _____

_____

9. Ethan Allen: _____

_____

10. William Howe: _____

_____

11. William Prescott: _____

_____

12. George Washington: _____

_____

13. John Hancock: _____

_____

14. John Adams: _____

_____

15. John Burgoyne: _____

_____

16. George Clinton: _____

_____

17. Henry Knox: _____

_____

18. Thomas Paine: _____

_____

19. Thomas Jefferson: _____

_____

20. Crispus Attucks: _____

_____

21. Frederick II: _____

_____

22. Horatio Gates: _____

_____

23. Daniel Morgan: _____

_____

24. Bernardo de Gálvez: _____

_____

25. Benedict Arnold: _____

_____

26. Lafayette: _____

_____

27. Friedrich von Steuben: _____

_____

28. Henry Clinton: _____

_____

29. Charles Cornwallis: _____

_____

30. Nathanael Greene: _____

_____

31. Philip Freneau: _____

_____

32. George Rogers Clark: _____

_____

TOPIC: An Unlikely Soldier
TIME: One to two class periods
TIME PERIOD: During study of the Revolutionary War

BACKGROUND

Deborah Sampson Gannett's childhood was not an easy one. Her father deserted the family when she was an infant. Her mother could not support herself and her children, and when Deborah was five her mother sent Deborah and her brothers and sisters to live with various families. The elderly woman who adopted Deborah died three years later, and Deborah ended up as an indentured servant to the family of Benjamin Thomas, a deacon and farmer. While other girls her age were learning the finer points of becoming "young ladies," Deborah, by choice, was working the farm. The deacon allowed Deborah to accompany his sons to the schoolhouse, and she was an avid student. Deborah was freed from service when she was 18 years old, but she remained with the Thomas family for another two years. At the age of 20 Deborah's adventurous spirit won out, and she decided that the best way to experience the world was to dress as a man. She first tried to enlist in the American Army in the spring of 1782 but was found out. Later that spring she tried again and was successful. She signed up as a private in the 4th Massachusetts Regiment, using her brother's name, Robert Shurtleff. Deborah Sampson Gannett's diary of her experiences as a soldier in the Revolutionary War sank to the bottom of the North River in 1783. Herman Mann wrote a biography of Deborah called *The Female Review*, which Deborah helped him revise. (The source used for this teaching strategy, *Weathering the Storm: Women in the American Revolution*, by Elizabeth Evans, is a fascinating and informative resource on women during the Revolutionary War period.) In this teaching strategy students will read excerpts of the biography, as well as excerpts from an address that Deborah gave to audiences in Massachusetts and New York. Students will use their historical imagination to write entries for Deborah's lost journal.

MATERIALS

1. A transparency or copies of the illustration of the Revolutionary War soldier
2. Copies of the handouts with the excerpts by Deborah Sampson Gannett

SUGGESTED PROCEDURE

1. Before class begins write the following statement on the chalkboard:

   Boston, August 1, 1786

   These may certify that Robert Shurtleff was a soldier in my regiment in the Continental Army, for the town of Uxbridge in the Commonwealth of Massachusetts, and was enlisted for the term of three years; that he had the confidence of his officers, did his duty as a faithful and good soldier, and was honorably discharged the army of the United States.

   Henry Jackson, late Colonel in the American Army

2. Read the statement to the class. Explain that an honorable discharge means that a soldier has behaved well and has completed his or her commitment to the army. Display the transparency or distribute copies of the illustration of the Revolutionary War soldier. Then ask students the following questions:
   a. What do you think a Revolutionary War soldier was like? (Elicit qualities such as age, occupation, education, sex, and so on.)
   b. What kinds of duties do you think a "faithful and good soldier" would perform? (Possible answers: following orders, helping fellow soldiers, performing well in battle, and so on.)
3. Tell students that Robert Shurtleff was not the real name of the soldier in the statement by the colonel and that the soldier's real name was Deborah Sampson Gannett. Ask students:
   a. From what you have learned about women who lived during the colonial period, do you think many women served in the army during the Revolutionary War? (Students will probably say no.)

b. Tell students that women were not allowed to serve in the army. Ask: How do you think a woman was able to join the army?

4. Provide students with the background information on Deborah Sampson Gannett. Distribute the handouts and ask volunteers to read the selections aloud. Discuss the following words and concepts that may be unfamiliar to students:

paroxysm	subjugation	habiliment
philanthropist	pinnacle	phalanx of war
analogous	abyss of destruction	palladium of peace

5. Organize students into groups of four. Each group member should write one diary entry for Deborah Sampson Gannett's lost journal. Students should use their historical imagination and the information from the excerpts to make their entries realistic. They should include thoughtful speculations as to why Deborah Sampson Gannett joined the army. Students should attempt to write their journal entries in the style of the excerpts. Have the groups share their journals with the class.

Parade Dress 1781

Excerpts from *The Female Review*

By Herman Mann, revised with Deborah Sampson Gannett

In June of 1782 Deborah was wounded when she and 30 other soldiers volunteered to flush out armed Tories in East Chester.

I considered this as a death wound, or as being equivalent to it; as it must, I thought, lead to the discovery of my sex. Covered with blood from head to foot, I told my companions I fear I had received a mortal wound; and I begged them to leave me to die on the spot: preferring to take the small chance I should in this case have of surviving, rather than be carried to the hospital. To this my comrades would not consent; but one took me before him on his horse, and in this painful manner I was borne six miles to the hospital of the French army, at a place called Crompond. On coming in sight of the hospital, my heart again failed me. In a paroxysm of dispair, I actually drew a pistol from the holster, and was about to put an end to my life. That I did not proceed to the fatal act, I can ascribe only to the interposition of Divine Mercy.

The French surgeon, on my being brought in, instantly came. He was alert, cheerful, humane. "How you lose so much blood at this early hour? Be any bone broken?" was his first salutation; presenting me and the other wounded men of our party with two bottles of choice wine. My head having been bound up, and a change of clothing becoming a wounded soldier being ready, I was asked by the too inquisitive French surgeon whether I had any other wound. He had observed my extreme paleness, and that I limped in attempting to walk. I readily replied in the negative: it was a plump falsehood! "Sit you down my lad; your boot say you fib!" said the surgeon, noticing that the blood still oozed from it. He took of my boots and stockings with his own hands with great tenderness, and washed my leg to the knee. I then told him I would retire, change my clothing, and if any other wound should appear, I would inform him.

Meanwhile I had procured in the hospital a silver probe a little curved at the end, a needle, some lint, a bandage, and some of the same kind of salve that had been applied to the wound in my head. I found that the ball had penetrated my thigh about two inches, and the wound was still moderately bleeding. The wine had revived me, and God, by his kind care, watched over me. At the third attempt I extracted the ball. . . .

Before the wound in my thigh was half healed, I rejoined the army on the lines. But had the most hardy soldier been in the condition I was when I left the hospital, he would have been excused from military duty.

An Address
Delivered at the Federal-Street Theater, Boston
Four Successive Nights of the Different
Plays, Beginning March 22, 1802
By Mrs. Deborah Gannett

Excerpted

Before Deborah Sampson Gannett delivered her speech, she went through 27 maneuvers of the Manual Exercise of the American Army, dressed in her blue and white uniform and carrying her musket. The following are excerpts from her address.

Not unlike the example of the patriot and philanthropist, though perhaps perfectly so in effect, do I awake from the tranquil slumbers of retirement, to active, public scenes of life, like those who now surround me. . . .

Know then, that my juvenile mind early became inquisitive to understand—not merely whether the principles, or rather the seeds of war are analogous to the genuine nature of man—not merely to know why he should forego every trait of humanity and assume the character of a brute; or, in plainer language, why he should march out tranquilly, or in a paroxysm of rage against his fellow man to butcher, or be butchered? . . .

But most of all, my mind became agitated with enquiry—why a nation, separated from us by an ocean more than three thousand miles in extent, should endeavor to enforce on us plans of subjugation, the most unnatural in themselves, unjust, inhuman in their operations, and unpractised even by the uncivilized savages of the wilderness? . . .

Wrought upon at length by an enthusiasm and frenzy that no could brook no control, I burst the tyrant bonds which held my sex in awe, and clandestinely, or by stealth, grasped an opportunity, which custom and the world seemed to deny, as a natural privilege. And whilst poverty, hunger, nakedness, cold and disease had dwindled the American armies to a handful—whilst universal terror and dismay ran through our camps, ran through our country—while even Washington himself, at their head, though like a god, stood, as it were, on a pinnacle tottering over the abyss of destruction, the last prelude to our falling a wretched prey to the yawning jaws of the monster aiming to devour—I threw off the soft habiliment of my sex, and assumed those of the warrior, already prepared for battle.

Thus I became an actor in that important drama, with an inflexible resolution to persevere through the last scene; when we might be permitted and acknowledged to enjoy what we had so nobly declared we would possess, or lose our lives—freedom and independence! . . .

You may have heard the thunderings of a volcano; you may have contemplated, with astonishment and wonder, the burial of a city by its eruptions. Your ears then are yet deafened from the thunderings of the invasion of York Town. . . .

Three successive weeks, after a long and rapid march, found me amidst this storm. But, happily for America, happily for Europe, perhaps for the whole world, when, on the delivery of Cornwallis's sword to the illustrious, immortal Washington, the sun of liberty and independence burst through a sable cloud, and his benign influence was, almost instantaneously, felt in our remotest corners! The phalanx of war was thus broken through, and the palladium of peace blossomed on its ruins.

TOPIC: Diplomacy and the Treaty of Paris (1783)
TIME: One to two class periods
TIME PERIOD: During study of the Treaty of Paris of 1783

BACKGROUND

Negotiations to end the Revolutionary War began soon after the surrender of Cornwallis in October 1781. Four American commissioners were chosen to represent America in the negotiations: Benjamin Franklin, John Jay, John Adams, and Henry Laurens. The Americans were fortunate to be so ably represented. They were also fortunate that Great Britain was eager to see a quick end to the war. Spain and France were not involved in the negotiations, and if they had been, the Americans probably would have gained only their independence. Instead, they gained independence; established territorial boundaries, gaining all the land between the Appalachian Mountains and the Mississippi River from the Great Lakes south to Florida; protected American fishing rights in Canada; and guaranteed navigation of the Mississippi River. In return, the Americans promised to recommend the restoration of Loyalist property confiscated during the war and to recommend the repayment of private debts owed by Americans to the English.

France was not represented in the peace talks until these decisions had already been reached. France was angry as well as surprised that the United States and Great Britain had agreed upon peace terms. Franklin had to use all of his arts of persuasion to smooth the ruffled feathers of the French leaders. His success in negotiating the final Treaty of Paris in 1783 proved his great skill as a diplomat. In this teaching strategy students will learn about and participate in the steps involved in the process of diplomacy.

SUGGESTED PROCEDURE

1. Provide students with the background information about the Treaty of Paris. Ask students to define the following words: treaty, diplomat, negotiate, compromise. Explain to or elicit from students the following steps used in the process of diplomacy.
   a. A diplomat represents the country to protect the country's interests in dealing with foreign nations.
   b. The diplomat goes through a process of negotiation with representatives of other nations. Compromises are reached during the negotiations. The diplomat receives and analyzes the information and sends reports back to the United States. More negotiation and compromise may be needed for both sides to reach agreement.
   c. The final step is the writing of a document setting forth the agreements between or among the nations.
2. Have students explain how the Treaty of Paris followed these steps of diplomacy.
3. Tell students that they are going to play the role of diplomats. Organize students into groups of two. One student will play the part of a teenager and the other student will play the part of a parent. Students must identify the issues, follow the steps of diplomacy (except for reporting back to the United States), and write a final document that clearly expresses the terms of agreement. Students may choose from the following suggested problems or they may use one of their own.
   a. The teenager wants a dog, but the parent says the teenager is not responsible enough to take care of it.
   b. The teenager wants the parent to buy the teenager a pair of $100 famous-brand tennis shoes that "everybody is wearing." The parent says that the shoes are not affordable.
   c. The teenager wants to participate in an after-school activity, but the parent says that the teenager must come home right after school to complete homework assignments.
   d. The teenager's bedtime has been nine o'clock since the teenager was 10 years old, and the teenager thinks that the hour should be extended to 10 o'clock. The parent does not agree.
   e. The teenager has been invited to a party on Saturday night, but the teenager has been "grounded" as punishment for not doing assigned chores.
   f. The teenager has saved up money to buy an electric guitar, but the parent says that the guitar will be too noisy.
   g. The teenager wants to spend the night at a friend's house, but the parent needs the teenager to babysit for a younger sibling.
   h. The teenager wants to spend Sunday with friends, but the parent wants the teenager to stay home because the teenager's grandparents are coming to visit.

4. Ask volunteers to read their written documents to the class. Then discuss with students the following questions:

    a. Were there any problems involved in the negotiations?

    b. How did you solve those problems?

    c. What qualities do you think a diplomat from the United States negotiating with a foreign country should have? (Elicit qualities such as intelligence, loyalty, dedication to country, skill in foreign languages, and so on.)

    d. What have you learned about Benjamin Franklin that makes you think he was a good diplomat?

Creative Strategies for Teaching American History

Governing the New Nation
1777–1803

TOPIC: The Need for a Constitution
TIME: One or two class periods
TIME PERIOD: During study of the Articles of Confederation and the Constitutional Convention

---

BACKGROUND

After declaring their independence in 1776, the colonies needed to develop a plan of government to replace British rule. This was a two-part task, for the colonists needed to form governments on both the state and national levels. As Congress attended to the task of a national constitution, the individual colonies began forming their own governments and writing their own constitutions. Soon all of the colonies had written and adopted constitutions, thus becoming states.

In November of 1777 Congress revealed its plan to unify the states—the Articles of Confederation. (A confederation is an association that allows many governments to work toward goals shared by all.) The Articles of Confederation made no real changes in the way "The United States of America" was already operating. It simply put into writing the powers that the Continental Congress was already exercising. By stressing the independence of the individual states, the Articles set up what was basically a "league of friendship" among them.

The Articles limited the powers of the central government. Although it could deal with other countries, make war and peace, and issue and borrow money, the central government had little authority. The states retained all control over trade and over taxation. Much of the content of the Articles of Confederation was a reaction to British rule. The writers of the Articles intentionally created a weak central government.

The government under the Articles did accomplish several important goals. It ended the Revolutionary War, negotiated the Treaty of Paris of 1783, and established a system for the development of western lands. The end of the Revolutionary War was a great blessing. But the end of the war also brought out the problems of a government that was only a league of friendship. States bickered among themselves. Problems with trade and money convinced many people that the United States needed to revise the Articles.

The trade problem almost ruined many American merchants and manufacturers. After the war British manufacturers began selling their products in America at very low prices. The British government also placed severe restrictions on United States trade with the West Indies. High United States tariffs on British imports might have persuaded the British to remove trade restrictions and would have protected American businesses. But the government did not have the power under the Articles of Confederation to put tariffs on foreign goods.

The money problem was equally threatening to American welfare. Under the Articles the government was denied the power to tax. The system of asking the states for money never worked well. To pay its bills and war debts the government simply printed more and more paper money, called Continental dollars. Because so much of this money was in circulation, it soon became worthless. People lost confidence in it. The same thing happened to money printed by the states. Everyone wanted payment in gold or silver, not paper. But there was not enough gold and silver to go around.

Shays' Rebellion was the final straw. When the Massachusetts legislature decided to raise taxes, the poor farmers in the western part of the state were hit very hard. Many farms were seized and sold. Daniel Shays, a farmer and Revolutionary War veteran, led a group of farmers into Springfield. Although the state militia put down the disturbance, the message was clear. The national government needed the power to handle certain problem situations.

In this teaching strategy students will imagine themselves as American citizens living under the Articles of Confederation. They will come to see that most of the problems that Americans were having could not be solved under the form of government established by the Articles.

MATERIALS

1. Copies of problem statement worksheets for each group. Separate the sections after you copy them.
2. Copies of the "Congressional Checklist" for members of the Congress of Confederation

SUGGESTED PROCEDURE

1. Provide students with the background information on the Articles of Confederation and the situation after the Revolutionary War.

2. Organize the class into eight groups, and give each group a problem statement worksheet. Tell the groups to imagine that they are members of the group described on the handout. They should discuss their problem and decide what they want the government to do to solve it. They should write this request on the worksheet along with the reasons that they think the solution will work. The group should come up with one solution, but each group member should complete his or her own worksheet. If the group members cannot come up with a solution, have them leave the space blank, but they should explain why they were unable to arrive at a solution.

3. Once the groups have completed their worksheets, have students select 13 classmates to represent the states in Congress. There should be at least one student from each group. Give each of these students a "Congressional Checklist." Tell them that they are to decide what to do about each of the problems about to be presented. Remind them, however, that the Articles of Confederation are specific about what they may and may not do. Point out the powers and limitations in the Articles at the top of the checklists. Have them refer to their checklists as they make their decisions.

4. Have a spokesperson from each group read the group's request and reasoning. Encourage the members of Congress to take notes on their checklists under the appropriate problem number. After they have heard all of the requests, have the members of the Continental Congress briefly discuss the problems aloud and vote on solutions. Remind them that they have only the powers granted by the Articles and that they must consider all related requests when creating a solution.

5. Display on an overhead projector the powers and limitations in the Articles (from the "Congressional Checklist"), or write them on the chalkboard so that the entire class may see them. Have a spokesperson from the Congress of Confederation read their decision about each group's problem. Allow the eight groups to react to the solutions. Then ask the class if the solution would work under the Articles. (For example, Congress could establish an army but could not draft troops!)

6. As a closure activity, discuss the following question: What could be done to make the central government more effective? (Suggested response: the government needs more specific and general authority, and most importantly, it needs to be able to enforce the laws that it passes.)

Problem Statement Worksheet 1

Directions: Imagine that you are members of the group described below. Discuss your problem and then decide what you want the government to do about it. Write your request to the government along with your reasons that you think this solution will solve your problem.

_____

You are a group of frontier settlers. During the last year the Indians on the frontier have raided your settlements, killing several settlers, burning farms and homes, and stealing livestock. The Indians then escape into the woods across the borders of neighboring states or into unclaimed territory. What do you want the government to do?

Request

_____

_____

Reasons

_____

_____

_____

- -

Problem Statement Worksheet 2

Directions: Imagine that you are members of the group described below. Discuss your problem and then decide what you want the government to do about it. Write your request to the government along with your reasons that you think this solution will solve your problem.

_____

You are a group of merchants. During the war you built a prosperous trade throughout all the colonies. You shipped goods through seaports and over roads. Now several states have begun to tax goods coming into their states. They even tax goods shipped *through* their states to other destinations. Your business is suffering. You have had to add the cost of the taxes to your price, making it impossible for you to compete with local merchants. It also is difficult to ship your trade around the states charging the taxes. What do you want the government to do?

Request

_____

Reasons

_____

_____

_____

Problem Statement Worksheet 3

Directions: Imagine that you are members of the group described below. Discuss your problem and then decide what you want the government to do about it. Write your request to the government along with your reasons that you think this solution will solve your problem.

_____

You are a group of poor farmers. Since the end of the war the value of farm products has fallen. It is impossible for you to raise enough money to pay your mortgages and to buy supplies. There just does not seem to be enough money to go around. Some of your neighbors want to take up arms and raid the banks in the area. What do you want the government to do?

Request

_____
_____
_____

Reasons

_____
_____
_____

Problem Statement Worksheet 4

Directions: Imagine that you are members of the group described below. Discuss your problem and then decide what you want the government to do about it. Write your request to the government along with your reasons that you think this solution will solve your problem.

_____

You are a group of frontier settlers. Residents in your area have always enjoyed a good relationship with the local Indians. In recent months, however, settlers from a neighboring state have stormed across the state border and attacked the Indians in your area. The settlers claim that they are seeking revenge for Indian attacks on their settlements, but now the settlers are attacking innocent Indians in your state. The Indians in your area are preparing to call a war council. What do you want the government to do?

Request

_____
_____

Reasons

_____
_____
_____

Problem Statement Worksheet 5

Directions: Imagine that you are members of the group described below. Discuss your problem and then decide what you want the government to do about it. Write your request to the government along with your reasons that you think this solution will solve your problem.

You are a group of typical early American families. In recent months supplies of many items, necessities and luxuries, have dried up. It is harder and harder to find the goods that you want and need. The merchants claim they can no longer ship goods to your state because the state now charges taxes on all items shipped into the state. The state claims that it needs the taxes to maintain roads and pay the state militia. What do you want the government to do?

Request

_____

_____

Reasons

_____

_____

_____

- -

Problem Statement Worksheet 6

Directions: Imagine that you are members of the group described below. Discuss your problem and then decide what you want the government to do about it. Write your request to the government along with your reasons that you think this solution will solve your problem.

You are a group of wealthy citizens. Some states have begun to print more state currency. You absolutely oppose this plan. The more money that is in circulation, the less your money is worth. What do you want the government to do?

Request

_____

_____

Reasons

_____

_____

_____

Problem Statement Worksheet 7

Directions: Imagine that you are members of the group described below. Discuss your problem and then decide what you want the government to do about it. Write your request to the government along with your reasons that you think this solution will solve your problem.

_____

You are a group of business owners. The banks in your state have just changed their policy. They will no longer honor currency from other states. Now you may only use money issued by your state. You must exchange all other currency for state money. The banks will give only one dollar for every three dollars of other currency. Since you do much of your business with customers in other states, this will soon put you out of business. What do you want the government to do?

Request

_____
_____

Reasons

_____
_____
_____

- -

Problem Statement Worksheet 8

Directions: Imagine that you are members of the group described below. Discuss your problem and then decide what you want the government to do about it. Write your request to the government along with your reasons that you think this solution will solve your problem.

_____

You are a group of concerned citizens that live in areas that border lands held by Great Britain. A neighboring state encouraged the British to build a fort nearby, which they did. You have noticed large numbers of troops entering the fort near your lands. There must be 10,000 by now. You and your neighbors are afraid that the British and their Indian allies are preparing to attack. Still, people in the neighboring state are encouraging the British to settle the area because it is good for their businesses. What do you want the government to do?

Request

_____
_____

Reasons

_____
_____
_____

Congressional Checklist

Directions: As members of the Continental Congress, your job is to try and solve the problems brought to you by the American citizens. In the space provided, take notes as each group presents its problem. As you look for solutions, keep in mind the following powers and limitations in the Articles of Confederation.

Power to

- Issue and borrow money
- Establish weights and measures
- Establish a postal system
- Appoint military officers
- Establish an army and a navy
- Handle diplomatic affairs with foreign nations
- Handle affairs with American Indians
- Arbitrate differences between states

NO power to

- Enforce its own laws
- Collect taxes
- Control trade among the states
- Raise troops
- Establish national courts to hear disputes between states

Problem 1: _____
_____
_____
_____

Problem 2: _____
_____
_____
_____

Problem 3: _____
_____
_____
_____

Problem 4: _____

_____

_____

_____

Problem 5: _____

_____

_____

_____

Problem 6: _____

_____

_____

_____

Problem 7: _____

_____

_____

_____

Problem 8: _____

_____

_____

_____

TOPIC: The Constitutional Convention—The Key Was Compromise
TIME: One to two class periods
TIME PERIOD: During study of the Constitutional Convention

BACKGROUND

On May 25, 1787, the delegates to the Constitutional Convention got down to business. They decided to keep the proceedings secret so that all the delegates could speak freely. No formal journal was kept; however, James Madison was allowed to take notes. Without his notes we would know very little about what went on behind those closed doors in Philadelphia.

Most of the representatives were quite young. James Madison, often called the Father of the Constitution, was 36 years old. The oldest delegate was Benjamin Franklin, age 81, but the average age of the delegates was 42. The framers represented a new generation in America that had grown up during the revolution against England. They had experienced self-government under the Articles of Confederation. The delegates came from various backgrounds. They included farmers, merchants, businessmen, and politicians. The group included some of the most notable figures in America, but because of their diverse backgrounds and interests, conflicts arose from the very beginning of the convention. Delegates stomped out. Several times the convention was almost called off. The key to the success of the convention and the document that evolved was compromise.

In this teaching strategy students will become familiar with three of the chief compromises made at the convention: the compromise over the powers of the national government, the "Great Compromise" over representation in Congress, and the compromise over the slavery issue. By portraying delegates at the convention, students will become better acquainted with the unique group of people who wrote the Constitution.

MATERIALS

Copies of the "Compromise Committee" worksheets

SUGGESTED PROCEDURE

1. Ask the class to define the word *compromise*. Ask volunteers to relate experiences in which they have had to compromise. Then provide students with the background information.
2. Organize the class into six groups. Assign two groups to each compromise. Distribute the appropriate "Compromise Committee" worksheet to all students in each group. Tell students to imagine that they are members of a compromise committee at the Constitutional Convention. Depending on group size, have each student choose one of the committee members listed on the handout. If there are more than four students in a group, more than one student may portray a committee member.
3. Allow the groups 15 minutes to discuss and arrive at a compromise. Remind students to think about the states that their particular committee members represent and to use their historical imaginations to stay in the character of their committee members.
4. Have a spokesperson from each group read their group's compromise. Allow the class to discuss each compromise, explaining why they think the compromise would or would not work.
5. After all the groups have presented their compromises, have each group find the actual compromise in the Constitution that was reached by the delegates to the Constitutional Convention. Have the groups discuss the similarities and differences between their compromises and the compromises contained in the Constitution.

Compromise Committee on the Powers
of the National Government

Directions: Choose one of the following delegates to portray. Then, with your group, work out a compromise for the problem discussed below.

For a strong national government:
Oliver Ellsworth—Connecticut
James Wilson—Delaware

Against a strong national government:
Luther Martin—Maryland
John Lansing—New York

You are on the compromise committee to solve the disagreement over how much power the national government and state governments should have under the new Constitution. You all agree that under the Articles of Confederation the central government did not enough power to control the states. But just how much power should the new national government have over the state governments and their citizens? Think about the following questions as you arrive at your compromise.

1. What should the states be prohibited from doing?

2. What should the national government be prohibited from doing?

3. What powers should the national government have?

4. What powers should the state governments have?

5. Who should enforce the laws?

6. How can the states be protected from invasion or domestic violence?

7. Should the national government's laws and the new Constitution be the supreme law of the land, or should the state governments' constitutions and laws be the supreme law of the land?

Compromise Committee on Representation in Congress

Directions: Choose one of the following delegates to portray. Then, with your group, work out a compromise for the problem discussed below.

___

Equal representation:

Gunning Bedford Jr.—Delaware

Jonathan Dayton—New Jersey

Proportionate representation, based on population:

Edmund Randolph—Virginia

William Houstoun—Georgia

You are on the compromise committee to solve the disagreement over representation in Congress. Small states want equal representation. Large states want representation to be in proportion to a state's population. This disagreement is threatening to break up the convention. A compromise must be reached. Think about the following questions as you arrive at your compromise.

1. How many houses of Congress should there be?

2. On what basis should representatives to the house(s) be elected?

3. Which house should have the power to develop bills for taxing and government spending? Why?

4. How will you know how many people live in each state?

Compromise Committee on the Issue of Slavery

Directions: Choose one of the following delegates to portray. Then, with your group, work out a compromise for the problem discussed below.

For continuation of the slave trade:
Hugh Williamson—South Carolina
Abraham Baldwin—Georgia

Against continuation of the slave trade:
George Mason—Virginia
Gouverneur Morris—Pennsylvania

You are on the compromise committee to solve the disagreement over the issue of slavery. Several of the southern states will not agree to the new Constitution unless they continue to have the right to import foreign slaves. Most northern states are opposed to slavery and the importation of foreign slaves, but they want and need the southern states' approval of the Constitution. Think about the following questions as you arrive at your compromise.

1. Since slaves cannot vote, should they be counted if the number of representatives from each state is being determined by population?

2. Should the importation of foreign slaves be abolished now or later?

3. What will happen to the economy of the South if the slave trade is abolished?

4. Should slaves who have escaped to free states be returned to their owners?

TOPIC: What Is in the Articles?
TIME: One class period, with homework
TIME PERIOD: During study of the content of the articles of the Constitution

BACKGROUND

Understanding the organization and the content of the Constitution is of primary importance for students. This teaching strategy focuses on the seven articles and uses a game in which students review this information. The game played in this strategy is based on the *Jeopardy!* game-show format. Students will be given an answer and they must come up with the question for the answer. Each answer and question is worth a certain number of points. The more difficult the answer and question, the more points are awarded. Most students will be familiar with the game, and they should enjoy this method of learning the information contained in the seven articles.

MATERIALS

Transparencies or copies of the "answers" for "Constitution," "Double Constitution"

SUGGESTED PROCEDURE

1. At the end of the class period during which students have been studying the articles of the Constitution, tell them that during the next class period they will be playing a game based on the seven articles. Organize the class into groups of four. Ask students if any of them have ever seen the game show *Jeopardy!* Have a student explain to the rest of the class how the game works. If students are not familiar with the game, explain the basic format: An answer to a question will be given. Students must come up with the question for the answer. Each question and answer combination will be worth from one to five points. The more difficult the combination, the more points it is worth. Tell students that to prepare for the game, they should reread the seven articles of the Constitution.

2. Choose one student from each group to be the announcer—the person who states the answers and calls on the three other group members to give the questions. Give the announcer a copy of the game answers to take home. As homework, that student should find in the Constitution the correct questions for the answers. Ask the announcer not the reveal the questions and answers to other students.

3. At the beginning of the next class period, ask students to meet with their groups. To begin the game, one group member asks for a category and a point value. (For example, the student might say, "Article I for two points.") The announcer reads the answer and calls on the first group member to raise his or her hand. That student states the question for that answer. The response must always be in the form of a question. If the question is incorrect, the announcer calls on another group member. The student with the correct question chooses the next category and point value. If no one knows the correct question, then the student who chose that category and point value chooses again. Have the announcer record the points for each group member.

4. When all groups have finished, call the whole class together. The student with the most points from each group will go on to play "Double Constitution" with the winning members from all of the groups. "Double Constitution" should be played as a class, with you or an appointed student acting as the announcer. The winners from each group should stand at the front of the class. The rest of the class may participate by writing the questions to the answers as they are given. Stress that class members must not shout out the answers. Ask a student to record points. The three students with the most points will go on to play "Final Constitution." These three students will have 30 seconds to write the question to the "Final Constitution" answer. Decide on an appropriate reward for the student (or students) who writes the correct question to the "Final Constitution" answer.

"Final Constitution" answer: The man who was president of the constitutional convention (Who was George Washington?)

"Questions" to Student "Answers"

"Constitution"

Points	Article I	Article II	Article III
1	What is the legislative branch?	What is the executive branch?	What is the judicial branch?
2	What is Congress?	What is 35 years old?	What is the Supreme Court?
3	What is two?	What is four years?	What is treason?
4	What is the Senate?	What is commander in chief?	What is "good"?
5	What are *ex post facto* laws?	What is the Senate	What is Congress?

"Double Constitution"

Points	Articles IV, V, VI, & VII	Checks & Balances	Grab Bag
1	What is national supremacy?	What is the executive branch?	Who is the president?
2	What is nine?	What is the legislative branch?	What is the legislative branch?
3	What is a religious test?	What is the judicial branch?	What is the Preamble?
4	What is a republican form of government?	What is the executive branch?	What is the House of Representatives?
5	What is three-fourths of the states?	What is the legislative branch?	What are electors?

Constitution!

Points	Article I	Article II	Article III
1	*1* Branch of government discussed in Article I	Branch of government discussed in Article II *6*	Branch of government discussed in Article III *9*
2	*2* The body of government consisting of the House of Representatives and the Senate	*3* Minimum age a president can be	*4* Highest court in the United States
3	*4* Number of senators from each state	*5* Term of office for the president	The word for giving aid and comfort to an enemy of the United States
4	*7* The only house of Congress that can try impeachments	*8* The president is "this" of the army and navy	Judges hold office during "this" kind of behavior
5	*10* Laws that punish people for doing something that was legal before the law was passed	*11* The house of Congress that consents to treaties made by the president	*12* The body of government that establishes inferior courts

Double Constitution!

Points	Articles IV, V, VI, & VII	Checks & Balances	Grab Bag
1	What Article VI discusses 13	This branch can veto a law passed by Congress 14	The person who gives a state of the union address 15
2	Number of states needed to ratify the Constitution	This branch can impeach a president 16	The branch with the power to coin and regulate money 17
3	This kind of test is *not* required for qualification of government officials	This branch decides on the meaning of the laws 18	What the introduction to the Constitution is called 19
4	The form of government guaranteed to every state	This branch enforces the laws 20	Bills for raising money originate in this house 21
5	The number of states needed to ratify an amendment	This branch can refuse to approve appointment of judges	What the people who elect the voters are called 22

TOPIC: The Debate over Ratification
TIME: One to two class periods
TIME PERIOD: During study of the ratification of the Constitution

BACKGROUND

A monumental task took place behind closed doors from May 25, 1787, until September 17, 1787. In just four months a group of men argued, theorized, fought, debated, compromised, and finally drafted the Constitution of the United States. Seventy-nine men were invited to the Constitutional Convention. Fifty-five attended. Thirty-nine signed the document on September 17. George Mason of Virginia walked out, saying that he could not sign a document that gave such tyrannical power to a central government. Alexander Hamilton left the Convention, saying that the document did not give the central government enough power. He later returned to Philadelphia to sign.

But the battle for making the Constitution a working form of government had just begun. The Constitution needed to be ratified. James Madison proposed the method of ratification. Fearful that Congress or the state legislatures would not ratify a document the writing of which had not received their permission, Madison proposed that the people from each state vote to elect delegates to special ratifying conventions. Moreover, he proposed that approval be necessary from only nine of the 13 states. Opposition to this plan came from the Antifederalists, people against the ratification of the new Constitution. They protested on the grounds that Madison's method was "unconstitutional." Under the Articles of Confederation, the approval of all 13 states was needed for the document to be amended. And until the Constitution was ratified, the Articles were the Constitution.

The Antifederalists had been given that unfortunate name because the Federalists had cleverly chosen their name first. The Federalists were basically nationalists. They were in favor of a strong central government. The Antifederalists were in favor of federalism, or a close association of the states. The Antifederalists tried to make the Federalists look bad by calling themselves "Anti-Rats" and calling the Federalists "Rats." Prominent Antifederalists included Richard Henry Lee of Virginia, who wrote a piece in opposition to the Constitution titled *Letters from the Federal Farmer*. Other Antifederalists included the playwright Mercy Otis Warren, Patrick Henry, Robert Yates, John Lansing, Jr., and George Mason.

On the Federalists' side were James Madison, Benjamin Franklin, George Washington, Alexander Hamilton, and John Jay. Under the pseudonym of "Publius," Madison, Hamilton, and Jay wrote a series of newspaper essays in favor of the new Constitution. The 85 essays were later published in two volumes titled *The Federalist*.

The Federalists had the advantage. They were well-organized and had prepared well for the battle for ratification. But the Antifederalists put up a good fight. On June 12, 1788, New Hampshire's delegates voted to ratify the Constitution. New Hampshire was the necessary ninth state. But everyone knew that unless the rich and powerful states of New York and Virginia ratified, the new government would never be successful. Virginia ratified on June 25, 1788, and New York on July 26, 1788. The Constitution could be put into action.

In this teaching strategy students will develop an understanding for both sides of the debate over ratification. Students will learn how and why the Bill of Rights was added to the Constitution. They will learn that although the Constitution is not perfect, it has provided an organized form of representative government that has survived for more than 200 years.

MATERIALS

1. Copies of the "Federalist Information Sheet"
2. Copies of the "Antifederalist Information Sheet"
3. Copies of the "Ballot: Should the Constitution Be Ratified?"

SUGGESTED PROCEDURE

1. Provide students with the background information. Explain to students that the Antifederalists and the Federalists were all Americans. Both groups had fought for independence from Britain. Both groups had

lived under the Articles of Confederation and wanted the best government for their country. Their basic difference lay in the amount of power the central government should have while still allowing representation by state and local governments and preserving individual liberties. Remind students that the basic principle behind the Magna Carta, the English Bill of Rights, and the Declaration of Independence was the security of the rights of the people.

2. Tell students that they are going to participate in the debate for ratification in the state of New York. Ask them to imagine that they live on the East Coast in 1787. Organize the class into three equal groups.

   a. One group will portray the Federalists. Give each member of the Federalist group the "Federalist Information Sheet."

   b. One group will portray the Antifederalists. Give each member of the Antifederalist group the "Antifederalist Information Sheet."

   c. One group will portray delegates to the ratifying convention to the state of New York. Give each group member a copy of the "Federalist Information Sheet" and a copy of the "Antifederalist Information Sheet."

3. Explain to students that the Federalists will be debating the Antifederalists about ratification of the Constitution. You should act as moderator. The delegates to the ratifying convention will ask members of the other two groups specific questions about their thoughts on the Constitution. One delegate at a time will pose a question to a member of either the Antifederalist group or the Federalist group. That person will answer the question and then the opposing side will have a chance to respond.

4. Allow students to work in their groups to discuss their information sheets. Tell students that they will need to refer to specific parts of the Constitution. Students should fill in the reasons and/or proofs on the worksheets. Each side will have to be prepared to provide an answer to an argument of the other side. The delegates will need to be prepared to question both sides.

5. To begin the debate, you, as moderator, should introduce the groups. Ask a delegate to begin the debate by posing a question to one member of either the Federalists or Antifederalists and proceed from there. Keep the class in order, but allow them to participate fully in the debate. Remind students to refer to specific parts of the Constitution in their arguments and to use their historical imaginations to stay in character.

6. After groups have exhausted the topics on the information sheets, distribute the ballots and ask students to vote for or against ratification of the Constitution. They should vote as if they lived in 1787 and had no knowledge of history after that date. Tell the Federalists and Antifederalists that they do not have to vote for their side. It may be that the other side presented such a good case that they have changed sides.

7. Have several students help you tally the vote and announce the result to the class. Ask students: What was the most important factor in your vote? (Most students will probably say the addition of a bill of rights.)

ANTIFEDERALIST INFORMATION SHEET

1. The Constitution allows for a national government that is far too strong. It takes power away from the state and local governments.
   Reason 1: _____
   Reason 2: _____
   Reason 3: _____

2. The executive branch has more power than either the legislative or judicial branch.
   Reason 1: _____
   Reason 2: _____
   Reason 3: _____

3. The "necessary and proper" clause gives Congress too much power.
   Reason 1: _____
   Reason 2: _____
   Reason 3: _____

4. The Constitution does not give the voters enough control over the officials running the federal government.
   Reason 1: _____
   Reason 2: _____
   Reason 3: _____

5. The country is too big and too populated for one government to keep the peoples' best interests in mind.
   Reason 1: _____
   Reason 2: _____
   Reason 3: _____

6. The Constitution does not include a bill of rights. The government will rob the people of their liberties.
   Reason 1: _____
   Reason 2: _____
   Reason 3: _____

FEDERALIST INFORMATION SHEET

1. The Constitution divides powers between the federal and state governments.
    Proof 1: _____
    Proof 2: _____
    Proof 3: _____

2. The Constitution is based on a system of separation of powers and checks and balances.
    Proof 1: _____
    Proof 2: _____
    Proof 3: _____

3. The Constitution provides for a strong central government to manage the economic and other problems facing the new nation.
    Proof 1: _____
    Proof 2: _____
    Proof 3: _____

4. The Constitution provides for a representative government.
    Proof 1: _____
    Proof 2: _____
    Proof 3: _____

5. The country is big and diverse. It needs a central government to protect peoples' rights and promote the general welfare.
    Proof 1: _____
    Proof 2: _____
    Proof 3: _____

6. The Constitution organizes the government in such a way that it is impossible to violate the rights of the people.
    Proof 1: _____
    Proof 2: _____
    Proof 3: _____

BALLOT

SHOULD THE CONSTITUTION BE RATIFIED?

_____

YES ☐
REASONS:

_____
_____
_____
_____
_____
_____
_____
_____

NO ☐
REASONS:

_____
_____
_____
_____
_____
_____
_____
_____

TOPIC: The History Behind the Bill of Rights
TIME: One to two class periods
TIME PERIOD: During study of the Bill of Rights

BACKGROUND

Alexander Hamilton was one of the opponents of the addition of the Bill of Rights to the Constitution. He gave four arguments against adding a bill of rights. First, he said that the Constitution already protected rights. He reminded people that the Constitution promised writs of *habeas corpus* and that it did not allow *ex post facto* laws. His next argument was that it was much more important for the states to promise rights to the people than for the national government to do so. The states, he said, would be making laws and decisions about all sorts of things, whereas the national government would be making laws for only a few general purposes. Thus the national government would have fewer reasons to violate rights. Hamilton's third argument was that the main purpose of a bill of rights was to limit the powers of a king in order to protect the rights of the people. The new government, however, would belong to the people themselves. The new Constitution did not allow titles of nobility, and kings would not rule the country. His fourth argument was that there was little need to limit a government's power if that government did not possess power in the first place. If the government did not have the power to limit freedom of the press, then there was no need to write down the right to freedom of the press. In fact, Hamilton thought that writing down limits to powers that the government did not possess might even be dangerous. Writing down limits to power might confuse people about what powers the government *did* possess.

By now students will have learned that the addition of the Bill of Rights to the Constitution was a compromise by the Federalists to the Antifederalists. But why were the Antifederalists and many other Americans so insistent about a bill of rights? In this teaching strategy students will use their historical imaginations and their knowledge of English and American history to suggest reasons that the Bill of Rights was added to the Constitution.

MATERIALS

Copies of the "We Demand Our Rights!" worksheets. Separate the sections after you copy them.

SUGGESTED PROCEDURE

1. Remind students that the addition of the Bill of Rights to the Constitution was the principle condition of several states for their ratification of the Constitution. Provide students with the background information about Alexander Hamilton's four arguments against adding a bill of rights to the Constitution.
2. Organize students into 10 groups. Tell the class that they will imagine themselves as American citizens in 1789. Assign each group one of the amendments to the Bill of Rights. Distribute the "We Demand Our Rights!" worksheet to each group. Tell the groups that they will be responsible for researching the reasons that the American people wanted the assigned amendment added to the Constitution. They should use their textbooks and other classroom resources. Remind students to research English history as well as American history. Each student in the group should play the part of an American citizen of their choice in 1789. Tell students that they should be prepared to explain their point of view to a "congressional committee" (the rest of the class).
3. Allow the groups about 30 minutes to prepare for the "congressional hearing." Call on groups in turn to present their arguments for their particular amendment.
4. After all groups have presented their amendments, have the class reach a consensus about which amendments should be included in the Bill of Rights.

WE DEMAND OUR RIGHTS!

Study the amendment written below. Each member of your group should portray an American citizen in 1789 and use that character's point of view to argue for the inclusion of your amendment in the Bill of Rights. For example, if you are assigned Amendment 1, one member of your group might choose to play the part of a Quaker. Another group member might choose to play the part of a newspaper editor. Each group member should complete his or her worksheet, based on the character that the group member has decided to portray. Use your textbook and other resources to find historical reasons for your arguments.

Amendment 1. Religious and Political Freedom

Congress shall make no law respecting an establishment of religion, or prohibiting the free exercise thereof; or abridging the freedom of speech, or of the press; or the right of the people peaceably to assemble, and to petition the Government for a redress of grievances.

  1. American citizen you will portray: _____

  2. Your arguments for the addition of this amendment to the Bill of Rights:

    _____

    _____

    _____

- -

WE DEMAND OUR RIGHTS!

Study the amendment written below. Each member of your group should portray an American citizen in 1789 and use that character's point of view to argue for the inclusion of your amendment in the Bill of Rights. For example, if you are assigned Amendment 1, one member of your group might choose to play the part of a Quaker. Another group member might choose to play the part of a newspaper editor. Each group member should complete his or her worksheet, based on the character that the group member has decided to portray. Use your textbook and other resources to find historical reasons for your arguments.

Amendment 2. Right to Bear Arms

A well regulated militia, being necessary to the security of a free State, the right of the people to keep and bear arms, shall not be infringed.

  1. American citizen you will portray: _____

  2. Your arguments for the addition of this amendment to the Bill of Rights:

    _____

    _____

    _____

WE DEMAND OUR RIGHTS!

Study the amendment written below. Each member of your group should portray an American citizen in 1789 and use that character's point of view to argue for the inclusion of your amendment in the Bill of Rights. For example, if you are assigned Amendment 1, one member of your group might choose to play the part of a Quaker. Another group member might choose to play the part of a newspaper editor. Each group member should complete his or her worksheet, based on the character that the group member has decided to portray. Use your textbook and other resources to find historical reasons for your arguments.

Amendment 3. Quartering of Soldiers

No soldier shall, in time of peace be quartered in any house, without the consent of the owner, nor in time of war, but in a manner to be prescribed by law.

1. American citizen you will portray: _____

2. Your arguments for the addition of this amendment to the Bill of Rights:

_____

_____

_____

WE DEMAND OUR RIGHTS!

Study the amendment written below. Each member of your group should portray an American citizen in 1789 and use that character's point of view to argue for the inclusion of your amendment in the Bill of Rights. For example, if you are assigned Amendment 1, one member of your group might choose to play the part of a Quaker. Another group member might choose to play the part of a newspaper editor. Each group member should complete his or her worksheet, based on the character that the group member has decided to portray. Use your textbook and other resources to find historical reasons for your arguments.

Amendment 4. Search and Seizure

The right of the people to be secure in their person, houses, papers, and effects, against unreasonable searches and seizures, shall not be violated, and no warrants shall issue, but upon probable cause, supported by oath or affirmation, and particularly describing the place to be searched, and the persons or things to be seized.

1. American citizen you will portray: _____

2. Your arguments for the addition of this amendment to the Bill of Rights:

_____

_____

_____

WE DEMAND OUR RIGHTS!

Study the amendment written below. Each member of your group should portray an American citizen in 1789 and use that character's point of view to argue for the inclusion of your amendment in the Bill of Rights. For example, if you are assigned Amendment 1, one member of your group might choose to play the part of a Quaker. Another group member might choose to play the part of a newspaper editor. Each group member should complete his or her worksheet, based on the character that the group member has decided to portray. Use your textbook and other resources to find historical reasons for your arguments.

Amendment 5. Criminal Process; Due Process of Law

No person shall be held to answer for a capital, or otherwise infamous crime, unless on a presentment or indictment of a Grand Jury, except in cases arising in the land or naval forces, or in the militia, when in actual service in time of war or public danger; nor shall any person be subject for the same offense to be twice put in jeopardy of life or limb; nor shall be compelled in any criminal case to be a witness against himself, nor be deprived of life, liberty, or property, without due process of law; nor shall private property be taken for public use, without just compensation.

1. American citizen you will portray: _____

2. Your arguments for the addition of this amendment to the Bill of Rights:

_____

_____

_____

WE DEMAND OUR RIGHTS!

Study the amendment written below. Each member of your group should portray an American citizen in 1789 and use that character's point of view to argue for the inclusion of your amendment in the Bill of Rights. For example, if you are assigned Amendment 1, one member of your group might choose to play the part of a Quaker. Another group member might choose to play the part of a newspaper editor. Each group member should complete his or her worksheet, based on the character that the group member has decided to portray. Use your textbook and other resources to find historical reasons for your arguments.

Amendment 6. Right to a Jury Trial

In all criminal prosecutions, the accused shall enjoy the right to a speedy and public trial, by an impartial jury of the State and district wherein the crime shall have been committed, which district shall have been previously ascertained by law, and to be informed of the nature and cause of the accusation; to be confronted with the witnesses against him; to have compulsory process for obtaining witnesses in his favor, and to have the assistance of counsel for his defense.

1. American citizen you will portray:_____

2. Your arguments for the addition of this amendment to the Bill of Rights:

_____

_____

_____

WE DEMAND OUR RIGHTS!

Study the amendment written below. Each member of your group should portray an American citizen in 1789 and use that character's point of view to argue for the inclusion of your amendment in the Bill of Rights. For example, if you are assigned Amendment 1, one member of your group might choose to play the part of a Quaker. Another group member might choose to play the part of a newspaper editor. Each group member should complete his or her worksheet, based on the character that the group member has decided to portray. Use your textbook and other resources to find historical reasons for your arguments.

Amendment 7. Civil Trials

In suits at common law, where the value in controversy shall exceed twenty dollars, the right of trial by jury shall be preserved, and no fact tried by a jury, shall be otherwise reexamined in any court of the United States, than according to the rules of the common law.

1. American citizen you will portray: _____

2. Your arguments for the addition of this amendment to the Bill of Rights:

_____

_____

_____

- -

WE DEMAND OUR RIGHTS!

Study the amendment written below. Each member of your group should portray an American citizen in 1789 and use that character's point of view to argue for the inclusion of your amendment in the Bill of Rights. For example, if you are assigned Amendment 1, one member of your group might choose to play the part of a Quaker. Another group member might choose to play the part of a newspaper editor. Each group member should complete his or her worksheet, based on the character that the group member has decided to portray. Use your textbook and other resources to find historical reasons for your arguments.

Amendment 8. Punishment for Crimes

Excessive bail shall not be required, nor excessive fines imposed, nor cruel and unusual punishments inflicted.

1. American citizen you will portray: _____

2. Your arguments for the addition of this amendment to the Bill of Rights:

_____

_____

_____

WE DEMAND OUR RIGHTS!

Study the amendment written below. Each member of your group should portray an American citizen in 1789 and use that character's point of view to argue for the inclusion of your amendment in the Bill of Rights. For example, if you are assigned Amendment 1, one member of your group might choose to play the part of a Quaker. Another group member might choose to play the part of a newspaper editor. Each group member should complete his or her worksheet, based on the character that the group member has decided to portray. Use your textbook and other resources to find historical reasons for your arguments.

Amendment 9. Other Rights
The enumeration in the Constitution, of certain rights, shall not be construed to deny or disparage others retained by the people.

    1. American citizen you will portray: _____

    2. Your arguments for the addition of this amendment to the Bill of Rights:

    _____

    _____

    _____

- -

WE DEMAND OUR RIGHTS!

Study the amendment written below. Each member of your group should portray an American citizen in 1789 and use that character's point of view to argue for the inclusion of your amendment in the Bill of Rights. For example, if you are assigned Amendment 1, one member of your group might choose to play the part of a Quaker. Another group member might choose to play the part of a newspaper editor. Each group member should complete his or her worksheet, based on the character that the group member has decided to portray. Use your textbook and other resources to find historical reasons for your arguments.

Amendment 10. Powers Reserved to the States
The powers not delegated to the United States by the Constitution, nor prohibited by it to the States, are reserved to the States, respectively, or to the people.

    1. American citizen you will portray: _____

    2. Your arguments for the addition of this amendment to the Bill of Rights:

    _____

    _____

    _____

TOPIC: Amending the Constitution
TIME: One class period
TIME PERIOD: During study of the procedure for amending the Constitution

BACKGROUND

The Constitution is a "living document" in that the framers provided for the future in several ways. One way involved the amendment process. The writers of the Constitution knew that the document would need changing and updating. They did not, however, make the amendment process easy. Over the years more than 10,000 amendments to the Constitution have been proposed. Since 1789 only 26 amendments have been added to the Constitution, 10 of them in 1791—the Bill of Rights.

In this teaching strategy students will review the amendment process laid out in Article V of the Constitution. They will learn that because of the diversity of the population and the great range of interests found among the population, it is very difficult for an amendment to be added to the Constitution.

MATERIALS

Copies of the "Amendment Challenge" sheets. Separate the sections after you copy them. The activity is organized for students to work in eight groups, four students per group. If you have a smaller class you can organize the students into four or five groups and then evenly distribute the leftover amendment proposals.

SUGGESTED PROCEDURE

1. Have students review Article V of the Constitution. Ask students the following questions:
   a. What are the two ways in which a constitutional amendment can be proposed? (Congress can propose an amendment when two-thirds of both houses believe it is necessary; Congress can call a national convention for proposing an amendment when the legislatures of two-thirds of the states apply to Congress for the amendment.) Tell students that the second option has never been used.
   b. What are the two ways in which a constitutional amendment can be ratified? (Legislatures of three-fourths of the states can ratify the amendment; three-fourths of special conventions in each state can ratify the amendment.) Tell students that this option has been used only once—in the repeal of prohibition, the 21st Amendment.
2. Ask students: Do you think it is a good idea or a bad idea that the amendment procedure is so difficult? Why? (Students should understand that the Constitution should be reserved for very important changes. If the amendment procedure were easy, the Constitution would be cluttered with many shallow laws or laws that were in the best interest of only one group of people.)
3. Ask students to open their textbooks to the amendments to the Constitution. Explain to students that the existing amendments have been passed for only a few objectives or purposes. Ask students to identify amendments that fit into each of the following categories:
   a. Protecting and extending rights (First 10 amendments; 13th, 14th, 15th, 19th, 23rd, 24th, and 26th amendments)
   b. Structural changes within the government (11th, 12th, 16th, 17th, 20th, 22nd, and 25th amendments)
   c. Reflection of changing ideas (18th, 19th, and 21st amendments)
4. Tell students that they are going to play an amendment game. Organize students into eight groups of four students each. Give each group a different "Amendment Challenge" sheet with two proposed amendments. Tell students that each group is to add two amendments to the list. Tell them to include the year that their made-up amendment was "proposed." Allow the groups about 15 minutes to think up their proposed amendments. Then call on each group to challenge the rest of the class to figure out which of the group's proposed amendments actually were proposed and which are the ones made up by the group.
5. To conclude the activity have each student write a paragraph describing a serious proposed amendment that the student thinks should be added to the Constitution. Students should explain why the amendment should be added and describe the amendment's objective or purpose (protecting and extending rights, structural changes within the government, or a reflection of changing ideas).

AMENDMENT CHALLENGE

The following amendments were proposed but not enacted. Your group will think up two "proposed" amendments to add to this list. Include the year that your amendment was "proposed." Make the amendments serious enough that your classmates will not be able to tell which are the real proposed amendments and which are the amendments you created.

1. 1933: No United States citizen shall have a personal wealth exceeding $1 million.

2. 1876: The Senate shall be abolished.

Your group's amendments:

3. _____

4. _____

AMENDMENT CHALLENGE

The following amendments were proposed but not enacted. Your group will think up two "proposed" amendments to add to this list. Include the year that your amendment was "proposed." Make the amendments serious enough that your classmates will not be able to tell which are the real proposed amendments and which are the amendments you created.

1. 1971: All citizens have an inalienable right to an unpolluted environment.

2. 1876: Religious leaders are forbidden to occupy government office and are denied all federal funding.

Your group's amendments:

3. _____

4. _____

AMENDMENT CHALLENGE

The following amendments were proposed but not enacted. Your group will think up two "proposed" amendments to add to this list. Include the year that your amendment was "proposed." Make the amendments serious enough that your classmates will not be able to tell which are the real proposed amendments and which are the amendments you created.

1. 1893: The nation shall hereafter be known as the United States of Earth.

2. 1947: Individual income shall be taxed at a rate no greater than 25 percent.

Your group's amendments:

3. _____

4. _____

AMENDMENT CHALLENGE

The following amendments were proposed but not enacted. Your group will think up two "proposed" amendments to add to this list. Include the year that your amendment was "proposed." Make the amendments serious enough that your classmates will not be able to tell which are the real proposed amendments and which are the amendments you created.

1. 1861: The institution of slavery shall not be declared unlawful.

2. 1878: The office of president shall be abolished and replaced with an executive Council of Three.

Your group's amendments:

3. _____

4. _____

- -

AMENDMENT CHALLENGE

The following amendments were proposed but not enacted. Your group will think up two "proposed" amendments to add to this list. Include the year that your amendment was "proposed." Make the amendments serious enough that your classmates will not be able to tell which are the real proposed amendments and which are the amendments you created.

1. 1914: The institution of divorce shall be prohibited.

2. 1916: All acts of war shall be put to a national vote. All those affirming shall be registered as a volunteer for service in the United States Armed Forces.

Your group's amendments:

3. _____

4. _____

- -

AMENDMENT CHALLENGE

The following amendments were proposed but not enacted. Your group will think up two "proposed" amendments to add to this list. Include the year that your amendment was "proposed." Make the amendments serious enough that your classmates will not be able to tell which are the real proposed amendments and which are the amendments you created.

1. 1938: Drunkenness in the United States and all the territories is forbidden.

2. 1948: The right of citizens to voluntarily segregate themselves shall not be denied.

Your group's amendments:

3. _____

4. _____

AMENDMENT CHALLENGE

The following amendments were proposed but not enacted. Your group will think up two "proposed" amendments to add to this lists. Include the year that your amendment was "proposed." Make the amendments serious enough that your classmates will not be able to tell which are the real proposed amendments and which are the amendments you created.

1. No United States citizen shall accept a title of foreign nobility.

2. 1888: Widows and spinsters shall be granted suffrage (the right to vote).

Your group's amendments:

3. _____

4. _____

TOPIC: The Constitution and Judicial Review
TIME: One class period
TIME PERIOD: During study of the interpretation of the Constitution

BACKGROUND

Amending the Constitution is not the only way in which the Constitution can be changed. The meaning of the Constitution also has changed. It is the responsibility of the judicial branch to interpret the meaning of the Constitution. As times change the members of the Supreme Court interpret the Constitution in different ways. The makeup of the Supreme Court also has a bearing on how the Constitution is interpreted.

It was established in 1796 that the Supreme Court could rule acts of state governments as unconstitutional. Article VI of the Constitution says that the Constitution and the federal laws are the "supreme law of the land." The question remaining concerned whether or not the Supreme Court could rule as unconstitutional acts of the legislative and executive branches of the federal government.

Until 1803 no one was really sure just how much power the Supreme Court held over the other branches of the federal government. But the case of *Marbury v. Madison* established the precedent of judicial review—the power of the Supreme Court to declare as unconstitutional laws passed by Congress. In this teaching strategy students will gain an understanding of judicial review by reading a case study of *Marbury v. Madison*. (For more case studies such as this one, see *The Constitution: Past, Present, and Future*.)

MATERIALS

Copies of the *Marbury v. Madison* case study

SUGGESTED PROCEDURE

1. Tell students that there is another way to change the Constitution besides the amendment procedure. Explain to students that conflicts about the meaning of the Constitution are settled by the Supreme Court. The decisions that the Supreme Court makes are called *precedents*. Conflicts arising about the meaning of the Constitution usually start in a lower court. Explain to students the following sequence of steps through which a conflict over a constitutional question passes.
   a. The constitutional question begins as a lower court case.
   b. The lower court decision is appealed to a higher court (the Supreme Court).
   c. The Supreme Court can refuse to hear the case, it can uphold the lower court's decision, or it can vote to change the decision.
2. Tell students that in the Supreme Court a majority vote is necessary to change a decision. Explain that currently there are nine members on the Supreme Court. The number of members is odd so that there will never be a tie vote.
3. Provide students with the background information. Distribute copies of the *Marbury v. Madison* case study. Call on students read the case study aloud. Then ask students the following questions:
   a. What is judicial review? (the power of the Supreme Court to decide if laws passed by Congress are constitutional)
   b. What kinds of cases does the Constitution state may be heard by the Supreme Court? (cases that pertain to the Constitution; cases involving laws or treaties of the federal government; cases involving ambassadors or public ministers and consuls; cases of admiralty and maritime jurisdiction; cases in which the United States is a party; disputes between states; disputes between a state and its citizens and a foreign country)
   c. If Chief Justice Marshall had not been eager to speak out on the subject of judicial review, how might his opinion have differed from the one he wrote? (Because Chief Justice Marshall was a strong Federalist, he might have wanted to ensure that Marbury received his commission. Marshall also may have felt personally responsible because it had been his job to deliver Marbury's commission.)
   d. If the judicial branch had not acquired the power of judicial review, then Congress would be its own judge of the constitutionality of its laws. Do you think it would be good or bad for Congress to have this power? Why? (Suggested response: If Congress could judge the constitutionality of the laws that it makes, it would probably judge them all to be constitutional.)

MARBURY V. MADISON (1803)

WHAT WAS THE CASE ABOUT?

The story. The time was early 1801. The Federalist party had been defeated by the Democratic–Republicans in the presidential and congressional elections. The winners of the election, however, were not due to take office until March 4. In the meantime the Federalists were determined to do whatever they could to hold their party's power.

One action they could take was to appoint supporters of the Federalist party to offices that were not filled by election. So, they chose a number of party supporters as justices of the peace in the District of Columbia. These people were nominated by the outgoing president, John Adams, and confirmed by the Senate at the last minute—on March 3. Their "midnight appointments" seemed to be just in time. But no one could take office as a new justice of the peace until his commission had been delivered to him.

The job of delivering the commissions fell to the acting secretary of state, John Marshall. The next day when the new president, Thomas Jefferson, took over, he found that John Marshall had not had time to deliver all of the commissions before his term of office ended. Jefferson was delighted. He immediately ordered his new secretary of state, James Madison, not to deliver the rest of the commissions. The people who had been confirmed by the Senate as justices of the peace could not take office after all!

William Marbury, one of the people whose commission was not delivered, sued James Madison. Marbury took advantage of a law passed by Congress (part of the Judiciary Act) that allowed him to make this kind of complaint directly to the Supreme Court. He asked the Court to order Madison to deliver the commission even though this request meant disobeying the president. Probably he expected the Court to do as he asked because John Marshall had been appointed chief justice of the Supreme Court. You remember that until James Madison took over as

secretary of state on March 4, John Marshall had held that job. Marshall was a strong Federalist. Moreover, the chief justice might have felt personal responsibility to Marbury because he had not been able to deliver Marbury's commission in time.

The question. As Chief Justice Marshall saw it, the question before the Court had three parts. First, did Marbury have a right to receive the commission? Second, if he did have a right to the commission, was the government now required to make amends? Finally, if the government was required to make amends, would it have to order Madison to deliver Marbury's commission, as Marbury had requested?

The issues. One might have thought that Chief Justice Marshall would want Marbury to receive his commission. Perhaps he did, but he cared even more about something else—the power of the Supreme Court itself. He considered it very important that the Court have a role in the system of checks and balances. Specifically, he wanted the Court to be able to decide if laws passed by Congress were constitutional. Whether or not the Court has this power of judicial review had not yet been decided. Marshall posed the question before the Court in the way he did in order to discuss judicial review.

HOW WAS THE CASE DECIDED?

Two years later, in an opinion written by the chief justice himself, the Court ruled against ordering Madison to deliver Marbury's commission. Is this ruling what you expected?

WHAT DID THE COURT SAY ABOUT GOVERNMENTAL POWERS?

First let's see how the Court reached its decision. Remember that Marshall had said that the question before the Court had three parts. Each part had to be answered before the Court could go on to the next part. So, the Court's reasoning went through three steps.

Step 1. Did Marbury have a right to the commission? Pointing to a law passed by

Congress, which told how justices of the peace should be appointed for the District of Columbia, the Court said that he did.

Step 2. Was the government required to make amends? The Court said that when governmental officials (such as Madison) hurt people (such as Marbury) by neglecting their legal duties (such as delivering commissions), our laws require that a remedy be found for the injury.

Step 3. If the government was required to make amends, did that mean that Madison must be ordered to deliver Marbury's commission as Marbury had requested? Marbury had asked that the Supreme Court simply order Madison to deliver the commission. Here Chief Justice Marshall did something surprising. Instead of giving a simple yes or no answer, he said yes, a court could issue such an order, but no, this was not the right court to issue it.

Why wasn't this the right court to issue it? Remember that Marbury had taken advantage of a part of the Judiciary Act that allowed complaints such as his to be taken straight to the Supreme Court instead of going through lower courts. Chief Justice Marshall, however, said that this law was unconstitutional. You know that the Constitution mentions several kinds of cases that can be brought straight to the Supreme Court. All other kinds of cases must go through lower courts first. Marbury's lawsuit, said the chief justice, was one of the kinds of cases that must go through lower courts first. It did not matter that Congress had passed a law saying something different, he said, because the Constitution is a higher law.

When two laws come into conflict, judges must obey the higher of them. Besides, judges take an oath to support the Constitution.

Do you see how cleverly Marshall wrote the Court's opinion? Sometimes in a game of chess a player gives up something in order to get something even better. The player allows a piece to be captured because it it the only way to get the other pieces into a stronger position. This example is something like what Marshall did. He gave up the power, granted to the Court by Congress, of hearing lawsuits such as Marbury's before lower courts had heard them. But the way that he gave up this power was to claim for the Court an even greater power. This greater power was the power of judicial review: the power to decide if laws made by Congress are allowed by the Constitution.

WHAT IMPLICATIONS DID THIS CASE HAVE FOR THE FUTURE?

Until 1803 nobody knew if judges really would be able to exercise such a power. In other words, nobody knew if the judicial branch would be able to play a role in the system of checks and balances at all. Without judicial review, Congress would decide for itself on the constitutionality of the laws it passed. By writing the opinion of the Court in *Marbury v. Madison,* Chief Justice Marshall changed all that forever. Today the judicial branch has taken its place as an equal to the legislative and executive branches. By deciding on the constitutionality of the actions of the other two branches, the judicial branch is the nation's final authority on the meaning of the Constitution itself.

Creative Strategies for Teaching American History

The New Nation
1789–1840

TOPIC: The Controversial Statue of George Washington
TIME: One class period
TIME PERIOD: During study of the role of George Washington in our nation's history

BACKGROUND

Americans in the late 1700s and early 1800s viewed the classics from Greece and Rome as either a legacy to be venerated, providing role models for the new American cultural and political ideas (as Jefferson and Adams thought), or as nonutilitarian, without the practical application of subjects such as mathematics. A tension existed between those who wanted to model the new American government after classical models and those who wanted to cut all ties with the past.

Architecture and fine arts frequently reflected the yearning for a classical model. Horatio Greenough, a distinguished American sculptor, was commissioned by Congress in 1832 to create a statue of George Washington on the occasion of the centennial of Washington's birth. Greenough took the advice of an advocate of Hellenism (an admirer of ancient Greek culture). Greenough modeled the statue after the colossal Olympian Zeus of Phidias, one of the wonders of the ancient world. This teaching strategy provides students with an opportunity to study the work of Greenough and the reactions to his work.

MATERIALS

1. One transparency of the photograph or a copy for each student
2. Copies of reviews

SUGGESTED PROCEDURE

1. Show the transparency or distribute copies to students. Ask students the following questions:
    a. Can you guess which American founding father this might be? How can you tell?
    b. Why do you think George Washington is shown this way? Is this the way he ordinarily dressed? Who did dress this way in everyday life?
    c. Why would the artist put Washington in a toga? (Suggested responses: to equate Washington with a Greek god; to show Greenough's respect for the great thinkers of ancient Greece)
    d. What do you suppose George Washington would have thought of this statue?
    e. How do you think the general public reacted to the statue?
2. Provide students with the background information. Some additional information that would be of interest to your students was written by Frank G. Carpenter in the Cleveland *Leader* some 40 years after the first appearance of the statue. Read the following article to the class.

> It took eight years for Horatio Greenough to make [the statue]. He did the work in Florence, Italy, where he chiseled out the Father of our Country in a sitting posture instead of standing, as the Act of Congress demanded.
> When the statue was completed, in 1840, the next question was how to get it from Italy to America. Congress haggled over the matter for weeks, finally sending a man-of-war to bring the statue across the Atlantic Ocean. But the marble George weighed twelve tons, and it took twenty-two yoke of oxen to haul him over the Italian roads. . . . When it arrived at the Washington Navy yard, Congressmen were horrified to see that our great hero had been carved, sitting in a chair, nude to the waist. The Virginia statesman General Henry A. Wise remarked at the time, "The man does not live, and never did live, who saw Washington without his shirt." . . . At the Capitol doors, it was found that the statue was too large. . . . The masonry had to be cut away and door enlarged. When it was finally installed the Rotunda floor began to sink so a pedestal was built under it to support it. It was soon decided that the Rotunda was not a suitable place for the statue, and at last, after a number of removals, it was taken to . . . the bitter cold, bleak air of the Capitol plateau. . . . One jokester, commenting on the outstretched sword

in the figure's hand, says he is sure Washington is crying, "Take my sword if you will, but bring me some clothes!"

Perhaps predicting the disappointment citizens would feel with Greenough's statue, a group of prominent citizens, with Chief Justice Marshall elected as the president of the Washington National Monument Society, decided to raise money and sponsor a competition for a monument to Washington. The Washington Monument was the result.

3. Distribute copies of the reviews to students. Then ask:
   a. Who defended the statue as a work of art? (an artist; Greenough)
   b. Who criticized the statue? Why? (the general public, because of the way Washington was dressed)
   c. What do you think of the statue?
4. Organize the class into small groups to discuss reasons that Americans greatly respected George Washington. The groups can then make charts of their reasons and present them in class.
5. Have students design a statue or monument honoring another famous American. Ask volunteers to describe and explain their designs.

REACTIONS TO STATUE OF GEORGE WASHINGTON

Sources: *Letters of Horatio Greenough,* edited by Frances B. Greenough; and
Horatio Greenough: The First American Sculptor, by Nathalia Wright

Excerpted

Greenough's great work has surpassed my expectations, high as they
were. It is truly sublime. The statue is of colossal grandeur. . . . In the
reversed sword the design of the artist was of course to indicate the
ascendency of the civic and humane over the military virtues, which
distinguished the whole career of Washington and which form the great
glory of his character. . . . To preserve the costume of the period, already
out of fashion, would have been unsuitable for effect in sculpture. The
colossal size, the antique drapery, the more youthful air of the face are
circumstances which, without materially impairing the truth to Nature,
increase very much the moral impression, and instead of furnishing
grounds of objection, are positive merits of high importance.

An Artist

[The statue] contains two of the most improving and sublime ideas that I
know of, and the most necessary to be felt, viz. the duty of all men toward
God—the duty of great men toward the human race. However, I may have
failed for want of art to make these ideas clear, speaking eloquent, I shall
never fail to feel a warmth in my bosom that I chose them for my
theme;—my Washington is . . . a conductor standing between God and
man, the channel of blessings from heaven, and of prayer and praise from
earth. I have struck a bold blow,—I have thrown to the winds the fear of
ridicule, carping and one-sided criticism; and I have made all the
enthusiasm, that a real American feels about his country, my guide. . . . I
have felt the hackneyed commonplaces of art alone—that will come of it I
know not.

Horatio Greenough

The bulk of popular opinion condemned or ridiculed the statue. A United
States senator objected to the prominence of the sword and said that
Washington should have been shown with his hand on the Constitution.
He also commented that Greenough should have been sent a suit of
Washington's clothes. Most of the objections were directed to the clothing
issue, and commentators repeatedly objected to the sculptor's decision not
to dress the hero in the clothing of the day. A piece in the New York
Herald by "George Porgy" described the figure as risen from a coffin
"with his winding sheet about him." The dress seemed to many people to
be foreign, pagan, and indecent. The General, one commentator said, was
"rigged out like an old Heathen instead of (in) buff and blue."

Various Critics

TOPIC: The Bill of Rights—Freedom of Religion
TIME: Three or four class periods
TIME PERIOD: During study of the Bill of Rights

BACKGROUND

During the Constitutional Convention the delegates debated on and voted against a bill of rights. At several state ratifying conventions, advocates of a bill of rights won pledges from the Federalists to work for the addition of specific civil liberties to the Constitution.

James Madison, a congressman representing Virginia, proposed several amendments to the First Congress of the United States, which met in 1789. There was a debate about the suitability of such a list of amendments, but in the end more than two thirds of the members voted for the amendments. The amendments were then sent to the states, in accordance with Article V. After three-fourths of the states ratified 10 of the amendments on December 15, 1791, the amendments became part of the Constitution.

This teaching strategy provides an in-depth study of the principle of freedom of religion in the First Amendment. Students will study the history of the writing of the principle, and they will learn the difference between the "establishment clause" and the "free exercise clause."

MATERIALS

1. Copies of handout "Freedom of Religion: Madison and Jefferson's Original Intent"
2. Copies of political cartoons
3. Copies of freedom of religion court cases

SUGGESTED PROCEDURE

1. Familiarize students with the following words from the handout on James Madison and Thomas Jefferson:

abridged	exclusion	proclaim
amendment	infringed	propagation
chaplain	observance	statute
conscience	petition	tyrannical

   Organize the class into groups of four and distribute the handout providing background information on James Madison and Thomas Jefferson's position regarding freedom of religion. As students take turns reading the handout aloud, circulate among the groups to check for understanding. Have each group answer the questions on the handout. A recorder from each group should write the group's answers on a sheet of paper. Compare groups' answers in a class discussion.

2. Distribute copies of the two cartoons. Ask the groups to suggest what they think the cartoonists' intended messages are. Have each group create captions for the cartoons. Compare all groups' ideas and captions in a class discussion.

3. Have the class reread the freedom of religion section of the First Amendment. Ask students how it is divided. Explain to students that these two clauses are commonly referred to as the "establishment clause" and the "free exercise clause." Distribute the handout with the short case summaries. Each group of students should try to reach a consensus on each case. Students must decide if each case involves the establishment clause or the free exercise clause. One member from each group should act as a recorder. Each group will then decide how they would have ruled in each case, and provide their reasoning for each decision. After students have completed the assignment, reveal the following Supreme Court decisions and allow time for students to compare their decisions with those of the Supreme Court.

Answers to Supreme Court Decisions (Page 100)

Case One: *State v. Massey*

It was decided that the city ordinance was a valid exercise of police power because the duties of police include protecting the lives, health, morals, welfare, and safety of the people. The value of public safety was ruled to be more important than this form of religious worship. (free exercise clause)

Case Two: *Sherbert v. Verner*

Adell Sherbert was ruled eligible for unemployment benefits because no state may "exclude individual Catholics, Lutherans, Mohammedans, Baptists, Jews, Methodists, Nonbelievers, Presbyterians, or the members of any other faith, because of their faith, or lack of it, from receiving the benefits of public welfare legislation." (free exercise clause)

Case Three: *Stone v. Graham*

The Court concluded that the posting of the Ten Commandments was not permissible under the establishment clause of the First Amendment, because the purpose of the law was religious in nature. (establishment clause)

Answers to Review Questions (Page 98)

1. He did not think it was right. He thought that people's civil rights should not depend on their religious opinions.
2. He warned that one sect of Christians could establish itself above all other sects of Christianity.
3. He said that there should be no national religion; he said that the civil rights of citizens should not depend on their religion; he said that rights of conscience should not be taken away.
4. Answers will vary. Students will notice that Congress inserted the clause "Congress shall make no law."
5. Congress took out the parts about civil rights and equal rights of conscience. They kept in the part about establishment of a national religion.
6. Madison and Jefferson did not want government involved in religion in any way. For example, Madison did not want official chaplains for Congress because they would be paid out of national taxes; Jefferson refused to set aside specific days for religious observance.

Freedom of Religion: Madison and Jefferson's Original Intent
Excerpted

James Madison and Thomas Jefferson were closely allied on the cause of religious freedom. Jefferson's draft of the Virginia Statute for Religious Freedom contained many ringing phrases.

> *To compel a man to furnish contributions of money for the propagation of opinions which he disbelieves is sinful and tyrannical . . . . Our civil rights have no dependence on our religious opinions, no more than on our opinions in physics and geometry.*

Introduced in 1777, it did not pass.

In 1785 James Madison anonymously wrote a petition that was circulated throughout Virginia and was signed by thousands. It argued against government support of the church. He wrote that religion

> *must be left to the conviction and conscience of every man; and it is the right of every man to exercise it as these may dictate. . . . Who does not see that the same authority which can establish Christianity, in exclusion of all other Religions, may establish with the same ease any particular sect of Christians, in exclusion of all other Sects?*

In 1789 Madison worked on the wording of the Bill of Rights. His first draft on freedom of religion was

> *The civil rights of none shall be abridged on account of religious belief or worship, nor shall any national religion be established, nor shall the full and equal rights of conscience be in any manner, or on any pretext, abridged.*

This draft was referred to a committee. On August 15 the House took up the question as

> *No religion shall be established by law, nor shall the equal rights of conscience be infringed.*

The amendment, however, was forwarded to the Senate as

> *Congress shall make no law establishing religion, or to prevent the free exercise thereof, or to infringe the rights of conscience.*

It was at this time that Madison introduced another amendment forbidding any violation of the rights of conscience, freedom of speech, and a free press. The House sent this to the Senate with the article on religion and 15 other amendments. Twenty-two senators combined some of the House amendments and dropped others. On September 9 the Senate reworded the article on religion:

> *Congress shall make no law establishing articles of faith, or a mode of worship, or prohibiting the free exercise of religion.*

The House refused to accept the change, so a joint committee, with Madison as chairperson, met and composed the following wording:

> *Congress shall make no law respecting an establishment of religion, or prohibiting the free exercise thereof.*

How does this compare with Madison's original wording? James Madison stood up for what he believed even when it was not popular to do so. For example, he opposed the appointment of official chaplains for Congress in 1789 because they would be paid out of the national taxes. He thought that the appointment of chaplains would be mixing religion and government and should not be allowed. He knew what he meant by *establish,* and he thought that government support should not be offered to any religious program. The majority of Congress did not agree with him.

When Thomas Jefferson became president he was criticized by many because, unlike Washington and Adams, he refused to proclaim certain days for religious observance. In 1802 he said that the First Amendment was intended to build "a wall of separation between church and state."

In 1791 the last of the necessary 11 states ratified the Bill of Rights. The First Amendment has been interpreted in various ways since that time.

Review Questions

1. What did Jefferson think about people being forced to pay taxes to support a state church?

2. What did Madison warn Christians about establishing Christianity as a state religion?

3. In Madison's first draft on freedom of religion for the Bill of Rights, what did he say about a national religion? What did he say abut the civil rights of citizens? What did he say about the rights of conscience?

4. Why do you think that Congress kept making changes in the wording?

5. Compare Madison's first draft with the final wording written by the committee.

6. In what other way did Madison show he was concerned about establishing a national religion? How did Jefferson show this same concern?

CHURCH AND STATE—NO UNION UPON ANY TERMS.

Freedom of Religion Court Cases

Directions: Decide if each of the following cases involves the establishment clause or the free exercise clause. Then write your group's decision for each case. Explain how you balanced individual freedoms against society's interests. Write your group's answer on a separate sheet of paper.

Case One: *State v. Massey* (1949)

Members of a religious group in North Carolina regularly handled poisonous snakes as part of their ceremonies. A law was passed by the city in which this group was located, forbidding the handling of "poisonous reptiles in such a manner as to endanger public health, welfare, and safety." The religious group continued to use the snakes, and some of its members were convicted of breaking the law. They appealed to the Supreme Court of North Carolina, saying that they handled snakes voluntarily as part of their religion and that they did not endanger the public health, welfare, or safety.

1. Did the religious group's appeal involve the establishment clause or the free exercise clause?

2. What is your group's decision? What are your reasons for reaching that decision?

Case Two: *Sherbert v. Verner* (1963)

Adell Sherbert was a member of the Seventh-Day Adventist Church, a church that prohibits its members from working on Saturday. She worked at a textile mill in South Carolina and was fired when she refused to work on Saturdays. She tried to get other jobs at mills, but they also required Saturday work. She finally applied for unemployment benefits. She was turned down because she had refused "available suitable work." Sherbert argued that her right to freedom of religion was being violated.

1. Did this case concern the establishment clause or the free exercise clause?

2. What is your group's decision? What are your reasons for reaching that decision?

Case Three: *Stone v. Graham* (1980)

The Kentucky state legislature passed a law requiring that the Ten Commandments be posted on the walls of all public-school classrooms. The small print at the bottom of each copy had to say, "The secular application of the Ten Commandments is clearly seen in its adoption as the fundamental legal code of Western Civilization and the Common Law of the United States." Some parents of Kentucky students asked for a court order to prevent the posting of the Commandments, saying that the law violated the First Amendment guarantees of freedom of religion.

1. Did this case concern the establishment clause or the free exercise clause?

2. What is your group's decision? What are your reasons for reaching that decision?

During a class discussion you will have the opportunity to compare your decisions with those of your classmates and learn what the actual Supreme Court decisions were in each of these three cases.

TOPIC: The Connection Between Education and Democracy
TIME: Three classroom periods, with homework
TIME PERIOD: During discussion of the presidency of Thomas Jefferson

BACKGROUND

This teaching strategy will assist students in understanding that people's attitudes toward education changed from colonial days through the early 1800s. There were also various ways for people to receive an education. Some people, such as Abigail Adams, were self-taught. Others, such as her husband, John Adams, were formally educated. The nation was growing in its commitment to public education, gradually realizing the value of an educated electorate.

To understand how attitudes changed from colonial times to Jefferson's time, students will engage in a series of readings and a map study. All of the exercises can be completed either by small cooperative groups or with the entire class.

MATERIALS

1. Copies of John Winthrop's essay
2. Copies of the Northwest Ordinance map
3. Copies of the handout concerning Abigail Adams
4. Copies of the handout describing a New England school in the early 1800s

SUGGESTED PROCEDURE

1. Ask students to name some of Thomas Jefferson's many accomplishments. Tell students that he was also known for the following quotation. (Write the quotation on the chalkboard.)

   If a Nation expects to be ignorant and free, in a state of civilization, it expects what never was and never will be.

   Ask students what they think Jefferson meant by this statement. (Possible response: A nation cannot be civilized if its citizens are not educated.)
2. Distribute the Winthrop reading and the land survey map of the Northwest Ordinance. Have volunteers read the excerpt. Then ask students the following questions:
   a. What reason did John Winthrop give for Mrs. Hopkins' loss of understanding and reasoning? (her passion for reading and writing)
   b. According to Winthrop, what was Mr. Hopkins' error? (He was loving and tender to her instead of forcing her to attend to the household affairs.)
   c. How did Mr. Hopkins solve his problem? (He sent her to live with her brother.)
   d. From what you have read, do you think that colonial girls had the same chance as boys for a formal education in Puritan communities? (Colonists did not think that girls needed to be formally educated.)
3. Allow students a few minutes to study the land survey map of the Northwest Ordinance. Tell them that each township was divided into 36 numbered lots (called sections) of 640 acres each. The land was sold by auction, and a section was the smallest unit that could be purchased at a price of no less than a dollar an acre. In each township Congress retained four sections for future sale and set aside one other for the support of public education. Ask students the following questions:
   a. What does this information tell us about what the nation's founders thought of education? (They thought education was important.)
   b. Why do you think education was important to the founders? (Possible answer: People need to be educated in order to be good citizens.)
   c. Do you think that education was more important to the founders because they were now citizens of an independent country and not a colony? Why? (Possible answer: Yes; people would need to be educated in order to govern themselves.)

4. Abigail Adams is one of the most admired presidential wives. Distribute the article on Abigail Adams from *The First Ladies* and ask volunteers to read the article aloud. Ask students the following questions:
   a. How did Abigail Smith Adams receive her education? (She was self-taught.)
   b. What evidence is there in this reading that Abigail Adams had keen intelligence? (She was curious and was an avid reader; she taught her four children; she wrote detailed letters; she performed well in her role as wife of the first United States Minister to Great Britain.)
   c. How did her education help others? (She taught her four children; she helped her husband by performing well in her roles as wife of the first United States Minister to Great Britain and as first lady.)
5. The last reading is a description of a New England school in the early 1800s. Distribute the reading and discuss with students how a New England school compares with schools today. Some topics for discussion include: time spent in school, size of classroom, punishment, how students were seated, recess, how reading grades were determined, when students learned to write, when students learned arithmetic, the most important subject, end-of-year examination. You might also want to include in the comparison the description of Ichabod Crane's classroom in "The Legend of Sleepy Hollow."

On the Education of Women

An account by John Winthrop in *The History of New England from 1630 to 1649,* edited by James Savage

Excerpted

Mr. Hopkins, the governor of Hartford upon Connecticut, came to Boston and brought his wife with him . . . who was fallen into a sad infirmity, the loss of her understanding and reason, which had been growing upon her diverse years, by occasion of her giving herself wholly to reading and writing; and she had written many books.

Her husband being very loving and tender of her, was loath to grieve her; but he saw his error when it was too late. For if she had attended to her household affairs, and such things as belong to women, and had not gone out of her way to meddle in such things as are proper for men, whose minds are stronger &c., she had kept her wits and might have improved them usefully and honorably in the place God had set her. He brought her to Boston and left her with her brother, one Mr. Yale, a merchant, to try what means might be had for her. But no help could be had.

THE NORTHWEST ORDINANCE, 1787

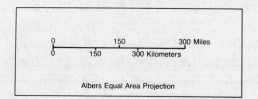

0   150   300 Miles
0   150   300 Kilometers

Albers Equal Area Projection

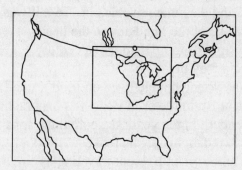

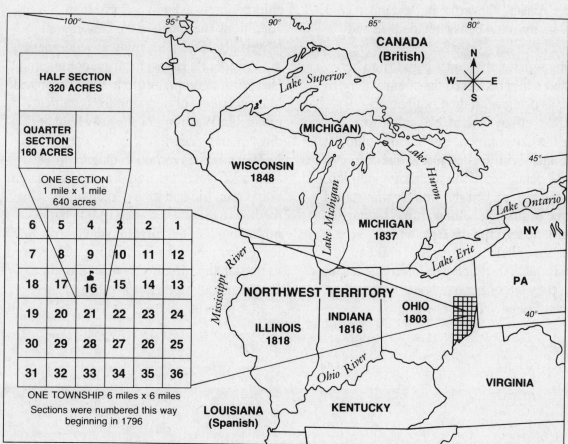

Abigail Smith Adams (1744–1818)

From *The First Ladies,* by Margaret Brown Klapthor

Inheriting New England's strongest traditions, Abigail Smith was born in 1744 at Weymouth, Massachusetts. On her mother's side she was descended from the Quincys, a family of great prestige in the colony; her father and other forebears were Congregational ministers, leaders in a society that held its clergy in high esteem.

Like other women of the time, Abigail lacked formal education; but her curiosity spurred her keen intelligence, and she read avidly the books at hand. Reading created a bond between her and young John Adams, Harvard graduate launched on a career in law, and they were married in 1764. It was a marriage of the mind and of the heart, enduring for more than half a century, enriched by time.

The young couple lived on John's small farm at Braintree or in Boston as his practice expanded. In ten years she bore three sons and two daughters; she looked after family and home when he went traveling as circuit judge. "Alass!" she wrote in December 1773, "How many snow banks devide thee and me. . . ."

Long separations kept Abigail from her husband while he served the country they loved, as delegate to the Continental Congress, envoy abroad, elected officer under the Constitution. Her letters—pungent, witty, and vivid, spelled just as she spoke—detail her life in times of revolution. They tell the story of the woman who stayed at home to struggle with wartime shortages and inflation; to run the farm with a minimum of help; to teach four children when formal education was interrupted. Most of all, they tell of her loneliness without her "dearest Friend." That "one single

expression," she said, "dwelt upon my mind and played about my Heart . . . ."

In 1784, she joined him at his diplomatic post in Paris, and observed with interest the manners of the French. After 1785, she filled the difficult role of wife of the first United States Minister to Great Britain, and did so with dignity and tact. They returned happily in 1788 to Massachusetts and the handsome house they had just acquired in Braintree, later called Quincy, home for the rest of their lives.

As wife of the first Vice President, Abigail became a good friend to Mrs. Washington and a valued help in official entertaining, drawing on her experience of courts and society abroad. After 1791, however, poor health forced her to spend as much time as possible in Quincy. Illness or trouble found her resolute; as she once declared she would "not forget the blessings which sweeten life."

When John Adams was elected President, she continued a formal pattern of entertaining—even in the primitive conditions she found at the new capital in November 1800. The city was wilderness, the President's House far from completion. Her private complaints to her family provide blunt accounts of both, but for her three months in Washington she duly held her dinners and receptions.

The Adamses retired to Quincy in 1801, and for 17 years enjoyed the companionship that public life had long denied them. Abigail died in 1818, and is buried beside her husband in United First Parish Church. She leaves her country a most remarkable record as patriot and First Lady, wife of one President and mother of another.

The District School in the Early 1800s

Based on *The School District As It Was,* by Warren Burton, 1835

In the early 1800s, most New England children attended public, town, or district schools. Generally these schools conducted three-month sessions in the summer and winter, allowing students time off in the spring and fall to help their families with planting and harvesting on the farm.

Generally, the school house was situated in the center of the district so that all residents would have equal access to the school.

As one entered the school, there was a small hallway often stocked with dry pine wood for making fires in the winter. On the left side of the hallway was the door leading into the one large classroom. The classroom measured about 20 feet by 10 feet. At one end of the room were seats and writing benches; at the other end, on a raised platform, was the teacher's desk. On the right side of the room the fireplace was located, as was a cloakroom. The cloakroom doubled as a punishment room when necessary. Through the rest of the room, rows of writing benches and log seats were located. Students were seated according to age, with the youngest near the teacher and the oldest at the back of the room.

The schoolroom was not a comfortable place. Students had no room on the writing benches to rest hands and arms. In winter, the roaring fire roasted those sitting near it, while those students far away huddled to keep warm.

The school mistress was very strict; students were to sit perfectly still. Common punishments for unruly or preoccupied students included ear twisting or a ruler snap on the head. Twice a day, in the morning and afternoon, students were allowed a five-minute recess, which had to be conducted quietly.

A good part of the school day was spent on reading aloud, or "reciting." Students were graded on speed and pronunciation, rather than on their understanding of the material. Beginning at the age of nine, students began learning to write. At 12, they began studying arithmetic, which was considered the most important subject for anyone wanting to enter a business occupation. At the end of each year, students were given an examination conducted by the town minister and the teacher.

TOPIC: The Louisiana Purchase—Jefferson's Difficult Decision
TIME: One class period
TIME PERIOD: During discussion of the Louisiana Purchase

BACKGROUND

Thomas Jefferson took a strict constructionist view of the Constitution. When confronted with the idea of the Louisiana Purchase he was torn between two strong ideas—his fear that the purchase would exceed the limited powers granted to the government by the Constitution and fear that Britain would claim these lands as a result of the Napoleanic Wars. Jefferson considered amending the Constitution in order to acquire the Louisiana territory. Finally, under great pressure and against his ethical objections, he allowed the purchase without a constitutional amendment. This teaching strategy provides students with an opportunity to use their historical imagination to debate Thomas Jefferson's decision.

SUGGESTED PROCEDURE

1. Have students review the section in their textbooks that covers the necessary and proper, or elastic, clause. Students should conclude that in this argument between Hamilton and Jefferson over the Bank of the United States, Jefferson claimed that Congress could only pass laws that were necessary, "not those which are merely 'convenient'." He opposed Hamilton's argument that the bank was a proper way to make use of the power of Congress to collect taxes and regulate trade. Then have students reread the circumstances of the Louisiana Purchase, making note of the difficulties with Spain and how France acquired the area. Point out on a wall map the area of the Louisiana Purchase.

2. Help students understand that Jefferson now faced a moral dilemma. Was the purchase of Louisiana territory constitutional? Could he invoke the elastic clause as his old archenemy Hamilton had years earlier? Does a president have a constitutional authority to acquire territory?

3. Organize the class into groups of four. Two members of each group will support the constitutional right of Jefferson and the American government to purchase the Louisiana territory and two members will oppose it. Each side will have 10 minutes to prepare a list of arguments to present to the other side in the group. Pairs may each take up to five minutes to present their side. After the presentation, pairs may challenge each other.

4. Now the pairs must switch sides. Those students previously arguing for the right of Jefferson to purchase the Louisiana territory must now argue against it. Those arguing against Jefferson's right must now support it. Each side prepares a new set of arguments and a new discussion follows.

5. After the final arguments, each group of four must try to reach a consensus as to which were the most valid arguments from both sides, summarize their findings in report form, and present the report to the class. In case of a deadlock in the groups, minority statements could be prepared.

TOPIC: "The Legend of Sleepy Hollow" by Washington Irving
TIME: Four classroom periods, with homework
TIME PERIOD: Anytime during study of the founding of the new nation in the 1700s

BACKGROUND

The post-Revolutionary War period will come alive for students with the reading of one of the most popular stories written during that era. Once students are acquainted with the vivid descendents of the original Dutch settlers of New York and the unforgettable pedagogue Ichabod Crane, they will have a much better idea of ordinary life during this period, including its humor.

Washington Irving was born in New York City in 1783. He studied law and was admitted to the bar. He published whimsical essays as well as more serious reading such as *A Chronicle of the Conquest of Granada* (1829) and a five-volume *Life of Washington* (1855–59). His best known short stories are "The Legend of Sleepy Hollow" and "Rip Van Winkle." Irving died in 1859, and he was elected to the American Hall of Fame in 1900.

MATERIALS

1. Copies of "The Legend of Sleepy Hollow" (check students' literary anthology; otherwise, obtain a copy from the library)
2. Copies of vocabulary list

SUGGESTED PROCEDURE

1. After a brief introduction, distribute the story and take time to read the beginning aloud so that students will become motivated to continue reading. Assign the rest of the story for homework. Distribute copies of the vocabulary list to help students with their understanding of the story.
2. Suggest group projects on the first day of teaching so that students will have enough time to complete their projects. Groups may be the same as the cooperative-learning groups, or you may wish to use different groupings for group projects. Allow time each day for students to work on their projects.
3. Use the cooperative-learning exercise on the second day of teaching to assess comprehension and to determine if more time should be spent on students' understanding of the story.
4. Use the discussion questions as an additional opportunity to assess comprehension.
5. Assign the role-playing exercise to help students come to conclusions about Ichabod's last night.
6. Use the last day for presentation of group projects.

SUGGESTIONS FOR GROUP PROJECTS

1. Make a gameboard of the story, including the major events and characters. The game will be more interesting if gimmicks such as bonus and bad luck cards are included.
2. Make dioramas or models of some of the characters or places in the story, such as the Headless Horseman, the Van Tassel mansion, or Ichabod's schoolhouse.
3. Write newspaper accounts of Ichabod Crane's arrival in Sleepy Hollow and his disappearance. Make a mock town newspaper and create the newspaper's name. Include other newsworthy events or advertisements that might have appeared on those two days.
4. Make a map of the Hudson River Valley, with historical sites noted. Include places mentioned in the story.
5. Research and report on Cotton Mather and the works that he published.
6. Use butcher paper to create set designs for each scene in the story.

COOPERATIVE LEARNING

Organize the class into groups of four. In each group, number students 1, 2, 3, and 4. Assign each number a section of questions to answer. In turn, all team members should share their respective answers. One spokesperson from each group will represent the group when the class compares information.

Questions for students numbered 1:
1. When does this story take place—before or after the Revolutionary War? How can you tell?
2. How does Irving describe Crane's appearance? Why is Crane a suitable name for this character?
3. Was Crane wealthy or poor? Support your answer with facts from the story.

Questions for students numbered 2:
4. How did Ichabod act with his students?
5. How did the females of the area react to Ichabod? Why?
6. Why do you think Ichabod wanted to gain the affections of Katrina?

Questions for students numbered 3:
7. How did Katrina act with Ichabod? How did she act with other males?
8. How did the neighbors feel about Brom Bones? Do you think people would have the same attitude today? Why or why not?
9. How can you tell that Baltus Van Tassel was wealthy?

Questions for students numbered 4:
10. How do you think Ichabod felt as he left the Van Tassel party? Why?
11. How did old Gunpowder react to events that occurred during the ride home from the party?
12. What do you think happened to Ichabod Crane?

DISCUSSION QUESTIONS

These questions can be discussed as a class or in small groups.
1. Is this setting the only place that this story could occur? Why or why not?
2. Is everything in the story believable? Does everything need to be believable?
3. What character (if any) in the story would you choose as a friend? Why?
4. Who do you think is the least likeable character? Why?
5. Did your feelings toward Ichabod Crane change during the story? Why?
6. How does the author stereotype women?
7. Why do you think that the author wrote this story?

ROLE-PLAYING

Organize the class into small groups to discuss the question "What do you think happened on Ichabod Crane's last night in Sleepy Hollow?" Students should consider the following factors:
1. How was he treated at the party? after the party?
2. What occurred on his ride from the Van Tassel's house?
3. What happened to him?

Ask the groups to enact their solutions to these questions before the class. After all groups have role-played their alternatives, discuss the solutions that have been presented. Which solution seemed most probable? If students think that Ichabod Crane ran away from Sleepy Hollow because he was humiliated, ask them if they think that his humiliation was a good reason to run away. Ask students what advice they would have given Ichabod.

GLOSSARY OF VOCABULARY

Here is a list of words from "The Legend of Sleepy Hollow" that you may not know. Use this list to help you with your understanding of the story. Use a dictionary to find the meaning of any other words in the story that you do not know.

advert: refer

apparition: a ghostly figure

arrant: unfavorably known

brake: here, a thicket or clump of brush

cavalier: knight

chivalry: qualities such as bravery, courtesy, and honesty that were idealized by knighthood

cognomen: a name, especially a nickname

Cotton Mather's . . . <u>Witchcraft</u>: Cotton Mather (1663–1728) was a noted American churchman and writer. He wrote about witchcraft, but he never published a book with the title given here.

erudition: learning

gainsay: denial; contradiction

harbinger: messenger

heretical: holding a view opposed to established opinion

Hessian trooper: soldier from Hessen (a part of Germany). Hessians were hired by the British to fight the Americans in the Revolutionary War.

husbandry: farming

inveterate: habitual

Major André: British officer hanged as a spy in 1780, during the American Revolution

Mynheer: Dutch for Mister

onerous: troublesome

pedagogue: school teacher

peradventure: perhaps

pertinacious: persistent

piazza: porch

portentous: ominous; warning of evil

potentate: person having great power

preceptor: teacher; tutor

propensity: tendency to

rantipole: a wild, reckless, sometimes quarrelsome person; unruly manner or attitude

Saardam: Holland

sequester: set apart, seclude

sojourn: stay temporarily

specter: ghost

stripling: youth

swain: young man

tête-à-tête: private conversation between two people

troop of Don Cossacks: horsemen along the Don River in Russia

whilom: at times

wight: human being

withe: willow twig

yeomen: here, farmers

Creative Strategies for Teaching American History

The Changing Nation
1800–1850

TOPIC: Planning a Wagon-Train Journey
TIME: Two to three class periods
TIME PERIOD: During study of the settlement of the West

BACKGROUND

Beginning in the 1830s groups of pioneers set off across the country in wagon trains. Some traveled for religious reasons, either seeking to convert the American Indians to Christianity or, in the case of the Mormons, to escape persecution for their religious beliefs. Others sought new homes in the reputedly fertile farmlands of the far West. In the 1840s, and even more after the discovery of gold in California in 1848, the trickle of transcontinental travelers became a flood.

Careful planning for the journey was vital. On the one hand, a variety of hardships would have to be faced, and the chance of getting new supplies either during the journey or at its end was small. Thus, pioneers felt the need to bring "a little bit of everything." On the other hand, a wagon could hold, and mules or even patient oxen could pull, only so much. Many families learned this to their sorrow as the trip wore on, and the sides of the trail through the desert soon became littered with furniture, tools, and other heavy objects discarded by desperate travelers trying to lighten their loads and save their animals.

Planning for the human element was important, too. Members of a wagon train had to be willing to work together to perform the daily duties of the camp and, on occasion, to protect the group against attacks by angry American Indians. Many trains split up because of disagreements within the group, thus often lessening their chances of survival. It was important, therefore, to select a leader who was both experienced in making the journey (or who could find a guide who was) and capable of enforcing an almost military discipline. In this teaching strategy students will plan a wagon-train journey across the country from two points of view: that of an individual family and that of the leader of a wagon train.

MATERIALS

1. Copies of handouts of the readings for each student
2. Family and wagon-train leader worksheets for each group

SUGGESTED PROCEDURE

1. Provide students with the background information on wagon-train journeys. Then give students copies of the readings.
2. Organize students into groups of five, and give each group a number. Tell each group that first it will imagine itself to be a family planning to make a wagon-train trip across the country in the 1840s. Have students in the group choose individual roles of father, mother, and children (they should decide what ages the children will be). Then the group will imagine itself to be the chosen leaders of an entire wagon train.
3. As homework, have students review their textbooks, the readings, and, if possible, other resources to learn more about wagon-train journeys. They should look for information on the supplies needed for the trip, the several routes (trails) used regularly by wagon-train travelers, and the problems and dangers faced by people making the journey.
4. During the next class meeting, have students meet in their groups to make decisions and fill in the worksheets related to family and wagon-train planning for their journey across the United States.
5. Have groups present their family and wagon-train plans to the class.
6. As an evaluation of the strategy, have students write answers to the following questions:
   a. If you were making the wagon-train journey, which group (refer to the group number) would you join? Why?
   b. What do you think are the five most important things for a family making the wagon-train journey to think about or remember?
   c. What do you think are the five most important things for the leaders of a wagon train to think about or remember?

WAGON-TRAIN TRIP LEADERS' PLANNER

Directions: Record your answers and explain why you made each choice.

1. About how big will your group be? (how many people? how many wagons?)

   _____

   _____

   _____

2. Who will you allow to join your group? (just single people? just families? both? any other requirements or restrictions?)

   _____

   _____

   _____

3. Will you have your wagons pulled by oxen, mules, or horses? Why?

   _____

   _____

   _____

4. What duties will you expect people in each wagon to perform for themselves?

   _____

   _____

   _____

5. What duties will you expect people to take turns doing for the whole group?

   _____

   _____

   _____

6. How will you expect people to deal with each of the kinds of danger you are likely to meet?

   _____

   _____

   _____

7. What rules (besides those related to duties) will you expect people in your group to obey?

   _____

   _____

   _____

FAMILY WAGON-TRAIN TRIP PLANNER

Keep in mind the following facts:

- Your journey will last at least four months.

- The animals drawing each wagon can pull only about one ton of weight.

- Everything must fit in a wagon bed about 10 feet long, 4 feet wide, and (counting its cloth cover) about 5 feet high.

- You will be able to hunt in some places and get fresh water in most (but not all) places, but you will have few or no chances to replace other supplies. Tools and supplies in California and Oregon, if available at all, will be quite expensive.

- Dangers you may face during the journey include cholera and other sicknesses, attacks by American Indians, deep rivers and high mountains difficult to cross, and deserts where water is unavailable or poisonous.

Directions: Record your answers in the space provided.

1. Which trail will you follow? Why?

   _____

   _____

   _____

2. Will you want someone to be in charge of your wagon train? If so, what powers do you want the leader or leaders to have? What powers do you *not* want them to have? What qualities or characteristics do you want them to have?

   _____

   _____

   _____

3. What will you take with you?
   a. Clothes:

   _____

   _____

   b. Food:

   _____

   _____

   c. Tools:

   _____

   _____

   _____

d. Wagon parts:

_____

_____

_____

e. Other (including personal belongings):

_____

_____

_____

4. If you have to leave things behind on the trail, what things will you leave?

_____

_____

_____

Excerpts from *The Prairie Traveler*

By Randolph B. Marcy, written in 1859

Routes to California and Oregon.
Emigrants or others desiring to make the overland journey to the Pacific should bear in mind that there are several different routes which may be traveled with wagons, each having its advocates in persons directly or indirectly interested in attracting the tide of emigration and travel over them. . . .

There is no doubt that each one of these roads has its advantages and disadvantages, but a judicious selection must depend chiefly upon the following consideration, namely, the locality from whence the individual is to take his departure, the season of the year when he desires to commence his journey, the character of his means of transportation, and the point upon the Pacific coast that he wishes to reach.

Persons living in the Northeastern States can, with about equal facility and dispatch, reach the eastern terminus of any one of the routes they may select by means of public transport. And, as animals are much cheaper on the frontier than in the Eastern states, they should purchase their teams at or near the point where the overland journey is to commence.

Those living in the Northwestern States, having their own teams, and wishing to go to any point north of San Francisco, will of course make choice of the route which takes its departure from the Missouri River.

Those who live in the middle Western States, having their own means of transportation, and going to any point upon the Pacific coast, should take one of the middle routes.

Others, who reside in the extreme Southwest, and whose destination is south of San Francisco, should travel the southern road running through Texas, which is the only one practicable for comfortable winter travel. The grass upon a great portion of this route is green during the entire winter, and snow seldom covers it. This road leaves the Gulf coast at *Powder-horn,* on Matagorda Bay, which point is difficult of access by land from the north, but may be reached by steamers from New Orleans five times a week. . . .

Many persons who have had much experience in prairie traveling prefer leaving the Missouri River in March or April, and feeding grain to their animals until the new grass appears. The roads become muddy and heavy after the spring rains set in, and by starting out early the worst part of the road will be passed over before the ground becomes wet and soft. This plan, however, should never be attempted unless the animals are well supplied with grain, and kept in good condition. They will eat the old grass in the spring, but it does not, in this climate, as in Utah and New Mexico, afford them sufficient sustenance. . . .

Upon the head of the Sweetwater River, and west of the South Pass, alkaline springs are met with, which are exceedingly poisonous to cattle and horses. They can readily be detected by the yellowish-red color of the grass growing around them. Animals should never be allowed to graze near them or to drink the water.

Organization of Companies. After a particular route has been selected to make the journey across the plains, and the requisite number have arrived at the eastern terminus, their first business should be to organize themselves into a company and elect a commander. The company should be of sufficient magnitude to herd and guard animals, and for protection against Indians.

From 50 to 70 men, properly armed and equipped, will be enough for these purposes, any any greater number only makes the movements of the party more cumbersome and tardy.

In the selection of a captain, good judgement, integrity of purpose, and practical experience are the essential requisites, and these are indispensable to the harmony and consolidation of the association. His duty should be to direct the order of march, the time of starting and halting, to select the camps, detail and give orders to guards, and, indeed, to control and superintend all the movements of the company.

An obligation should then be drawn up and signed by all the members of the association, wherein each one should bind himself to abide in all cases by the orders and decisions of the captain, and to aid him by every means in his power in the execution of his duties; and they should also obligate themselves to aid each other, so as to make the individual interest of each member the common concern of the whole company. To insure this, a fund should be raised for the purchase of extra animals to supply the places of those which may give out or die on the road. . . .

In case of failure on the part of any one to comply with the obligations imposed by the articles of agreement after they have been duly executed, the company should of course have the power to punish the delinquent member, and, if necessary, to exclude him from all the benefits of the association. . . .

The advantages of an association such as I have mentioned are manifestly numerous. The animals can be herded together and guarded by the different members of the company in rotation, thereby securing to all the opportunities of sleep and rest. . . .

When a captain has once been chosen, he should be sustained in all his decisions unless he commit some manifest outrage, when a majority of the company can always remove him, and put a more competent man in his place. Sometimes men may be selected who, upon trial, do not come up to the anticipations of those who have placed them in power, and other men will exhibit, during the course of the march, more capacity. Under these circumstances, it will not be unwise to make a change. . . .

Wagons and Trains. A company having been organized, its first interest is to procure a proper outfit of transportation and supplies for the contemplated journey.

Wagons should be of the simplest possible construction—strong, light, and made of well-seasoned timber, especially the wheels, as the atmosphere, in the elevated and arid region over which they have to pass, is so exceedingly dry during the summer months that, unless the wood-work is thoroughly seasoned, they will require constant repairs to prevent them from falling to pieces. . . .

There has been much discussion regarding the relative merits of mules and oxen for prairie traveling, and the question is yet far from being settled. Upon good firm roads, in a populated country, where grain can be procured, I should unquestionably give the preference to mules, as they travel faster, and endure the heat of summer much better than oxen; and if the journey be not over 1000 miles, and the grass abundant, even without grain, I think mules would be preferable. But when the march is to extend 1500 or 2000 miles, or over a rough sandy or muddy road, I believe young oxen will endure better than mules; they will, if properly managed, keep in better condition, and perform the journey in an equally brief space of time. Besides, they are much more economical, a team of six mules costing six hundred dollars, while an eight-ox team only costs upon the frontier about two hundred dollars. Oxen are much less liable to be stampeded and driven off by Indians, and can be pursued and overtaken by horsemen; and finally, they can, if necessary, be used for beef. . . .

Cows will be found very useful upon long journeys when the rate of travel is slow, as they furnish milk, and in emergencies they may be worked in wagons. I once saw a small cow yoked beside a large ox, and driven about six hundred miles attached to a loaded wagon, and she performed her part equally well with the ox. It has been by no means an unusual thing for emigrant travelers to work cows as their teams.

Stores and Provisions. Supplies for a march should be put up in the most secure, compact, and portable shape.

Bacon should be packed in strong sacks of a hundred pounds to each; or, in very hot climates, put in boxes and surrounded with bran, which in a great measure prevents the fat from melting away. . . .

Flour should be packed in stout double canvas sacks well sewed, a hundred pounds in each sack.

Butter may be preserved by boiling it thoroughly, and skimming off the scum as it rises to the top until it is quite clear like oil. It is then placed in tin canisters and soldered up. This mode of preserving butter has been adopted in the hot climate of southern Texas, and it is found to keep sweet for a great length of time, and its flavor is but little impaired by the process.

Sugar may be well secured in India-rubber or gutta-percha sacks, or so placed in the wagon as not to risk getting wet.

Desiccated or dried vegetables are almost equal to the fresh, and are put up in such a compact and portable form as easily to be transported over the plains. They have been extensively used in the Crimean war, and by our own army in Utah, and have been very generally approved. They are prepared by cutting the fresh vegetables into thin slices and subjecting them to a very powerful press, which removes the juice and leaves a solid cake which, after having been thoroughly dried in an oven, becomes almost as hard as a rock. A small piece of this, about half the size of a man's hand, when boiled, swells up so as to fill a vegetable dish, and is sufficient for four men. . . .

In making up their outfit for the plains, men are very prone to overload their teams with a great variety of useless articles. It is a good rule to carry nothing more than is absolutely necessary for use upon the journey. One can not expect, with the limited allowance of transportation that emigrants usually have, to indulge in luxuries upon such expeditons. . . .

The allowance of provisions for each grown person, to make the journey from the Missouri River to California, should suffice for 110 days. The following is deemed requisite, viz.: 150 lbs. of flour, or its equivalent in hard bread; 25 lbs. of bacon or pork, and enough fresh beef to be driven on the hoof to make up the meat component of the ration; 15 lbs. of coffee, and 25 lbs. of sugar; also a quantity of saleratus or yeast powders for making bread, and salt and pepper.

These are the chief articles of subsistence necessary for the trip, and they should be used with economy, reserving a good portion for the western half of the journey. Heretofore many of the California emigrants have improvidently exhausted their stocks of provisions before reaching their journey's end, and have, in may cases, been obliged to pay the most exorbitant prices in making up the deficiency. . . .

I once traveled with a party of New Yorkers *en route* for California. They were perfectly ignorant of everything relating to this kind of campaigning, and had overloaded their wagons with almost every thing except the very articles most important and necessary; the consequence was, that they exhausted their teams, and were obliged to throw away the greater part of their loading. They soon learned that Champagne, East India sweetmeats, olives, etc., etc., were not the most useful articles for a prairie tour.

Excerpts from *The World Rushed In*

By J. S. Holliday

Through April and the first two weeks of May, the Californians crowded the streets of Independence, St. Joseph and the smaller frontier towns. . . . Most were busy buying salted bacon, salertus, hard bread, dried fruit, pistols, rifles, percussion caps, medicines, tin stoves, India-rubber blankets, bowie knives, rope, lanterns and a score of other recommended necessities. At nearby corrals they debated whether to buy oxen or mules.

Of all their decisions in preparing for the overland journey, the choice of teams was most important and difficult. Many complained that every resident of Independence and St. Joseph seemed to have either oxen or mules to sell or sought to promote the interest of friends who had one or the other. Despite the contradictory recommendations, decisions were made, sometimes with such certainty that arguments broke out between members of the same company, some demanding purchase of oxen, others insisting on mules. A few companies split over the issue.

From information and general discussion heard in Independence, Swain and his friends judged that oxen were preferable to mules, in part because they sold for $40 to $50 per yoke, while mules cost $50 to $70 each. As well, the perversity of mules, especially for a city man, dissuaded many from choosing the long-ears. For those who did, Mexicans could be hired in Independence and St. Joseph to break the wild mules that had been sold with the assurance "they would be as handy as sheep."

Better than half of the companies chose oxen. Only a few hitched up horses to their wagons. Some companies bought pack saddles for their mules to carry food and supplies, thus saving the cost of wagons. But packing was known to be a demanding experience without a place to rest or, if necessary, to carry a sick comrade. And worse, with pack mules the companies could not carry the array of equipment they expected to need in the mines—everything from underwater diving suits and bells to gold-washing machinery, in addition to all the food and gear required on the trail. Wagons would allow room for everything. . . .

For all but a few, the tradition of earlier travelers to Oregon and California showed the way to go—by wagon and in organized companies or associations. No one faced the vast distance with just one wagon and four or five companions. Though motivated by individual ambition, indeed by an independence of spirit that had sent them off from home, the goldseekers knew that the journey would require joint effort and cooperation . . . in the face of wilderness uncertainties and dangers. Therefore, back home or at the frontier they organized joint-stock companies that served not only as business partnerships to meet the costs of purchasing wagons, teams and supplies, but also provided governmental or military decision-making authority and leadership. For defense against Indian attack, regulation of guard duty to protect the animals, decisions as to where to camp each night, it had been proved in years past that officers with authority, sometimes enhanced by uniforms, could best manage a company of greenhorns. . . .

The Rangers' success in reaching California would depend first on the health and strength of their teams and second on the durability of their wagons. James Pratt, as the Wolverines' agent, had purchased their wagons in Chicago and had them shipped to Independence. Like those of other companies on the frontier, they were simple farm wagons, such as had been used in earlier years by Oregon and California settlers. They were not at all like the heavy, sway-backed Conestoga wagons used in Pennsylvania in the mid-eighteenth century and adapted for the Santa Fe trade where the cargoes required size and heft. The gold rush wagons were standard vehicles, common on farms across America—and seldom, if ever, were they called "prairie schooners." Light but sturdy, they had three basic parts—the bed, the running gear, and the top. The bed was a wooden box about nine or ten feet long and four feet wide, with the sides and ends about two or three feet high. The axles and tongues were made of well-seasoned hickory, ash, oak or other hardwood; many companies carried extras, for these parts were known to snap and give way at stream crossings and steep declines. The wheels had to be extremely tough, and the rims or tires were made of iron. The tops or covers, made of canvas or some other thick cloth that had been waterproofed with linseed or other oil, were stretched over five or six bows of hickory. Inside the "covered wagon" an enclosed space about five feet high from bed to peak provided storage space and shelter. Because these simple wagons had no brakes (and, of course, no springs), the teamsters learned how to tie chains around the rear wheels to lock them, and thus provide a drag when the teams started down a steep slope.

Excerpts from "How to Make the Trek"
From *Route and Distances to Oregon and California* by J. M. Shively, written in 1846

When you start over these wide plains, let no one leave dependent on his best friend for any thing; for if you do, you will certainly have a blow-out before you get far. I would advise all young men who have no families to have nothing to do with the wagons nor stock. . . .

Those who emigrate with families, and consequently, wagons, stock, etc., cannot expect to accomplish the journey in less than four months, under the most favorable circumstances; and, in order that they be prepared in the best possible manner, first buy a light strong wagon, made of the best seasoned materials; for, if the timbers be not well seasoned, your wagon will fall to pieces when you get to the dry, arid plains of the mountains; let the bed of your wagon be made of maple if you can get it, and let the side and end boards be one wide board, without cracks; let them so project the sides and ends of the bottom of the bed as to turn off the water from the bottom. Next, let your wagon sheet be either linen or Osnaburg, well oiled or painted, and fixed to fasten well down the sides; let the bed be straight; procure wooden boxes of half or three-quarter inch pine boards, of the same convenient height, and let them fit tight in the bed of your wagon. In these boxes place your provisions, clothing, ammunition, and whatever articles you choose to take along; close the boxes by hinges or otherwise, and on them is a comfortable place for women and children to ride through the day, secure from dust or rain, and a place to sleep at night for a small family. Take as much tea, coffee, sugar, and spices as you please; but above all take plenty of flour and well cured side bacon to last you through if you can. Let each man and lad be provided with five or six hickory shirts, one or two pair of buckskin pantaloons, a buckskin coat or hunting shirt, two very wide brimmed hats, wide enough to keep the mouth from the sun. For the want of such hat thousands suffer nearly all the way to Oregon, with their lips ulcerated, caused by sunburn. Take enough of coarse shoes or boots to last you through—three or four pair a-piece will be sufficient—moccasins will not protect your feet against the large plains of prickly pear along the road. However much help your wives and daughters have been to you at home, they can do but little for you here—herding stock, through either dew, dust, or rain, breaking brush, swimming rivers, attacking grizzly bears or savage Indians, is all out of their line of business. All they can do, is to cook for camps, etceteras, &c.; nor need they have any wearing apparel, other than their ordinary clothing at home.

TOPIC: Life in Spanish California
TIME: Two class periods
TIME PERIOD: During study of the West and Southwest between 1800 and 1850

BACKGROUND

The land that is now California was originally occupied by numerous tribes of Indians, mostly peaceful hunter-gatherers. In 1542 Juan Rodriguez Cabrillo, a Spaniard, became the first European to explore this land. The Spanish did not show much further interest in California, however, until the visit of the Englishman Sir Francis Drake in 1769 made them fear that the English might take over the area. The first Spanish settlement in Alta (Upper) California, at San Diego, was established in the same year.

Spain, declining in power in Europe, paid little attention to its California holdings. Most European-descended settlers in California during the time Spain owned it were either missionaries or military men. The missionaries Christianized and controlled the Indians, using them as unpaid labor. Until the 1820s the missions controlled most of the land as well and were the area's major economic centers. The soldiers lived in presidios, or military towns, the most important of which were San Diego, Santa Barbara, Monterey, and San Francisco. A few pueblos, or civilian towns, also existed: San Jose, Los Angeles, and Santa Cruz.

After Mexico gained its independence from Spain in 1821, it took over California. Like Spain, Mexico had neither the power nor the interest to keep firm control over California. Mexican rule did bring important changes, however, by removing restrictions on foreign trade and allowing most of the mission lands to be "secularized" and distributed to ranchers.

These two changes greatly increased the importance of ranching in California. Ships from the United States (which the Spanish Californians called "Boston," because most of the ships came from that city) visited California in increasing numbers after the 1820s, and hides and tallow (hardened fat, used for candles, soap, and other purposes) from California cattle became the area's main exports. Beaver and sea otter furs were also much sought after by American and Russian traders alike.

The "golden age" of Spanish California is usually considered to be between the time of Mexican takeover in the 1820s and the time of American takeover in the mid-1840s. This is the period described in this teaching strategy. During this time the aristocratic families of California (*gentes de razon,* or "people of reason"), soldiers or ranchers or both, held most of the area's land and wealth. These families claimed Spanish descent, even though few were purely Spanish. The Lugo family, shown in the photograph, was one of these families. Middle-class people—artisans and so on—were Mexican or of mixed blood (including black, in some cases). The Indians, treated virtually as slaves, were at the bottom of the social ladder.

A group of Californians led by the American soldier and explorer John C. Frémont declared California independent of Mexico after the so-called Bear Flag Revolt in 1846. In 1848, at the end of the Mexican War, Mexico ceded California and other lands to the United States. Nine days before the treaty ceding the land was signed, an event perhaps even more important for California history occurred: gold was discovered at Sutter's Mill. The next year brought a huge influx of gold seekers from the United States, and California soon became a state.

The new settlers quickly found ways to take over most of the land covered by the old Spanish and Mexican land grants, many of which had been imprecise in designating boundaries. As a result, most of the wealth and power of the Spanish-descended aristocratic families vanished, and the way of life of Spanish California disappeared or was integrated into the very different ways of life brought by the miners and farmers.

The first reading, by Paul Horgan, describes Spanish–American culture in New Mexico during a time perhaps a little earlier than the 1820s. Most of Horgan's remarks, however, also apply to the life of Californians of Spanish descent. The title of his book, *The Heroic Triad,* refers to the three groups that contributed to Southwestern culture: the Indians, the Spanish Americans, and the Anglo Americans.

The second reading is by Richard Henry Dana, a Bostonian who became a sailor and wrote about his experiences in *Two Years Before the Mast,* first published in 1840. He visited California in 1834. Students should note and discuss some of the prejudices expressed in Dana's writing.

Hubert Howe Bancroft was a famous historian who wrote about California during the late nineteenth century. The third reading is from his book *California Pastoral,* first published in 1888.

This teaching strategy encourages students to use their historical imagination and the readings to become better acquainted with life in Spanish California. They will consider how the takeover of California by the United States changed life in Spanish California.

MATERIALS

1. Transparency or copies of the photograph of the Lugo family
2. Copies of the readings about Spanish California

SUGGESTED PROCEDURE

1. Provide students with the background information and review the textbook material on Spanish California.
2. Show the transparency or distribute copies of the photograph of the Lugo family, one of the aristocratic ranch families of Spanish California. Ask students the following questions:
   a. How many generations do you see in the picture? (three)
   b. What can you suggest about family life in Spanish California from the picture? (Answers will vary. Students may suggest that all generations of a family lived together.)
   c. Do you think this family was wealthy or poor? Why? (Possible answers: The family may or may not own the house in which they are being photographed. Their dress may indicate wealth, but point out that the family probably dressed in their best clothes to have the photograph taken.)
3. Distribute the readings about life in Spanish California, and allow time for students to read the material. Students who do not finish the readings in class should complete them for homework. Encourage students to research additional material on Spanish California that is available from textbooks and library books.
4. At the beginning of the following class period, instruct students to use information from the photograph, the written material, and their research to write an account of an imaginary visit to an aristocratic Spanish-California family's rancho some time between 1825 and 1840. They may wish to imagine that they (like Dana) are sailors on a Yankee ship, that they are visiting Spanish California in a time machine, that they are Indian servants in a rancho, or that they are relatives visiting from Mexico. Their accounts should tell what they see and do, what they eat, how their hosts behave, and so on. If this assignment seems too difficult for individuals, you might have students prepare their stories in groups, with each individual writing part of the story. Students may illustrate their stories if they wish.
5. When students have finished their writings, post the stories on the bulletin board and/or have volunteers read their stories aloud.
6. As a closure activity, discuss the following question: Based on what you know of Spanish-California culture and the culture of the United States during this period, how would you expect life in Spanish California to change after about 1850? (Suggested response: As pioneers to the West began taking land from the Spanish Californians, their whole way of life would probably change. No longer would they have large land holdings to raise horses and cattle. The cultures, religions, and language of the incoming settlers would probably start to dominate.)

Excerpts from *The Heroic Triad*

By Paul Horgan

The house of a big hacienda was an image in earth of the family. Through generations it grew as the family grew. Its life faced inward. The outer walls were blind against the open country with its Indian dangers and were entered by wide covered passageways as deep as a room, and barred with heavy wooden doors that were secured with massive iron locks. Within, the rooms all opened on a patio in which trees grew, that in time towered over the roofs. Where the clay hives of the classic Indian towns grew upward in terrace above terrace, the hacienda, built of the same materials, and using many of the pueblo's details in style and method, expanded along the ground in a single story. Beginning with one system of rooms about a square patio, the house, as new lives came, grew into another patio, and even another. The walls were often three feet thick, built of weighty adobe blocks and plastered with earth mixed with straw. Ceiling beams were peeled tree poles, and between them were laid peeled sapling sticks. . . . Windows facing the patio held sections of selenite or small panes of imported glass, and were shuttered with carved wooden panels, hung from iron or leather hinges or upon round wooden pegs fitted into carved wooden rings. The floors were of packed earth. Within the patios, an extension of the roof made a porch on all sides. . . .

The . . . house threw its high clay wall around all the purposes and needs of life. There was a great room, or *sala,* for grand occasions—dances, receptions, family gatherings. A family chapel sat at one corner of the oldest patio, and over its door might be a belfry with a bell from Mexico. Each parental bedroom was also a sitting room with its own fireplace. The kitchen was a long room where the family sat down to meals. Near it were long dark storerooms in one of which meat and game were hung. In another, dried fruits were stored, and piñones in bags, and grain of wheat and corn in jars. Beyond the walls of these rooms, and reached by a heavy rear gate, sparkled a little ditch, bringing a vein of water from the main ditch that drank of the river. Rooms for servants ran along the rear. A blacksmith shop with forge, anvil, and leather bellows and a tool house with carpentry supplies and hides stood side by side in a work patio, where pens for chickens and sheep, a stable for horses and a shed for milk cows closed the square. . . .

In its essential form, the room was simple, and very close to the Indian's. The Indian at first lived on his floor. Later he made an earthen bench that hugged his wall, and if he sat, he had his wall to lean against. His very house was his furniture. The humble Spaniard made his earthen bench too, and in using it was tied to his wall. But the rich Spaniard moved away from the wall to the free center of the room, where he placed furniture, which was heavy, dark, and formal. Its character reflected his. If he sat in his chair, he must sit bolt upright, for the seat was narrow and shallow, its back straight, its arms high and hard, its legs tall. . . .

Placed against the stark earthen walls of a valley house, imported furnishings and precious objects even at their richest never seemed out of place. Inlaid woods, gold leaf, velvets, crystal, pure silver, turned the master's rooms . . . into the apartments of a Castilian palace. Profuse trade with the Indies brought European articles to New Spain, and some of these found their way to the northern kingdom, where they made references of nostalgia, pride, and respect for the past. . . .

The Mexico-Orient trade brought curious, gleaming fabrics from China, and for its rarity and strange richness of gold and silver thread, a strip of Chinese brocade was sometimes hung flat on the white wall. By daylight the room was cool and dim, for the patio windows were deep and low, and shaded outside by the overhang of the porch. The room was lighted at night by candles, held in iron candelabra, or others carved of wood, covered with gesso, and finished with gold leaf. . . .

The kitchen was in many ways the richest room in the house. Its graduated copper pots, hanging above the fireplace and its iron oven, shone like treasure. On its wooden shelves gleamed rows of dishes and glass. . . .

There were piles of silver dinner plates, and rows of cups and saucers, mugs, pitchers, chocolate pots; knives, forks, and spoons. Some of it was made in Spain, and bore Spanish hallmarks; much of it in Mexico. . . . Though massive, the silver pieces had grace, and though treasured, they bore the little pits and dents of daily use. To eat in the kitchen, off silver—in this were both the Spaniard's earthy simplicity and his pride. . . .

For in its own scale the family was as rigid and formal as the court of the King in respect to authority, reverence, and responsibility. So long as he lived the father was the lord, to be obeyed, respected, and loved. In turn he must provide the goods of life to those for whose lives he was responsible, and lead them wisely, and guide their work. The mother, in rich family or poor, was the lady of all, and worked harder than any at the endless household duties. Reverence was due to her, for she brought life and gave it to the world, and in doing so through the years received wisdom to which all would do well to listen. If her lord died before her, she until her death was the head of the family, and to the love and respect paid to her was now to be added obedience. Her ways were the right ways, no matter what the world tried to teach. She knew them without learning. Often in the colonial family, if the father represented the earth's life and its work of seasons and its secrets of strength, the mother was the fire and the spirit, the divined imagination at the heart of things, which she seemed the older she lived to perceive the more brightly. Her sons and daughters dared to risk humor with her, though rarely with their father. The grandchildren and great-grandchildren—for

the families in their homemade sustenances were long-lived—stood in awe of their august forebears. . . .

Children, who wore miniatures of their parents' clothes, early echoed their parents' formality. They soon learned to stop crying over trifles. . . .

While children played in the patio, under the prattling cotton woods, and talked to their parrots, the mother had many tasks to oversee. For her embroidery and knitting, there was wool to be dyed. Favorite colors came in the Mexican trade—reds and blues from cochineal, indigo, and brazilwood. But these were scarce, and the old Indian dyes, used for centuries on sacred feathers, and kachina masks, now colored the threads for embroidering bedspreads, altar cloths, upholstery, and clothing: yellow from rabbit brush, blue from larkspur, pink from the tag alder, blue-green from copper ore. Wool from brown and black sheep was used unchanged. With homespun yarns the women knitted stockings and wove brown and white rugs for the slippery floors. They made toilet soap from animal fats, adding melon seeds, rosemary, wild-rose leaves and bran starch, and grinding the whole mixture to paste, forming it in cakes, and setting them in the sun to dry. . . . The women made candles, dipping a long cotton string into melted tallow or beeswax and hanging it up to cool. When it was cool, they dipped it again, and again, until the candle was as big as they liked. In the spring, they gathered up the blankets in the house, heaped them on a cart and drove them to the river to be washed. By the riverside a fire was built, water was heated in big copper kettles, and yucca root was beaten and thrown into a long wooden trough into which hot water was poured. The women, bare-armed and barefooted, knelt by the trough and flailed the water until they made suds. The blankets were then immersed, rubbed, and wrung until the country's unfading dye colors came clear again. At the river's edge . . . they rinsed the heavy cloths in the current, and then spread them in the meadow grass to dry.

Excerpts from *Two Years Before the Mast*
By Richard Henry Dana

Wednesday, Jan 6th. Set sail from Monterey, with a number of Spaniards as passengers, and shaped our course for Santa Barbara. . . .

Among our passengers was a young man who was the best representation of a decayed gentleman I had ever seen. . . . He was of the aristocracy of the country, his family being of pure Spanish blood, and once of great importance in Mexico. His father had been governor of the province, and having amassed a large property, settled at San Diego, where he built a large house with a courtyard in front, kept a great retinue of Indians, and set up for the grandee of that part of the country. His son was sent to Mexico, where he received the best education and went into the first society of the capital.

Misfortune, extravagance, and the want of funds . . . soon ate the estate up, and Don Juan Bandini returned from Mexico accomplished, poor, and proud, and without any office or occupation, to lead the life of most young men of the better families—dissolute and extravagant when the means are at hand; ambitious at heart, and impotent to act; often pinched for bread; keeping up an appearance of style, when their poverty is known to each half-naked Indian boy in the street, and they stand in dread of every small trader and shopkeeper in the place.

He had a slight and elegant figure, moved gracefully, danced and waltzed beautifully, spoke the best Castilian with a pleasant and refined voice and accent, and had throughout, the bearing of a man of high birth and figure. Yet here he was, with his passage given him (as I afterward learned), for he had not the means of paying for it, and living upon the charity of our agent.

He was polite to everyone, spoke to the sailors, and gave four *reales*—I dare say the last he had in his pocket—to the steward who waited upon him. I could not but feel a pity for him, especially when I saw him by the side of his fellow passenger and townsman, a fat, coarse, vulgar, pretending fellow of a Yankee trader, who had made money in San Diego, and who was eating out the very vitals of the Bandinis, fattening upon their extravagance, grinding them in their poverty; having mortgages on their lands, forestalling their cattle and already making an inroad upon their jewels, which were their last hope. . . .

Sunday, January 10th. Arrived at Santa Barbara. . . .

Great preparations were making on shore for the marriage of our agent, who was to marry Dona Anneta De G——, youngest daughter of Don Antonio N——, the grandee of the place, and the head of the first family in California. . . .

On the day appointed for the wedding, we took the captain ashore in the gig, and had orders to come for him at night, with leave to go up to the house and see the *fandango*. . . .

As we drew near, we heard the accustomed sound of violins and guitars, and saw a great motion of the people within. Going in, we found nearly all the people of the town—men, women, and children—collected and crowded together, leaving barely room for the dancers for on these occasions no invitations are given, but everyone is expected to come. . . .

The old women sat down in rows, clapping their hands to the music, and applauding the young ones. The music was lively, and among the tunes, we recognized several of our popular airs, which we, without doubt, have taken from the Spanish.

In the dancing, I was much disappointed. The women stood upright, with their hands down by their sides, their eyes fixed upon the ground before them, and slided about without any perceptible means of motion; for their feet were invisible, the hem of their dresses forming a perfect circle about them, reaching to the ground. They looked as grave as if they were going through some religious ceremony. . . .

The men did better. They danced with

grace and spirit, moving in circles round their nearly stationary partners, and showing their figures to great advantage.

A great deal was said about our friend Don Juan Bandini, and when he did appear, which was toward the close of the evening he certainly gave us the most graceful dancing that I had ever seen. He was dressed in white pantaloons, neatly made, a short jacket of dark silk, gayly white stockings and thin morocco slippers upon his very small feet.

His slight and graceful figure was well calculated for dancing, and he moved about with the grace and daintiness of a young fawn. . . .

The great amusement of the evening—which I suppose was owing to its being carnival—was the breaking of eggs filled with cologne, or other essences, upon the heads of the company. One end of the egg is broken and the inside taken out, then it is partly filled with cologne, and the whole sealed up.

The women bring a great number of these secretly about them, and the amusement is to break one upon the head of a gentleman when his back is turned. He is bound in gallantry to find out the lady and return the compliment, though it must not be done if the person sees you. . . .

Excerpts from *California Pastoral*
By Hubert Howe Bancroft

The usual fare in well-to-do families was as follows: first the *desayuno,* at daybreak, milk mixed with a little pinole of maize, finely sifted, and a small quantity of sugar; some had, instead of milk, chocolate, or coffee with or without milk, and bread or biscuit with butter; next, between 8 and 9 a.m. was served the *almuerzo,* or regular breakfast, consisting of good fresh beef or veal, roasted, or otherwise prepared, well fried beans, and a cup of tea or coffee, with milk. Some used bread made of wheaten flour, others a kind of bread made of maize, of a circular shape, flattened out very thin, baked over a slow fire on a flat, earthen pan, and which was known as tortilla de maíz, to distinguish it from the one made of wheaten flour with a little fat, which was called tortilla de harina. Dinner took place at noon, and consisted of good broth, á la española, made usually of beef or mutton, and to thicken the broth rice, garbanzos, good cabbage, etc. were boiled with it. After the broth came soups á la española made with rice, vermicelli, tallarines, maccaroni, punteta, or small dumplings of wheaten flour, bread, or tortilla de maíz. The next course was the puchero, which usually was the meat and vegetables from which the broth had been made, with sauce to stimulate the appetite. This sauce was generally confectioned in summer with green peppers and red tomatoes, minced onions, parsley, or garlic. In winter the sauce was made with dried peppers. Lastly, there were fried beans. With this meal the tortilla de maíz was generally eaten, and sometimes some dulce or sweetmeat, which made a drink of water after it quite palatable. In the afternoon, chiefly in summer, a cup of chá, as tea was called in California, or coffee, was taken, by the women with milk, and by the men with a small glass of liquor. At night there was a light supper of meat ragout, or roast, finishing with beans. These were the usual meals among the principal classes. It is hardly necessary to say that fish of every kind, where it could be had, was frequently used, especially on Fridays, and other days when the church inhibited the use of flesh. . . .

The people at large lived almost entirely on beef, reddish beans, and tortillas. They used but little flour. Corn they ate in the form of tortillas. Beef was frequently cut in slices or strips, and roasted before an open fire on an iron spit. Peppers and beans, as well as the corn, were raised, and the peppers were used to season almost everything. . . .

They began to ride almost as soon as they could walk, and such children as were not killed in the beginning became expert riders. A boy as soon as he had the strength would go out upon the hills, lasso a wild colt, halter and mount it, and then let it go flying over the open country until exhausted. . . . Corrals were formed by driving poles (estantes) into the ground; these were secured by ledges (latas) tied with thongs. . . .

Coronel says that the men occupied themselves exclusively in caring for the cattle and horses, but this only during the season of the rodeos . . . and when the slaughter of the cattle took place, in order to collect the hides and tallow wherewith to make purchases and the payment of their debts—for these articles served in lieu of money. They were not devoted to agriculture; for at the missions they obtained what grain they wanted. Some, however, cultivated land for their own use, and later, as the missions decayed, all were compelled to pay some attention to cultivating their land. At this time the men of a certain age still preserved the character of their Spanish progenitors. Formal and upright, imperious yet honorable, in their business transactions—however great the value involved—no aid of men learned in the law, or even that of witnesses, was sought or needed. But these characteristics rapidly disappeared. . . .

The few who were not good riders were looked upon with a sort of contempt. Their attachment to their steeds was as great as the Arab's, and the greatest token of friendship between man and man was the present of the best horse.

The Californians always galloped. . . . When the horse tired, the traveller would catch the first other one he saw, and so continue changing his steed, always sure of recovering it on returning. The hat was small in the opening and a string was put on to secure it. The rider usually had his mouth open as if to keep the hat-string tight, and the hat secure; often as he rode along he filled the air with popular ditties. If rain overtook the horseman, he would ride into the first house he came to, if there were no outhouses or sheds. . . .

Serrano remarks that when California women ride on horseback they use the same trappings and saddles as men, though without ornaments; some are exceedingly skilful in managing a horse, mounting alone and with agility. As the saddles on which they ride have the saddle-bow and stirrups taken off, they use as a stirrup for one foot a silk band, one end being made fast at the pommel, the other at the cantel.

TOPIC: Alexis de Tocqueville on the Restless Americans
TIME: One class period
TIME PERIOD: During study of the settlement of the West

BACKGROUND

Alexis-Charles-Henri Clérel de Tocqueville (1805–1859) was a French political scientist and historian. Trained as a judge, he spent two years in the United States in the early 1830s. The original purpose of his visit was to learn about American prisons, but he ended up making a detailed analysis of the society and political system of the United States. This analysis appeared in his two-volume work *Democracy in America,* which was first published in 1835. This work considers how the society and daily life of the United States affects and is affected by the country's democratic and egalitarian ideals. The reading used in this teaching strategy is taken from the second volume. Students will evaluate Tocqueville's ideas as an explanation of the westward movement in the first half of the nineteenth century and will consider the degree to which Tocqueville's observations apply to Americans today.

MATERIALS

Copies of the handout "Why the Americans Are Often So Restless in the Midst of Their Prosperity"

SUGGESTED PROCEDURE

1. Provide students with the background information on Tocqueville and the excerpt from *Democracy in America.*
2. Organize the class into groups of four. Distribute copies of the handout, and have students take turns reading the excerpt aloud. One student in each group should act as a researcher to find in the dictionary any unfamiliar words from the reading. Ask students to answer the questions at the end of the reading. A recorder from each group should write the group's answers on a sheet of paper. Compare the groups' answers in a class discussion.
3. Have students review textbook material and other readings on the westward movement in the United States during the first half of the nineteenth century. Then have students discuss or write answers to the following questions:
   a. What aspects of the westward movement (people's reasons for going, the effort they put into getting there, what they did when they got there, and so on) fit with Tocqueville's ideas about American restlessness? Which aspects do not fit his ideas? (Possible answers for aspects that fit: the "feverish ardor" that Tocqueville says Americans have, which would explain the immense effort they put into crossing the country; his idea that Americans have the longing to "hurry after some new delight" fits with the pioneers' desire for new land, adventure, and wealth (gold). Possible answers for aspects that do not fit his ideas: his ideas that Americans have a "taste for physical pleasures" and that "men are often less afraid of death" than of hardship do not fit with the enormous risk and hardship the pioneers undertook when they crossed the country.)
   b. How well do you think Tocqueville's ideas fit Americans today? Explain your answer. (Answers will vary. Students might point out peoples' current desire for getting things done quickly, using tools such as fax machines, car telephones, and computers; students might point out that today some people are materialistic in that they must have the best cars, the best clothes, the best entertainment systems, and so on.)

Answers to Review Questions (Page 136)
1. They never stop thinking about what they do not have.
2. In a democratic society in which all people are equal, a person alone is powerless because he or she is faced with the competition of all other people. Students may or may not agree with Tocqueville, but they should support their answers with sound reasoning.
3. Tocqueville seems to think that the restlessness causes more trouble and discontent than it is worth.

Excerpts from *Democracy in America*, Vol. II, Chapter 13

By Alexis de Tocqueville

"WHY THE AMERICANS ARE OFTEN SO RESTLESS IN THE MIDST OF THEIR PROSPERITY"

In certain remote corners of the Old World you may sometimes stumble upon little places which seem to have been forgotten among the general tumult and which have stayed still while all around them moves. The inhabitants are mostly very ignorant and very poor; they take no part in affairs of government, and often governments oppress them. But yet they seem serene and often have a jovial disposition.

In America I have seen the freest and best educated of men in circumstances the happiest to be found in the world; yet it seemed to me that a cloud habitually hung on their brow, and they seemed serious and almost sad even in their pleasures.

The chief reason for this is that the former do not give a moment's thought to the ills they endure, whereas the latter never stop thinking of the good things they have not got.

It is odd to watch with what feverish ardor the Americans pursue prosperity and how they are ever tormented by the shadowy suspicion that they may not have chosen the shortest route to get it.

Americans cleave to the things of this world as if assured that they will never die, and yet are in such a rush to snatch any that come within their reach, as if expecting to stop living before they have relished them. They clutch everything but hold nothing fast, and so lose grip as they hurry after some new delight.

An American will build a house in which to pass his old age and sell it before the roof is on; he will plant a garden and rent it just as the trees are coming into bearing; he will clear a field and leave others to reap the harvest; he will take up a profession and leave it, settle in one place and soon go off elsewhere with his changing desires. If his private business allows him a moment's relaxation, he will plunge at once into the whirlpool of politics. Then, if at the end of a year crammed with work he has a little spare leisure, his restless curiosity goes with him traveling up and down the vast territories of the United States. Thus he will travel five hundred miles in a few days as a distraction from his happiness. . . .

The taste for physical pleasures must be regarded as the first cause of this secret restlessness betrayed by the actions of the Americans, and of the inconstancy of which they give daily examples.

A man who has set his heart on nothing but the good things of this world is always in a hurry, for he has only a limited time in which to find them, get them, and enjoy them. Remembrance of the shortness of life continually goads him on. Apart from the goods he has, he thinks of a thousand others which death will prevent him from tasting if he does not hurry. This thought fills him with distress, fear, and regret and keeps his mind continually in agitation, so that he is always changing his plans and his abode.

Add to this taste for prosperity a social state in which neither law nor custom holds anyone in one place, and that is a great further stimulus to this restlessness of temper. One will then find people continually changing path for fear of missing the shortest cut leading to happiness.

It is, however, easy to understand that although those whose passions are bent on physical pleasures are eager in their desires, they are also easily discouraged. For as their ultimate object is enjoyment, the means to it must be prompt and easy, for otherwise the trouble of getting the pleasure would be greater than the pleasure when won. Hence the prevailing temper is at the same time ardent and soft, violent and enervated. Men are often less afraid of death than of enduring effort toward one goal.

Equality leads by a still shorter path to the various effects I have just described.

When all prerogatives of birth and fortune are abolished, when all professions are open to all and a man's own energies may bring him to the top of any of them, an ambitious man may think it easy to launch on a great career and feel that he is called to no common destiny. But that is a delusion which experience quickly corrects. The same equality which allows each man to entertain vast hopes makes each man by himself weak. His power is limited on every side, though his longings may wander where they will.

Not only are men powerless by themselves, but at every step they find immense obstacles which they had not at first noticed.

They have abolished the troublesome privileges of some of their fellows, but they come up against the competition of all. The barrier has changed shape rather than place. When men are more or less equal and are following the same path, it is very difficult for any of them to walk faster and get out beyond the uniform crowd surrounding and hemming them in.

This constant strife between the desires inspired by equality and the means it supplies to satisfy them harasses and wearies the mind.

Review Questions

1. According to Tocqueville, why are Americans so restless?
2. Why did Tocqueville think that people in a democratic society are more likely to be restless and discontented than people under other forms of government? Do you agree with him? Why or why not?
3. Did Tocqueville seem to think that the restlessness of Americans is a good quality or a bad one? Why did he think so? Do you agree?

TOPIC: The Work of Pioneer Women
TIME: One class period
TIME PERIOD: During study of the lives of the settlers in the West

BACKGROUND

In 1836 Narcissa Whitman and Eliza Spalding, both missionaries, became the first white women to settle in Oregon. They were followed by many others, missionary and otherwise. Most women made the hard journey across the country in trains of covered wagons with their husbands and, often, children. Filled with hardships as that journey was, it merely marked the beginning of the pioneer women's work. Men, women, and children all had to work as hard as they could simply to survive in the new land. Sometimes their struggle wore them down, but many pioneer women developed a strength of character that was perhaps not equaled in the easier times of later generations.

Some pioneer women kept diaries. Others were interviewed in their old age by reporters who asked them about their early memories. Some of the quotations used in this teaching strategy come from interviews conducted by Fred Lockley for the *Oregon Journal* in the 1920s and early 1930s. Students will read the first-hand accounts of the lives of pioneer women, and they will have the opportunity to consider the positive and negative effects of constant hard work on personal development.

MATERIALS

Copies of handouts with diary entries and interviews

SUGGESTED PROCEDURE

1. Provide students with the background information and review the textbook material on migration to and settlement in the far West.
2. Distribute the handouts. Before you ask for volunteers to read the selections, instruct students to make charts with columns headed *Food, Clothing, Care of Children and Infants,* and *Other.* Ask students to classify the tasks mentioned in the selections into these categories. After the selections have been read, instruct students to add any other tasks that they have read about in other sources or think that pioneer women might have done.
3. Then ask students the following questions:
   a. What resources did pioneer women in Oregon and Washington have? (Possible answers: wool for spinning into thread to make clothes; bark from trees to dye the cloth; cows for milk, butter, and cheese; small game for food and hides; lumber to make logs for cabins.) What resources did they lack that would have been available to women in an eastern city? (Possible answers: stores in which to shop for things such as food, clothes, and other necessities; the company of other women; shelter other than tents or log cabins.)
   b. Recall that some of the pioneer women believed that women of pioneer times were better than women of later times. In what ways did they think they were better? (They thought themselves more kindly, thoughtful, and considerate; more self-reliant, self-sacrificing, and useful.) Why might the conditions of pioneer life make people better in those ways? (Hard work and the difficulties of survival contributed to those qualities.)
   c. In what way might the conditions of pioneer life harm or stunt the development of a woman's personality or character? (Answers will vary but might include: isolation may have stunted their development; just trying to survive meant that there was no time for anything else.)
   d. Overall, do you think pioneer people, especially women, were likely to have been better human beings than people who had more comforts and conveniences? Why or why not?

Excerpts from *Westward the Women*

By Nancy Wilson Ross

A woman on the Rogue River has left scraps of a journal from the fifties. . .

> Alone all day finish a new dress. Wish I had some new book to read to
> pass off time with some prophet or advantage. . . . O! dear I am tyred of
> the same dull monotony of time. . . .
> Think if I had the company of some lively female acquaintance I would
> feel better. . . .
> Today Oh! horrors how shall I express it, is the dreded washing day. . . .
> O! could I see through the future if but one step.
> O! dear today I have so much to do. Mr. B is agoing to have his house
> raised and I have got to get dinner for about twenty persons besides being
> bothered with two lady visitors. . . . Dinner is over and I am hartly glad of
> it for I never did like to cook.

Mary Richardson Walker, a missionary wife who came in the late thirties to Tshimakain,
near the present city of Spokane, has left an invaluable record of a lively mind functioning
in wilderness isolation. . . .
It is good to read stout-hearted Mary's strong and simple phrasing on the day of her
delivery:

> Rose about five. Had early breakfast. Got my house work done about
> nine. Baked six loaves of bread. Made a kettle of mush and have now a
> suet pudding and beef boiling. . . . I have managed to put my clothes away
> and set my house in order. May the merciful be with me through the
> unexpected scene. Nine o'clock p.m. was delivered of another son.

Though there were long days of solitude for Mary in the lonely countryside, there was,
always, endless work to be done. Just to read the chores enumerated in her wilderness
journal makes the back ache. Her work day averaged sixteen hours. Sixteen hours of
washing, ironing, sewing, mending, painting, carpentering, baking, repairing roofs and
chimneys, helping the invalid Mrs. Eells ("cleaned Mrs. E's earthen ware. Cooked for both
families") milking six cows night and morning, making soap and butter. Even
cheese-making was added. . . . She also made all the family's garments and their shoes: "cut
out eight pairs of shoes." She salted beef, cleaned tripe, wove carpets, churned, tried tallow,
dipped candles: "sat up all night . . . dipped twenty-four dozen"—and all this labor was
accomplished without even the primitive equipment that at the time passed for
conveniences among more favored American women. . . .

Excerpts from *Conversations with Pioneer Women*
By Fred Lockley

From interview with Catherine Thomas Morris

For my 13th birthday I was given a spinning wheel. This was in 1854. Mother was a good hand at carding wool. People used to bring in their wool, and we washed, carded, spun and wove it on shares, so we soon had plenty of clothes. Mother used alder bark to dye the cloth brown and oak bark to dye it butternut color. . . .

Each generation thinks that it is a great improvement on past generations. In a way I suppose this is true or we would make no progress, but in some ways I cannot help thinking that, as busy as they were, the pioneers of Oregon had more time to be kindly, thoughtful, and considerate than the people of today. When I was a girl, if a woman got sick she didn't have to hire a trained nurse. Her neighbors came in, did the housework, took her children to their homes to care for till she was well, brought her home-made bread and jellies and other things, and if a man met with an accident or was sick, all the men in the neighborhood would put in his crop for him or reap his grain, making it a day's picnic, just as if they were going to a house-raising. If he was out of wood they would haul wood and cut it up, and in every way the neighbors showed a spirit of helpfulness and service.

In these days many families have no children and others have one child. In those days there were usually from 10 to 15 children in the family so that children had no chance to grow up spoiled and selfish. They had to learn to share their things and to help each other. Both the boys and the girls had certain duties that they had to perform, so they had very little time to get into mischief. . . .

From interview with Marilla R. Washburn Bailey

I am 87 years old and as I look back to my girlhood I cannot help thinking how much more is done for the girls of today than was done for the girls of my day and generation. They have liberty that in our day was undreamed of. Sometimes I wonder if the girl of today is as self-reliant, self-sacrificing and as useful as girls were when I was a girl.

I was married at 15, and was not only a good cook and housekeeper, but I knew how to take care of babies, from having cared for my brothers and sisters. I had ten babies of my own and never had help. I could paddle my canoe on the river or handle the oars in a rowboat as well as an Indian. When my husband was away I could rustle the meat on which we lived, for I could handle a revolver or rifle as well as most men. I have shot bears, deer, and all sorts of smaller game. . . . In fact, I became so expert with a revolver that at 50 to 100 feet I could beat most men.

During the early days I lived in tents, in log pens, and in log cabins. The modern mother would think twice before she let her 15-year-old daughter move out on a tract of timber, miles away from any other settler, where she would have to kill the game for meat, cook over a fireplace, take care of the children, make soap and make clothes for the children. In those days we could not run into some handy store to get supplies.

From interview with Rebecca Heater Hess

During the 66 years I have lived on that farm I have managed to keep busy, taking care of my ten children, cooking for harvest hands, and milking six or seven cows night and morning besides making bread, doing my housework, and keeping the children's clothes mended.

From interview with Sarah Booth Hockett

As I look back to my girlhood I realize how busy my mother was rearing her large family of children and doing all of the work of the home, for in those days there were no labor-saving conveniences. Mother carded and spun the wool and made the clothes for all of us children. She also made Father's overcoats and made his white shirts. She did all of the sewing by hand and at first did the cooking over the fireplace. She molded all of the candles we used, and knitted socks and stockings for all of us and also knitted socks for sale.

TOPIC: Folk Songs of the Forty-Niners
TIME: One to three class periods
TIME PERIOD: During study of the California gold rush and the Forty-Niners

BACKGROUND

In 1849, following the discovery of gold at Sutter's Mill in California, thousands of Americans left their homes in the East and journeyed across the country. Some went by sea, either around Cape Horn or across Panama; others crossed the land by wagon train. All endured great hardships during the three or four months that their journey took. Hardships of the land journey included cholera and other sicknesses, attacks by American Indians, and the crossing of deep rivers, waterless deserts, and snowy mountains. Most of the Forty-Niners hoped to find gold, become rich, and return East, but some remained in the western lands and established farms or businesses there.

"The Sioux Indians" describes an attack by American Indians on a wagon train from the point of view of the people in the wagon train. It may or may not have been exaggerated. The Indians undoubtedly would have had a different tale to tell, of increasing hordes of people encroaching on their land and their way of life. The chorus repeats the last line of the song.

"Sweet Betsy from Pike" exists in many versions, with different verses and different nonsense syllables in the chorus. The song celebrates the strength, resourcefulness, and humor of the women as well as the men who faced the dangers of the westward journey. The tune comes from an old English ballad. The place referred to is Pike County, Missouri.

The tune of "The Old Settler's Song" comes from an Irish air. The song tells the story of a miner who failed in his golden dreams, moved north to Washington state, and eventually learned to love the new land—more or less. In this teaching strategy students will use their study of folk songs and other research to draw conclusions about the nature and hardships of the Forty-Niners' experiences.

MATERIALS

Copies of the three song sheets

SUGGESTED PROCEDURE

1. Provide students with the background information and review the textbook material on the Forty-Niners and their transcontinental journeys, especially the land journey by wagon train.
2. If possible, play records or tapes of singers performing "The Sioux Indians," "Sweet Betsy from Pike," "The Old Settler's Song," or other folk songs about the Forty-Niners and their journeys.
3. Distribute the song sheets. Provide the background information on the songs and have students sing them.

• To extend the strategy you may wish to do one or more of the following activities:

4. Ask students to study the three songs. Have students write short descriptions of the hardships of the wagon-train journey and mining and farming in the far West.
5. Have students rewrite the lyrics to "The Sioux Indians" from the point of view of a Sioux Indian.
6. Organize the class into groups of three or four, and have students write an original song (using a traditional tune, if they wish) describing some aspect of the 49ers' life not covered in the first three songs. Possibilities include the sea journey (around Cape Horn or via Panama), life in a mining camp, life in San Francisco, the western journey from a woman's or child's point of view, and life in the West from the point of view of a person who is not a miner (for example, a storekeeper, a cook or laundrywoman, or a Chinese laborer). Have the groups perform their songs for the class.

The Sioux Indians

Pioneer Song

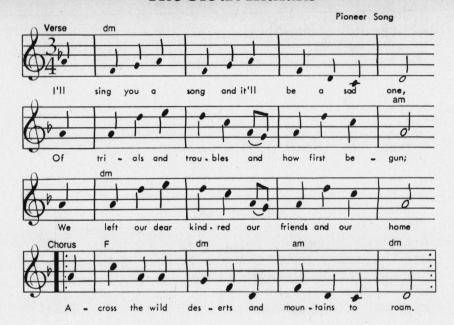

I'll sing you a song and it'll be a sad one,

Of tri-als and trou-bles and how first be-gun;

We left our dear kind-red our friends and our home

A-cross the wild des-erts and moun-tains to roam.

2. We crossed the Missouri and joined a large train,
   Which bore us o'er mountains and valleys and plains;
   And often of an evening out hunting we'd go,
   To shoot the fleet antelope and the wild buffalo.

3. We heard of Sioux Indians all out on the plains,
   A-killing poor drivers and burning their trains;
   A-killing poor drivers with arrows and bows,
   When captured by Indians, no mercy they'd show.

4. We traveled three weeks till we came to the Platte
   We set up our camp at the head of the flat;
   We spread down our blankets on the green grassy ground
   While our mules and our horses were grazing around.

5. While taking refreshment we heard a low yell;
   The whoop of Sioux Indians coming out of the dell
   We sprang to our rifles with a flash in each eye.
   "Boys," said our brave leader, "we'll fight till we die."

6. They made a bold dash and came near to our train,
   The arrows fell round us like showers of rain;
   But with our long rifles we fed them hot lead,
   Till many a brave warrior around us lay dead.

7. In our little band there were just twenty-four,
   And of the Sioux Indians, five hundred or more;
   We fought them with courage, we said not a word,
   The whoop of the Indians was all could be heard.

8. We shot their bold chief at the head of his band,
   He died like a warrior with his bow in his hand;
   When they saw their brave chief lying dead in his gore,
   They whooped and they yelled and we saw them no more.

9. We traveled by day, guarded camp in the night,
   Till Oregon's mountains look'd high in their might;
   Now in a green valley, beside a clear stream,
   Our journey has ended in the land of our dream.

Sweet Betsy from Pike

Traditional

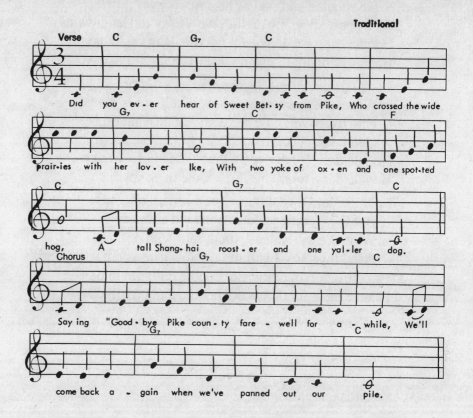

Did you ev-er hear of Sweet Bet-sy from Pike, Who crossed the wide prair-ies with her lov-er Ike, With two yoke of ox-en and one spot-ted hog, A tall Shang-hai roost-er and one yal-ler dog.

Chorus

Say ing "Good-bye Pike coun-ty fare-well for a -while, We'll come back a-gain when we've panned out our pile.

They swam the wild rivers and climbed the tall peaks,
   And camped on the prairies for weeks upon weeks.
   Starvation and cholera, hard work and slaughter,
   They reached Californy, spite of hell and high water.
Hoodle dang fol di dye do, hoodle dang fol di day,
Hoodle dang fol di dye do, hoodle dang fol di day.

They soon reached the desert, where Betsy gave out,
   And down on the sand she lay rolling about,
   While Ike in great wonder looked on in surprise,
   Sayin', "Get up now, Betsy, you'll get sand in your eyes."
Hoodle dang fol di dye do, hoodle dang fol di day,
Hoodle dang fol di dye do, hoodle dang fol di day.

The Indians came down in a wild yelling horde,
   And Betsy got skeered they would scalp her adored,
   So behind the front wagon wheel Betsy did crawl,
   And fought off the Indians with musket and ball.
Hoodle dang fol di dye do, hoodle dang fol di day,
Hoodle dang fol di dye do, hoodle dang fol di day.

The terrible desert was burning and bare,
   And Isaac he shrank from the death lurkin' there,
   "Dear old Pike County, I'll come back to you."
   Says Betsy, "You'll go by yourself if you do!"
Hoodle dang fol di dye do, hoodle dang fol di day,
Hoodle dang fol di dye do, hoodle dang fol di day.

One morning they climbed up a very high peak
  And with wonder looked down upon old Placerville,
  Ike shouted and said as he cast his eyes down
  "Sweet Betsy, my darlin', we've got to Hangtown."
Hoodle dang fol di dye do, hoodle dang fol di day,
Hoodle dang fol di dye do, hoodle dang fol di day.

Long Ike and Sweet Betsy attended a dance,
  Where Ike wore a pair of his Pike County pants,
  And Betsy was covered with ribbons and rings,
  Quoth Ike, "You're an angel, but where are your wings?"
Hoodle dang fol di dye do, hoodle dang fol di day,
Hoodle dang fol di dye do, hoodle dang fol di day.

Long Ike and Sweet Betsy got married, of course,
  But Ike, getting jealous, obtained a divorce,
  While Betsy, well satisfied, said with a shout,
  "Goodbye, you big lummox, I'm glad you backed out!"
Hoodle dang fol di dye do, hoodle dang fol di day,
Hoodle dang fol di dye do, hoodle dang fol di day.

The Old Settler's Song

2. For each man who got rich by mining,
   Perceiving that hundreds grew poor,
   I made up my mind to try farming,
   The only pursuit that was sure.

3. So rolling my grub in my blanket,
   I left all my tools on the ground;
   I started one morning to shank it
   To the country they called Puget Sound.

4. Arriving flat broke in midwinter,
   I found it enveloped in fog
   And covered all over with timber
   Thick as hair on the back of a dog.

5. When I looked on the prospects so
      gloomy,
   The tears trickled over my face;
   And I thought that my travels had brought
      me
   To the end of that jumping-off place.

6. I tried to get out of the country,
   But poverty forced me to stay;
   Until I became an old settler,
   Then nothing could drive me away.

7. And now that I'm used to the climate,
   I think that if man ever found
   A place to live easy and happy,
   That Eden is on Puget Sound.

8. No longer the slave of ambition,
   I laugh at the world and its shams
   As I think of my pleasant condition,
   Surrounded by acres of clams.

Last Refrain:
   Surrounded by acres of cla-a-ams,
   Surrounded by acres of clams;
   As I think of my happy condition,
   Surrounded by acres of clams.

(The choruses are formed by repetition of the fourth and third lines)

TOPIC: A New Kind of Political Campaign
TIME: One to two class periods
TIME PERIOD: During study of the presidential campaign of 1840

BACKGROUND

Although previous political campaigns had by not been free of personal attacks on candidates or other techniques that detracted from the real issues, the presidential campaign of 1840 reached new heights (or depths) of promoting style or symbolism over substance. This situation was particularly true of the successful campaign of the Whig party to elect William Henry Harrison, which concentrated on associating Harrison with certain popular attributes (some of which he did not possess) and on attacking Harrison's opponent, incumbent President Martin Van Buren. The campaign, with its many rallies and speeches in rural areas, succeeded not only in electing Harrison and many legislators associated with his party but also in producing the highest voter turnout of any election to that time.

Although the Whigs worked hard to associate Harrison with the folksy "log cabin" symbol, Harrison in fact was born (in 1773) on a plantation and belonged to an aristocratic Virginia family. As an adult he lived in Ohio and other parts of what was then known as the Northwest Territory, and he held various political offices there. He gained popularity as the author of a bill that made it easier for poor people to obtain government land grants. He also helped to pass the act that divided the Northwest Territory into Ohio and Indiana Territories and, in 1800, was appointed governor of Indiana Territory.

In 1811, while Harrison was still governor, he attacking the Indian village of Tippecanoe, defeating (at least temporarily) an American Indian uprising led by Chief Tecumseh. Harrison fought, not especially well, in the War of 1812 and served, not especially brilliantly, in Congress and as United States minister to Colombia until 1829, when he retired to his farm in North Bend, Ohio. The Whigs called him out of retirement to run against Van Buren. He did not succeed in 1836, but he garnered enough votes to be nominated again in 1840. Harrison died of pneumonia a month after his inauguration in 1841.

Martin Van Buren, Harrison's rival in the 1840 election, was of New York Dutch stock. He was well known as a wily politician. He had helped to get Andrew Jackson elected and had been Jackson's secretary of state and, later, vice president. He was sometimes called "little Van" because he was physically short (about five feet five). The Whigs portrayed him as an aristocrat and lover of luxury and suggested that he used government money to buy personal luxuries. This teaching strategy will enable students to consider the effects, significance, and ethics of a political campaign that focuses on symbols rather than on issues.

MATERIALS

Copies of handout

SUGGESTED PROCEDURE

1. Provide students with the background information on William Henry Harrison and the presidential campaign of 1840. Mention that the log cabin was a major symbol associated with Harrison by the Whigs in the election campaign. (If necessary, explain that a symbol is anything that stands for something else and has a shared meaning attached to it. Point out that symbols have often played important roles in politics. For example, the donkey is the symbol of the Democratic party and the elephant is the symbol of the Republican party.) Ask students the following questions:
   a. Why do you think the Whigs thought that associating Harrison with a log cabin would help their campaign? (Possible answer: It would make Harrison appeal to a wider range of voters, including farmers and the rural population.)
   b. What does the success of this symbol suggest about the values held by the American people at that time? (Possible answer: People were looking for a candidate who was a common, or simple, man such as Andrew Jackson professed to be.)
2. Mention that the Whig campaign often called Harrison "Old Tippecanoe" and used "Tippecanoe and Tyler Too" as a popular slogan. Ask students: What does the emphasis on Harrison's victory at Tippecanoe

suggest about American feelings and values of the time? (Possible answer: People admired men who had fought the Indians; people did not have much sympathy for Indians.)

3. Distribute the handout, and have students read the quotation. Discuss the following words and concepts:

   huzzas, no truck with issues, invective, Croesus, propaganda tracts, patronage brigades

   Then ask students the following questions:

   a. What were the effects of the Whigs' new style of campaigning? (More people voted than had ever before voted in a presidential election.)

   b. What does the campaign's success suggest about the values of the people of the time and about their feelings about politics? (Possible answer: People wanted a president they could relate to, who was representative of "simple folk" like them.)

- If you wish to complete this lesson in one class period, go directly to instructional procedure 6. To extend the lesson another class period, compete procedures 4–6.

4. Organize the class into groups of four to six. Have each group choose a presidential candidate (other than Harrison), successful or otherwise, from the period 1800–1850. For this candidate the group should design (a) a poster with a symbol and a slogan, (b) a rhyme or song, and (c) a short speech to be given by or for the candidate. In designing these materials, students should consider what they think were the values of the people of the appropriate period, reviewing textbook or other material as necessary, and should try to make the materials have maximum emotional appeal to those people.

5. Have the groups present their posters, rhymes or songs, and speeches to the class.

6. As a closure activity, have students discuss or write answers to the following questions:

   a. What seems good about the new style of campaigning? What seems bad? Overall, do you think the style is better or worse than those that preceded it? Why? (Answers will vary; most students will probably say that the new style of campaigning was worse than the style that preceded it because it did not portray the candidate honestly and did not address the issues. Students should mention that the new style of campaigning did, at least, get out the voters.)

   b. How are political campaigns today like the Harrison campaign? How are they different? (Answers will vary but might include: campaigns today are alike in that a lot of emphasis is put on a candidate's personality; smear campaigns still exist. They are different in that today more focus is put on the issues; campaigns today are conducted in the media.)

   c. What types of symbols and slogans do you think would appeal to the American people today? What do these symbols say about Americans' feelings, interests, and values? (Answers will vary. Accept all reasonable responses.)

Excerpts from *The Vineyard of Liberty*

By James MacGregor Burns

Whig leaders knew only too well the sorry fate of those Federalists and National Republicans who had allowed Jeffersonians and Jacksonians to pose as the "friends of the people." Whigs would now be more populist than those populists, more pleasing to the people. And where were the people? In the countryside. America in 1840 was still overwhelmingly rural; only about a tenth of the populace lived in places with more than 2,500 inhabitants. The Whigs would strike directly into the rural hinterlands that had sustained the old Republican party.

So Harrison was transformed from an aged general-politico, who had been born into a distinguished Virginia family in a fine plantation manor, into a simple farmer. Transparencies—an exciting media device of the day—showed him seated in front of his log-cabin "birthplace," a barrel of hard cider at his side. "Log-cabin boys" were organized to produce loud huzzas for the speechifying. Horny-handed farmers lumbered to the stage to present a pitchfork to Harrison.

The campaign brought marvelous theater into the villages and hamlets. Songs glorified the "Hero Ploughman" and his "Buckeye Cabin." Hawkers sold Tippecanoe buttons, tobacco, lithographs, canes surmounted by a miniature barrel, whiskey bottles in the shape of log cabins. Whigs would have no truck with issues; their convention adopted no party platform. In the absence of genuine issues, invective flourished. Whigs routinely pictured "Old Van" as living in regal splendor, in a palace fit for Croesus, playing billiards with ivory balls. Soon the crowds were chanting:

> Let Van from his coolers of
> silver drink wine,

> And lounge on his cushioned
> settee,
> Our man on a buckeye bench
> can recline
> Content with hard cider is he.

. . . Still, it was a battle more of party than of personality. Behind the scenes parties compiled master mailing lists of voters, mobilized state and local campaign committees, mustered the patronage brigades, ground out posters, leaflets, and propaganda tracts. Fifteen hundred newspapers—most of them partisan weeklies—carried news of the party battle even to the frontier. Whig newspapers were especially ingenious in publishing campaign sheets. Horace Greeley's *Log Cabin,* full of chatty news about Harrison and his campaign, quickly went through a first printing of 30,000 and then sold at a weekly rate of 80,000 copies. Stealing the tune of "Jefferson and Liberty," the *Log Cabin* published sheet music with lyrics ending "For HAR-RI-SON and LIB-ER-TY!"

The result was the greatest outpouring of voters the nation had seen. Harrison beat Van Buren by about 53 percent to 47 percent, by 234 electoral votes to the Democrats' 60. The Whigs carried the House elections, 133 seats to 102, and exactly reversed the Democrats' previous margin in the Senate, 28 to 22. Harrison won the swing states of New York and Pennsylvania. The turnout was perhaps more remarkable than the election results. Almost two and one half million voted—about 80 percent of the eligibles, compared with less than 60 percent four years before. . . . Campaign organization plus campaign hokum had mobilized the electorate.

TOPIC: Effects of the Telegraph
TIME: Two class periods, with homework
TIME PERIOD: During study of major inventions of the late 1800s and early 1900s

BACKGROUND

In 1844 Samuel F.B. Morse successfully demonstrated his electric telegraph, sending a message ("What hath God wrought?") by wire from Baltimore to Washington, D.C., 41 miles away. This demonstration persuaded observers that the telegraph was a feasible invention.

Morse is commonly credited with being "the inventor" of the telegraph, but this is not truly justified. Morse drew on the scientific work of Joseph Henry and others, who did the experiments in electromagnetism on which Morse's device was based. Morse did, however, improve the telegraph device (among other things, he added relays, which made it possible for messages to travel over a long distance). He also invented the dot-dash code that bears his name. Most important, perhaps, he made the telegraph widely known and commercially successful for the first time.

The telegraph consisted of two keys, each attached to a sounder and connected to each other by a wire and battery. Messages could be sent from either end of the device. When the sending key was pressed down, it closed the electrical circuit and caused a pulse of electricity to flow along the wire. When the pulse was received at the other end of the wire, it caused the sounder to click and also to move a pen that marked a paper tape. A short pulse produced a dot; a longer pulse produced a dash. Each letter of the alphabet was represented in Morse's code by a pattern of dots and dashes. Students may be interested in using the encyclopedia to see the entire Morse Code.

Before the telegraph was used, messages could be sent no faster than human beings and vehicles could travel—rarely more than 30 miles an hour. Telegraph messages, however, were received almost instantaneously. Telegraphy did not become widespread immediately. Wires had to be stretched from city to city by tying them to trees or by putting up a series of poles. People had to be trained to send, receive, and decode telegraph messages. Perhaps most important, people had to realize just how useful the new device could be. Telegraphy did spread, however, first in the northeast and then to the west. By 1861 a telegraph line stretched across the country. In this teaching strategy students will speculate about the effects of a major communication invention, the telegraph. After conducting research and summarizing gathered material, students will modify their speculations and draw conclusions about the effects of the telegraph.

MATERIALS

Question sheets for every student in each group, one topic per group. Separate the question sheets after you copy them.

SUGGESTED PROCEDURE

1. Provide students with the background information on the telegraph.
2. Organize the class into five groups. Give each group question sheets dealing with one type or area of the effect of the telegraph. Have each group draw on their knowledge of the telegraph and of the history of the time to speculate on the effects of the telegraph (up to about 1865) in their area. The question sheet will give them some ideas, but they should add to these. Have them record their speculations.
3. As a homework assignment, have students look in their textbooks or other resources to learn about the actual effects of the telegraph in their area.
4. At the beginning of the second class period, instruct students to meet in their groups to correct or add to their speculations. Ask each group to choose a member to describe to the rest of the class the telegraph's effects in that group's area. Encourage students to take notes.
5. Have the class reach a consensus about the two or three most important ways in which the telegraph changed American life (both what people did and how they felt about their world).

What were the effects of the telegraph on NEWS?

1. How did Americans learn about events outside their community before the telegraph became widespread? About how long did it take to receive information? How did the telegraph change the way in which people learned about distant events?

   _____

   _____

2. How might this change in the way people learned about distant events have affected the way they felt about those events? Why might people's feelings have changed in this way?

   _____

   _____

3. Why did many newspapers take on names like *The Daily Telegraph?*

   _____

   _____

   Your ideas:

   _____

   _____

   _____

- -

What were the effects of the telegraph on WAR?

1. The telegraph was available to American armies for the first time during the Civil War. What would the telegraph allow commanders to do that they could not do before?

   _____

   _____

2. During the Civil War the Union (the North) had most of the telegraph lines: 15,000 miles of lines to only 1,000 miles in the Confederacy (the South). How might this fact have helped the Union win the war?

   _____

   _____

   Your ideas:

   _____

   _____

   _____

What were the effects of the telegraph on RAILROADS?

1. Railroads were among the first businesses to use telegraphs extensively, and the telegraph became very important to railroads. Why?

_____

_____

2. How could the telegraph help make railroads safer? How could it help make them more dependable?

_____

_____

3. Before railroads and telegraphs became widespread, different cities, even those fairly close to each other, had different local times. One city's time might be five minutes ahead of another city 30 miles away, for example. This caused few problems. After the railroad and the telegraph became widespread, however, people—especially those connected with the railroads—began to see the need for standard time zones. Why would the spread of the telegraph and railroads increase the need for standard time zones?

_____

_____

Your ideas:

_____

_____

_____

- -

What were the effects of the telegraph on EVERYDAY LIFE?

1. What could people do in their everyday lives after the telegraph became widespread that they could not do, or could not do as easily, before?

_____

_____

2. What could businesspeople do because of the telegraph that they could not do before? Explain how the telegraph might have been useful in different kinds of businesses. For which kinds of businesses would it have been most useful?

_____

_____

3. Telegraph messages were relatively expensive. What kinds of messages did ordinary people probably send most often? What kinds of messages did businesses probably send most often? How do you think the average person felt when told that he or she had received a telegraph message?

_____

_____

Your ideas:

_____

_____

What were the effects of the telegraph on JOBS?

1. The Pony Express was started in 1860 as a new, very fast way of getting mail and messages across the United States. About a year later, it went out of business. Can you guess why?

_____

_____

2. What jobs would no longer be needed after the telegraph became widespread?

_____

_____

3. What jobs would be done differently after the telegraph became widespread? How and why would they be different?

_____

_____

4. What new jobs would be created when the telegraph became widespread?

_____

_____

Your ideas:

_____

_____

_____

TOPIC: Charles Dickens Describes the American People
TIME: One to two class periods
TIME PERIOD: After study of the Northeast during the mid-1800s

BACKGROUND

Charles Dickens (1812–1870) was one of nineteenth-century Britain's most famous writers. Raised in poverty, Dickens educated himself and became a writer of fiction, concentrating on life in London. *The Posthumous Papers of the Pickwick Club*, serialized in a magazine, became a best-seller in 1836. Among Dickens' best-known books are *A Tale of Two Cities, David Copperfield, Oliver Twist*, and *A Christmas Carol*.

Dickens' novels and short stories are famous for their wide variety of sharply observed, wittily described characters from all walks of life and for their commentary on the society of the time. Dickens brought these same skills and concerns to *American Notes*, a description of a trip to the United States that he made in 1842. The book includes accounts of rides on various kinds of American transportation (steamboat, canal boat, stagecoach, railroad), some of them wonderfully funny; descriptions of several American cities and the individuals that Dickens met in them; and grim pictures of slavery and of life in a solitary-confinement prison in Philadelphia. The selection used in this teaching strategy is taken from the last chapter of the book, in which Dickens sums up his view of the American character.

In this teaching strategy students will analyze the passage by Dickens and look for evidence from American history in the 1830s and 1840s that supports or contradicts Dickens' view. They will decide whether or not they think Dickens' view of the American people was valid (supported by factual evidence) at the time he wrote it and whether or not it is still valid today.

MATERIALS

Copies of the handout with the selection from Dickens

SUGGESTED PROCEDURE

1. Provide students with the background on Dickens and his trip. Distribute copies of the selection and call on students to read it aloud. Discuss any unfamiliar words or concepts. Point out how the meaning of some words has changed or has a British origin. For example, when Dickens uses the word *smart,* he means "clever, sharp-dealing." Ask students the following questions:
   a. What characteristics does Dickens see in the American people? (He thinks they are honest, brave, friendly, hospitable, and affectionate; he sees them as being universally distrusting; he thinks that they have a love and respect for "smart dealing.")
   b. Dickens sees "universal distrust" as harmful, but he claims that Americans see it as "freedom of opinion" and think that it is desirable. With which view do you agree? Why? Could this characteristic be both helpful and harmful? (Encourage students to discuss this issue, making sure they support their opinions.)
   c. What does Dickens mean by "smart dealing"? (clever, keen-witted, sharp)
2. As homework, have students go through their textbooks and other historical readings for the 1830s and 1840s to look for specific events, especially economic and political events, that either demonstrate or contradict each of the characteristics that Dickens describes.
3. During the first part of the next class period, have students report their findings. You might want to summarize these findings on the chalkboard in a chart with *Support* and *Contradict* as headings.
4. To conclude, ask students to discuss or write answers to the following questions:
   a. Overall, do you agree with Dickens' view of the American people in 1842? Why or why not?
   b. Based on your reading, would you modify, remove, or add any characteristics to Dickens' description? Explain your answer.
   c. Do you think the American people show any of Dickens' characteristics today? Give examples from current events to support your answer.
   d. What would you say are the three most striking characteristics of the American people today?

Excerpts from *American Notes*
By Charles Dickens (1842)

But I may be pardoned, if on such a theme as the general character of the American people, and the general character of their social system, as presented to a stranger's eyes, I desire to express my own opinions in a few words, before I bring these volumes to a close.

They are, by nature, frank, brave, cordial, hospitable, and affectionate. Cultivation and refinement seem but to enhance their warmth of heart and ardent enthusiasm; and it is the possession of these latter qualities in a most remarkable degree, which renders an educated American one of the most endearing and most generous of friends. . . .

These qualities are natural, I implicitly believe, to the whole people. That they are, however, sadly sapped and blighted in their growth among the mass; and that there are influences at work which endanger them still more, and give but little present promise of their health restoration; is a truth that ought to be told.

It is an essential part of every national character to pique itself mightily upon its faults. . . . One great blemish in the popular mind of America, and the prolific parent of an innumerable brood of evils, is Universal Distrust. Yet the American citizen plumes himself upon this spirit, even when he is sufficiently dispassionate to perceive the ruin it works. . . .

"You carry," says the stranger, "this jealousy and distrust into every transaction of public life. By repelling worthy men from your legislative assemblies, it has bred up a class of candidates for the suffrage, who, in their every act, disgrace your Institutions and your people's choice. It has rendered you so fickle, and so given to change, that your inconstancy has passed into a proverb; for you no sooner set up an idol firmly, than you are sure to pull it down and dash it into fragments: and this, because directly you reward a benefactor, or a public servant, you distrust him, merely because he *is* rewarded. . . . Any man who attains a high place among you, from the President downwards, may date his downfall from that moment; for any printed lie that any notorious villain pens, although it militate directly against the character and conduct of a life, appeals at once to your distrust, and is believed. . . . Is this well, think you, or likely to elevate the character of the governors or the governed, among you?"

The answer is invariably the same: "There's freedom of opinion here, you know. Every man thinks for himself, and we are not to be easily overreached. That's how our people come to be suspicious."

Another prominent feature is the love of "smart" dealing: which gilds over many a swindle and gross breach of trust . . . and enables many a knave to hold his head up with the best. . . . This smartness has done more in a few years to impair the public credit, and to cripple the public resources, than dull honesty, however rash, could have effected in a century. The merits of a broken speculation, or a bankruptcy, or of a successful scoundrel, are not gauged by its or his observation of the golden rule, "Do as you would be done by," but are considered with reference to their smartness. . . . The following dialogue I have held a hundred times: "Is it not a very disgraceful circumstance that such a man as So-and-so should be acquiring a large property by the most infamous and odious means, and notwithstanding all the crimes of which he has been guilty, should be tolerated and abetted by your Citizens? He is a public nuisance, is he not?" "Yes, Sir." "A convicted liar?" "Yes, Sir." "He has been kicked, and cuffed, and caned?" "Yes Sir." "And he is utterly dishonorable. . .?" "Yes, Sir." "In the name of wonder, then, what is his merit?" "Well, Sir, he is a smart man."

TOPIC: The Purposes of Education
TIME: One to two class periods
TIME PERIOD: During study of educational reform in the 1800s

BACKGROUND

Horace Bushnell, the author of the first quotation in this teaching strategy, was a minister in Hartford, Connecticut. He was interested in social reform and in planning the raising and education of children to lead them from their earliest years into a Christian life. He disagreed with Charles Grandison Finney and other ministers of the time who emphasized the importance of a conversion experience in adulthood. The quotation is taken from a book called *Views of Christian Nurture, and of Subjects Adjacent Thereto,* published in 1848.

Thomas Jefferson, the author of the second quotation, was interested in a wide variety of subjects, including education. His view that the main purpose of education was to prepare people for good citizenship was widely shared by Americans of the period. Jefferson wrote these suggestions for the objectives of primary education in 1818.

Francis Wayland, the author of the third quotation, was president of Brown University between 1827 and 1855. His background included medicine (although he never practiced) and the Baptist ministry. He stressed discipline, a combination of classical learning with practical application, and the desirability of education for all classes. He stressed the need to teach people things that would help them improve themselves and carry out their lives successfully, particularly in business. Rather than having all college students follow the same curriculum, Wayland urged flexibility so that "in so far as it is practicable, every student might study what he chose, all that he chose, and nothing but what he chose." In this teaching strategy students will analyze passages on the purposes of education and will work in groups to design curricula through which different educational purposes might be carried out.

MATERIALS

Copies of the quotations concerning the purposes of education

SUGGESTED PROCEDURE

1. Distribute copies of the quotations to each student. Provide the background information on the authors. Allow students time to read the quotations (individually or as a class) and discuss any words or phrases that they do not understand.
2. Organize the class into groups of four or five. Write the following questions on the chalkboard:
   a. What is the main purpose of education, according to each author? (Bushnell says the purpose is for a child to grow with a Christian education so that he or she will not wait to have a sudden conversion as an adult; he wants the child to "love what is good from his earliest years." Jefferson says that a person should be educated in order to perform intelligently in a democratic society. Wayland wants to broaden the curriculum to include all social classes.)
   b. Imagine that you are designing three different schools, one devoted to the educational aims of each author. For each school, tell what subjects you would teach students at your grade level. Name at least three. Explain how those subjects carry out each school's purpose.
3. Have each group work together for the rest of the class period to answer the questions.
4. During the first part of the next class period, have representatives of the groups describe their imaginary schools.
5. As a closure activity, have students discuss or write answers to the following questions:
   a. Suppose each of these men ran a school designed to carry out his purpose. In which school would you most like to be a student? Why?
   b. Based on your school experiences, what do you think the purpose or purposes of American education today is supposed to be? In what ways is that purpose different from the purposes proposed for American education in the early nineteenth century? In what ways is it similar?
   c. What do you think the purpose of education *should* be? Why do you think that purpose is important? If you were designing a school to carry out your purpose, what would you teach students?

The Purpose of Education According to Three Early Nineteenth-Century American Writers

In answer to the following question, "What is the true idea of Christian education?" Bushnell responded:

> I answer in the following proposition, which it will be the aim of my argument to establish, viz.: That the child is to grow up a Christian. In other words, the aim, effort, and expectation should be, not, as is commonly assumed, that the child is to grow up in sin, to be converted after he comes to a mature age; but that he is to open on the world as one that is spiritually renewed, not remembering the time when he went through a technical experience, but seeming rather to have loved what is good from his earliest years.
>
> —Horace Bushnell, 1848

The objects of primary education should be:

> To give every citizen the information he needs for the transaction of his own business;
> To enable him to calculate for himself, and to express and preserve his ideas, his contracts and accounts, in writing;
> To improve, by reading, his morals and faculties;
> To understand his duties to his neighbors and country, and to discharge with competence the functions confided to him by either;
> To know his rights; to exercise with order and justice those he retains; to choose with discretion the fiduciary of those he delegates; and to notice their conduct with diligence, with candor, and judgment;
> And, in general, to observe with intelligence and faithfulness all the social relations under which he shall be placed.
>
> —Thomas Jefferson, 1818

> Wherever an institution is established in any part of our country, our first inquiry should be, what is the kind of knowledge . . . which this portion of our people needs, in order to perfect them in their professions, give them power over principles, enable them to develop their intellectual resources and employ their talents to the greatest advantage for themselves and for the country? This knowledge, whatever it may be, should be provided as liberally for one class as for another. Whatever is thus taught, however, should be taught, not only with the design of increasing knowledge, but also of giving strength, enlargement and skill to the original faculties of the soul. When a system of education formed on these principles shall pervade this country, we may be able to present to the world the legitimate results of free institution.
>
> —Francis Wayland, 1855

TOPIC: "Bloomerism"—Feminism Meets Fashion
TIME: One class period
TIME PERIOD: During study of the woman's rights movement in the 1800s

BACKGROUND

Middle-class and upper-class women of the mid-nineteenth century wore many layers of clothing. All parts of the body except the face and hands were covered. Skirts trailed on the ground and used up many yards of material—sometimes 20 yards or more. Beneath her dress a lady wore several petticoats, some with bottom rims corded with horsehair or straw to make them stand out in a circle.

The fashion of the time dictated that women must appear to have very small waists. To produce this effect they wore stays or corsets—long strips of steel or whalebone set into a cloth framework. When the corset was laced tightly, the stiff strips pulled in the woman's abdomen and made her appear to have a small waist. Many women wore their stays laced as tightly as possible. Some probably suffered medical problems because of the compression of abdominal organs and reduction of circulation caused by the tight stays.

In the mid-1800s some American women attempted to revolt against these uncomfortable and confining clothes by wearing what came to be called the "Bloomer Costume," or bloomers. This outfit included full pantaloons gathered at the ankle, over which was worn a full skirt that came just below the knee. A relatively loose-fitting top, which could be worn without stays, completed the costume.

The costume was named after Amelia Jenks Bloomer (1818–1894). Bloomer was a close friend of Elizabeth Cady Stanton, the well-known woman's rights leader. Both women lived in Seneca Falls, New York, where the first women's rights convention was held in 1848. Stanton headed the convention, and Bloomer attended it. Bloomer published a journal, *The Lily,* which was devoted to temperance and woman's rights.

Bloomer did not in fact invent the "Bloomer" costume. She first saw a version of it worn by Stanton's cousin, Libby Miller. Miller had made the outfit as a traveling costume on a trip to Europe after hearing about an Englishwoman, Helen Weber, who wore something similar. But Bloomer took up the costume and also wrote about it in *The Lily.* Her name became attached to it in the popular press.

The bloomer costume never replaced the prevailing fashions for most women, but a number of women did wear it as a way of rebelling against uncomfortable, confining clothes and the attitudes that those clothes symbolized. Versions of the costume were used later in the nineteenth century by women who wanted to take part in physical activities, such as bicycle riding, that would have been difficult to do in a long skirt.

In this teaching strategy students will examine illustrations of conventional and unconventional women's costumes of the mid-1800s and draw conclusions about the costumes' physical effects on women and about the different attitudes toward women reflected in the costumes. Students will consider reactions to an unconventional costume for women and draw conclusions about the reasons for these reactions.

MATERIALS

Transparencies or copies of fashionable women's clothes of the mid-1800s, the Bloomer costume, and the cartoon "Popping the Question"

SUGGESTED PROCEDURE

1. Show the transparency or distribute copies of the illustration that shows fashionable women's clothing of the mid-1800s. Ask students: What kinds of things could someone do while wearing these clothes? What kinds of things could someone *not* do while wearing them? (Students should suggest that freedom of movement was greatly curtailed. A woman could sit or walk slowly in these clothes. She would not be able to run, bend with ease, or move quickly.)

2. Provide students with background information on women's clothing of the period, including stays. Ask students: How do you think women felt while wearing these clothes? (restricted and uncomfortable; fashionable) Why did they wear them? (for fashion reasons) What physical problems might the clothes have caused? (stomach and back problems) What do the clothes suggest about the way people expected

upper-class women to behave? (Women were not expected or encouraged to participate in activities requiring much movement.)

3. Show the transparency or distribute copies of the Bloomer costume. Ask students: In what ways is this costume different from the others you saw? (The skirt is not as long and heavy; the sleeves of the blouse are loose; the outfit does not include a tight-fitting jacket; pants are worn under the skirt; the wearer's shoes show; the hat has a wide brim.) In what ways is it the same? (The wearer's body is still completely covered; it also has a skirt.) What kinds of things could a woman do while wearing this costume that she could not do in the other clothes? (walk quickly or run, bend easily, sit more comfortably)

4. Provide students with background information on the Bloomer costume and how and why it was introduced, including information about Amelia Bloomer. Ask students: What kind of women probably wore the Bloomer costume? (a woman who was not afraid to go against the fashion; a woman who was in favor of the women's rights movement of the time)

5. Show the transparency of the cartoon "Popping the Question." Have students discuss what is going on in the cartoon and what is being satirized. Explain that many cartoons expressing the same basic idea appeared in American and British newspapers in the mid-1800s. Ask students: Judging from this cartoon, why did many people object to the Bloomer costume? To what larger idea were they objecting? (the idea that the woman was taking the man's position in society by dressing "like a man")

6. Ask students to imagine that they lived in the mid-1800s. Then write the following questions on the chalkboard and have students write a paragraph or two answering either one of the two questions.
   a. If you were a woman in the mid-1800s, would you have worn a Bloomer costume? Why or why not?
   b. If you were a man in the mid-1800s, would you have approved or disapproved of women wearing the Bloomer costume? Why?

THE BLOOMER COSTUME.

ONE OF THE DELIGHTFUL RESULTS OF BLOOMERISM.—THE LADIES WILL
POP THE QUESTION.

Superior Creature. "Say! Oh, say, Dearest! Will you be Mine?" &c., &c.

TOPIC: Ideal Communities
TIME: Two class periods
TIME PERIOD: During study of the age of reform in the 1800s

BACKGROUND

A number of American groups tried to set up ideal communities in the first half of the nineteenth century. Some of these groups, such as the Shakers and the Amish (the latter of which still exist), were bound together by religious ideals. Others, such as the Oneida community in New York and the New Harmony community in Indiana, were not religious but shared philosophical views.

Different communities had different rules. Some were controlled by councils of elders or leaders, whereas others were democratic. In many communities, though not all, individuals were allowed to own little or no property; everything belonged to the community. In many communities, individuals owed the community a certain amount of work time. Some communities united men and women in a sort of collective marriage, while others did not allow the sexes to meet at all except in formal public groups. In some, children were raised in a common nursery. Others had more traditional marital and family living arrangements.

Some communities required their members to live as simply as possible, wearing plain clothing and avoiding most forms of technology. Others did not have such requirements. Some urged their members to have as little contact with the outside world as possible, whereas others encouraged business contacts (especially the selling of handicrafts, farm produce, or other products of the community) that would make a profit for the community.

Most ideal communities did not last long. They floundered because of disagreements among the members, lack of a solid economic base, or both. The few that did survive tended to have members with unusually strong devotion to their ideals, rules that were not impossibly restrictive, and/or a good way of supporting themselves economically (good land and/or products that people wanted to buy).

In this teaching strategy students will create rules for their own ideal community. Then they will evaluate the rule-making process to understand why many ideal communities broke up and others did not.

MATERIALS

1. One "Rules for an Ideal Community" worksheet for each group
2. Copies of "Ideal Community Evaluation" sheet for each student

SUGGESTED PROCEDURE

1. Review the textbook material and provide the background material on American ideal communities of the early nineteenth century.
2. Organize the class into groups of five or six students. Tell the groups to imagine that they are going to set up ideal communities. Give each group a "Rules for an Ideal Community" worksheet and allow the groups the rest of the class period (or more time, if necessary) to discuss and work out the rules of their communities. Instruct each group to choose a secretary to record the rules on the worksheet as they are agreed on.
3. During the first part of the next class period, have a representative from each group present its rules for an ideal community. Have other members of the class (outside the group) comment on the rules and perhaps vote on whether they would be willing to join a community with those rules.
4. To conclude the activity, distribute the "Ideal Community Evaluation" sheets, and have each student complete the sheet.

Group Worksheet: Rules for an Ideal Community

Directions: Imagine that your group is going to set up an ideal community. You must decide on the rules by which your community will live. With your group, work out rules for each of the following.

1. Who, if anyone, will govern your community?

   _____

   _____

   _____

2. How will decisions affecting the community be made?

   _____

   _____

   _____

3. What will you do about people who disagree with these decisions?

   _____

   _____

   _____

4. What rules will you have about owning property (money, land, homes, personal possessions)? Will individuals be allowed to own property? If so, what kinds of property? What kinds of property, if any, will belong to the community?

   _____

   _____

   _____

   _____

5. How will people live? Will families live together, or will children live separately? Will men and women be allowed to marry and live together?

   _____

   _____

   _____

   _____

6. What work will people have to contribute to the community? What work or time will people have to themselves?

   _____

   _____

   _____

7. What beliefs, if any, will everyone in your community be expected to share? What part, if any, will religion play in your community?

_____

_____

_____

8. What contacts will the community have with the outside world?

_____

_____

_____

9. What things will the community supply for itself? How will it supply these things?

_____

_____

_____

10. How will the community get things it cannot supply for itself? What business dealings, if any, will the community have with the outside world? (Will you make or grow things to sell, allow community members to take outside jobs, or what?) To whom will profits from business dealings belong?

_____

_____

_____

_____

11. What rules, if any, will you have about clothing in your community?

_____

_____

_____

12. Name at least five rules of ethics or behavior that you will expect all members of your community to follow.

_____

_____

_____

_____

_____

Ideal Community Evaluation

Directions: Answer the following questions in the space provided.

1. How easy was it for your group to agree on rules for your imaginary community?

   _____

   _____

   _____

2. What problems, if any, did you have in working out rules?

   _____

   _____

   _____

   _____

3. Would you be willing to live under the rules of your imaginary community for at least a year? Why or why not?

   _____

   _____

   _____

4. What did your classmates (outside your group) think about your community rules? Why did they react that way?

   _____

   _____

   _____

5. Most ideal communities broke up after a few years. Based on what you know about communities and your own experience in trying to set up an ideal community, give at least two reasons why an ideal community might break up.

   _____

   _____

   _____

6. A few ideal communities lasted longer. Give three characteristics (such as size, kinds of business relationships with the outside world, or kinds of beliefs shared by members) that you would expect to find in a community that lasted.

   _____

   _____

   _____

7. If your ideal community had really been established in early nineteenth-century America, do you think it would have lasted more than a few years? Why or why not?

   _____

   _____

   _____

TOPIC: An Imaginary Panel Discussion
TIME: Two to three class periods
TIME PERIOD: During study of the reform movements of the 1800s

BACKGROUND

Emily Dickinson (1830–1886), one of America's great poets, was a shy person who lived a very isolated life. She was born in Amherst, Massachusetts, and spent most of her life in her family home there. She never married and did not have a wide circle of friends. She wrote thousands of poems but seldom showed them to others. Most were discovered only after her death. They show her close observation and love of nature and her profound understanding of human triumphs and tragedies, especially of death and the striving for immortality. Some, such as "I'm Nobody," show an impish sense of humor as well.

Charles Grandison Finney (1792–1875) was a key figure in the religious revival movement of the early nineteenth century. In 1821 he underwent a religious conversion and became an evangelist, or traveling preacher. His energetic speeches at Congregational and Presbyterian churches brought many converts but also opposition from more traditional church leaders. He eventually broke from the Presbyterian church and established his own "Tabernacle." Finney emphasized people's ability to reform themselves and brought his message to people of all classes.

Elizabeth Cady Stanton (1815–1902) was a leader in the woman's rights movement. She headed the 1848 meeting in Seneca Falls, New York, which was the first organized demand for women's suffrage. Stanton first became angry about laws that discriminated against women when she studied law in the office of her father, Daniel Cady. Stanton was also involved in abolitionism, the movement to abolish the enslavement of blacks.

Henry David Thoreau (1817–1862) was born and lived most of his life in Concord, Massachusetts. In his most famous book, *Walden,* he described his ideal of the simple life lived close to nature and detached from society, especially from affairs of business and government. The book was based on the two years (1845–1847) that he lived alone in the woods by Walden Pond, near Concord, in a small house that he built himself. Thoreau also wrote a famous essay explaining his belief in civil disobedience, or nonviolent refusal to obey a government of whose actions he disapproved. He spent a night in jail rather than pay a tax that he believed was unjust.

Walt Whitman (1819–1892) was a poet, but he lived a life very different from that of Emily Dickinson. In his early years he was a newspaper reporter and also had political ambitions. He supported western expansion and was against slavery. His famous book of poems, *Leaves of Grass,* was self-published at first (1855). The first poem in the volume begins, "I celebrate myself," but Whitman celebrated much else as well: nature, the wandering life, individualism and the importance of all beings, physical pleasure, spiritual growth, and the energy and spirit of the Americans (especially working-class Americans) whom he had met. "Here are the roughs and beards and space and ruggedness and nonchalance that the soul loves," he wrote in a preface to the poems. Whitman stressed the interdependence and equal importance of the body and the soul. His emphasis on the physical shocked many readers but delighted others. Whitman worked in military hospitals during the Civil War and wrote a book of war poems, *Drum-Taps,* which included two famous elegies on Lincoln's death.

In this teaching strategy students will learn about the beliefs of these five early nineteenth-century American thinkers and writers. They will impersonate one of these individuals in a panel discussion on the questions: "What is the best kind of life to live? What should a person's main purpose in life be?"

MATERIALS

Copies of the "Imaginary Panel Discussion" worksheet for each student

SUGGESTED PROCEDURE

1. Share with students the background information on Emily Dickinson, Charles Grandison Finney, Elizabeth Cady Stanton, Henry David Thoreau, and Walt Whitman.
2. Organize students into groups of five. Leftover students may be assigned as "doubles" to other groups or told to act as moderators during the group discussions.

3. Tell students that each will play the role of one of the above five thinkers and writers in an imaginary panel discussion on the questions: "What is the best kind of life to live? What should a person's main purpose in life be?" Each group should include all five characters (if an extra student has been added to the group, it might have, for example, two Emily Dickinsons). Students may select the characters they want to play, or you may assign characters.

4. Allow a minimum of one homework period, or longer if time permits, for each student to research the ideas of the character he or she will portray. Encourage students to read both biographical material about the characters and samples of the characters' own writings. Advise them to take notes on the character's beliefs about the purpose of life, perhaps even copying down quotations to use in the discussions.

5. Allow each group about 10 minutes to hold its panel discussion. Each student should wear a name tag showing the character that he or she represents and should express the ideas that he or she believes the character would have held. Encourage students to use their notes, to include any mannerisms and ways of speaking or behaving that they think their characters might have had, and to work actual quotations from the writers into their dialogue if possible. Have students express both agreements and disagreements among the characters. Tell them that the purpose of the discussion is to express all the characters' views rather than arriving at any single conclusion.

6. As an evaluation activity after all the discussions have been held, distribute the worksheets and have each student fill one out.

Imaginary Panel Discussion

1. Which student gave the best performance as each of the following? Why do you think so?

   a. Emily Dickinson:

   _____

   b. Charles Grandison Finney:

   _____

   c. Elizabeth Cady Stanton:

   _____

   d. Henry David Thoreau:

   _____

   e. Walt Whitman:

   _____

2. Based on what you have learned from the discussions, describe the ideas of each of the following people about the purpose of life.

   a. Emily Dickinson:

   _____

   b. Charles Grandison Finney:

   _____

   c. Elizabeth Cady Stanton:

   _____

   d. Henry David Thoreau:

   _____

   e. Walt Whitman:

   _____

3. Which of the five characters do you think would have been friends if they had known each other? Which ones probably would not have gotten along? Which characters would have agreed about some things but not others? Explain your answers.

   _____

   _____

   _____

   _____

   _____

4. Which character's view of the purpose of life comes closest to your own? With what parts of that view do you agree and disagree? Why?

   _____

   _____

   _____

   _____

   _____

TOPIC: Imaginative Recreation of Lives of Southern Farmers
TIME: Two class periods, with homework
TIME PERIOD: When beginning study of the South in the 1800s

BACKGROUND

This teaching strategy will help build historical empathy by involving students in an imaginative recreation of life in the South in the 1800s. Encourage students to imagine themselves in the time and setting in order to gain some understanding of how people actually lived.

The excerpt students will read is from *The Mind of the South,* the classic work by W. J. Cash. Cash was born in South Carolina and grew up and lived in North Carolina. In the excerpt Cash recreates the life of a large plantation owner, whose attainment of wealth and a place in the southern aristocracy was typical of many plantation owners. An immigrant and a settler on the frontier, he owed his success to hard work, luck, and the demand for cotton. Having a background different from that of southerners like Thomas Jefferson and John Calhoun, this man was representative of a far greater number of large plantation owners.

MATERIALS

Copies of the handout with the excerpt from *The Mind of the South*

SUGGESTED PROCEDURE

1. Have students work in small groups or with partners to read the excerpt, and help them to define any unfamiliar words. Explain that the man described is not a real person. He is an imaginative recreation based on actual information that historians have collected about the lives of plantation owners. Instruct students to underline sentences and phrases that give important information about the plantation owner's values, social position, participation in government, and so on.
2. With the class as a whole, ask the following questions to elicit information about the way many plantation owners accumulated wealth and obtained social and political power. These questions will also draw attention to the author's attempt to make the man seem real to readers by using factual information in an imaginative manner.
   a. What details show that the plantation owner was wealthy and successful? (He built and owned three houses; he acquired a carriage; when he died he left 2,000 acres, 114 slaves, and 4 cotton gins.)
   b. Do you think that the owner had begun farming at a fortunate time? Why or why not? (Yes; the cotton gin had just been invented, and cotton was becoming a valuable crop.)
   c. What is the meaning of the word *aristocrat?* (a member of the privileged class, especially a noble) Was the plantation owner an aristocrat? (Students should refer to his immigrant origins.) Did he eventually behave like an aristocrat? (Ask for examples.) Was he considered an aristocrat by others? (Yes.) What did the newspaper mean when it referred to him as "a gentleman of the old school" and "a noble specimen of chivalry"? (He was, indeed, considered to be an aristocrat.) What people and behavior are associated with chivalry? (medieval knights; honor, courage, gallantry)
   d. What opportunities did the planter's children have? (The boys received an education; the girls learned to play the piano.) What information do these details give about men and women's roles? (Men received higher education; women were not expected to go to college.)
   e. What part did slaves play in the owner's success? (They worked in his cotton fields.)
   f. How did the planter participate in government and politics? (He became a judge; he was a member of the legislature.)
   g. What does the author's description of the "big house" tell about plantation houses in general? (Though the houses looked impressive, in reality they were crude and simple.) What point is the author making? (Outward appearances were important.)
   h. How was this man different from other more famous plantation owners such as Thomas Jefferson and John Calhoun? (He was an immigrant; he started with very little.)

3. After you remind students that large plantation owners were not typical of southern farmers, have the class discuss the lives of small farmers in the South during this period in history. Tell the class that, throughout the early 1800s, plantation owners acquired large units of the most fertile land, leaving the less desirable land for small farmers. As time went on these small farmers could not hope to find better land even by moving beyond the Mississippi River, because the large planters had already spread into Arkansas and Texas with their slaves. (You may want to use the classroom map to locate the frontier, pointing out its movement westward.) Small farmers were left with small, rocky (or sandy) parcels of land on which they grew tobacco, corn, rice, raised hogs, and so on. Many sold some of their yield for use on the large plantations, but for some small farmers surpluses did not exist. Furthermore, there was no means of transporting crops to market. Existing roads and railroads, built primarily to transport cotton, rarely extended into the backcountry. Shut out of the political system by the large planters, farmers had little possibility of bettering their lives. The more successful farm families lived in frame or log houses that had seven or eight rooms, but many crowded into drafty one-room cabins that failed to provide protection against wind and rain. In a class discussion, ask students to contrast the way of life of the majority of southern farmers with that of the large plantation owners.

4. Finally, have students write two or three paragraphs describing the life of a typical small farmer, either a husband or a wife. Encourage students to use the W. J. Cash excerpt as a model so that they do not simply give facts but enter into the lives of the person they describe. Ask them to include details that give important but personal information about their subjects, as Cash did in describing the education and the expected future of the owner's son and in referring to obituaries appearing in newspapers after the owner's death. Have students follow these steps in writing their paragraphs:

Step 1: Prewriting
Have students work in small groups or with partners to make a list of details that give information about the lives of small farmers. (Lists should include the information you have provided on subsistence or near-subsistence farming, housing, lack of access to transportation, lack of educational opportunities, the difficulty of moving to new lands, and so on.)

Step 2: Writing a First Draft
Instruct students, as they work alone, to write a first draft that includes details from the lists they made in Step 1.

Step 3: Revising
Have students exchange their work with a partner from their group, who will refer back to the list of details made by the group and then critique the description and suggest improvements. Suggested improvements should include those that give interesting and informative details. Then have students revise.

Step 4: Proofreading
Students should proofread for errors in spelling, punctuation, grammar, and word usage.

Step 5: Writing a Final Copy
Have students write a final copy on clean paper. Collect the descriptions and display them in class so that students can read one another's work.

Excerpts from *The Mind of the South*

By W.J. Cash

A stout young Irishman brought his bride into the Carolina upcountry about 1800. He cleared a bit of land, built a log cabin of two rooms, and sat down to the pioneer life. One winter, with several of his neighbors, he loaded a boat with whisky and the coarse woolen cloth woven by the women, and drifted down to Charleston to trade. There, remembering the fondness of his woman for a bit of beauty, he bought a handful of cotton seed, which she planted about the cabin with the wild rose and the honeysuckle—as a flower. Afterward, she learned under the tutelage of a new neighbor, to pick the seed from the fiber with her fingers and to spin it into yarn. Another winter the man drifted down the river, this time to find the half-way station of Columbia in a strange ferment. There was a new wonder in the world—the cotton gin—and the forest which had lined the banks of the stream for a thousand centuries was beginning to go down. . . .

Land in his neighborhood was to be had for fifty cents an acre. With twenty dollars, the savings of his lifetime, he bought forty acres and set himself to clear it. Rising long before day, he toiled deep into the night, with his wife holding a pine torch for him to see by. Aided by his neighbors, he piled the trunks of the trees into great heaps and burned them, grubbed up the stumps, hacked away the tangle of underbrush and vine, stamped out the poison ivy and the snakes. A wandering trader sold him a horse, bony and half-starved, for a knife, a dollar, and a gallon of whisky. Every day now—Sundays not excepted—when the heavens allowed, and every night that the moon came, he drove the plow into the earth, with uptorn roots bruising his shanks at every step. Behind him came his wife with a hoe. In a few years the land was beginning to yield cotton—richly, for the soil was fecund with the accumulated mold of centuries. Another trip down the river and he brought home a . . . slave. . . . Next year the Irishman bought fifty acres more, and the year after another

black. Five years more and he had two hundred acres and ten Negroes. Cotton prices swung up and down sharply, but always, whatever the return, it was almost pure velvet. For the fertility of the soil seemed inexhaustible.

When he was forty-five, he quit work, abandoned the log house, which had grown to six rooms, and built himself a wide-spreading frame cottage. When he was fifty, he became a magistrate, acquired a carriage, and built a cotton gin and a third house—a "big house" this time. It was not, to be truthful, a very grand house really. Built of lumber sawed on the place, it was a little crude and had not cost above a thousand dollars, even when the marble mantle was counted in. Essentially, it was just a box, with four rooms, bisected by a hallway, set on four more rooms bisected by another hallway, and a detached kitchen at the back. Wind-swept in winter, it was difficult to keep clean of vermin in summer. But it was huge, it had great columns in front, and it was eventually painted white, and so, in this land of wide fields and pinewoods it seemed very imposing.

Meantime the country around had been growing up. Other "big houses" had been built. There was a county seat now, a cluster of frame houses, stores, and "doggeries" about a red brick courthouse. . . . The Irishman had a piano in his house, on which his daughters, taught by a vagabond German, played as well as young ladies could be expected to. One of the Irishman's sons went to the College of South Carolina, came back to grow into the chief lawyer in the country, got to be a judge, and would have been Governor if he had not died at the head of his regiment at Chancellorsville.

As a crown on his career, the old man went to the Legislature, where he was accepted by the Charleston gentlemen tolerantly and with genuine liking. Tall . . . and well-made, he grew whiskers after the Galway fashion—the well-kept whiteness of which contrasted very agreeably with the brick red of his complexion— donned the long-tailed coat, stove-pipe hat, and string tie of the statesmen of his period. . . .

When the old man finally died in 1854, he left two thousand acres, a hundred and fourteen slaves, and four cotton gins. The little newspaper which had recently set up in the county seat spoke of him as "a gentleman of the old school" and "a noble specimen of chivalry at its best."

TOPIC: GEOGRAPHY—The Mississippi River and the South
TIME: One class period
TIME PERIOD: During study of the deepening sectional conflicts in the mid-1800s

BACKGROUND

The Mississippi River became "a great highway" of commerce after the invention of the steamboat, which enabled boats to move upstream against strong currents. From New York boats filled with pine logs chugged down the Allegheny and the Ohio rivers and into the Mississippi, bound for New Orleans. From Illinois and Missouri came cattle and horses, corn, potatoes, and apples. Boats from Tennessee piled high with bales of cotton sailed south to New Orleans. The Mississippi became the heart of the nation's commerce, and New Orleans briefly became the city that Thomas Jefferson had envisioned it would be: "the mighty mart of the merchandise brought from more than a thousand rivers."

For a brief time the Mississippi seemed to be one of the strongest ties linking the North and South in economic interdependence and union. This tie, however, began to break as northerners, with the large amounts of capital they had accumulated from their factories, began to spend money for the building of railroads and refused to appropriate funds for improvements in river systems. The first railroad lines toward the West were built in Chicago. These lines connected with the system of northeastern railroads, lakes, and canals that carried to New York a greater and greater share of western produce—produce that had once flowed south to New Orleans.

By 1850 the importance of the Mississippi had rapidly declined. Railroads and canals linked the eastern and western parts of the country. Southerners, who had depended on the Mississippi for the movement of their crops, especially cotton, were no longer at the center of the nation's commerce. This teaching strategy furthers students' understanding of geography—of relative location, of human and environmental interaction, of the value placed on natural resources because of human need, and of human movement. It also provides an opportunity to explore the connection between geography and economics.

SUGGESTED PROCEDURE

1. Have students work with a partner to look at a map of the United States in their textbook. (Have them use the political map at the back of the textbook if there is one. If not, have them use any United States map that shows rivers and has major cities labeled.) Ask students to find the Mississippi River and the main rivers flowing into it. As volunteers name the rivers, write them on the chalkboard.

2. Explain to students that the invention of the steamboat made the Mississippi River into a "great highway" on which goods were transported from place to place. Have students refer to the list of rivers flowing into the Mississippi and help them determine how goods moved south from the North and the West.

3. Write on the chalkboard the names of the states that by 1850 grew the most cotton (South Carolina, Georgia, Florida, Alabama, Mississippi, Louisiana, Arkansas, and Tennessee). Then ask students to discuss how the Mississippi was important to these states.

4. Have students refer to the map in their textbook and name the major port on the Mississippi from which goods could be exported out of the country. Then give students these facts: In 1821 the value of exports from New Orleans was only slightly less than that of New York. In 1819 New Orleans had a population of 40,000, but by 1829 its population reached 50,000. By 1840 New Orleans was the third largest city in the nation, its commerce at times surpassing that of New York. Have students discuss how New Orleans and the Mississippi River were important to the economy of the South.

5. Have students recall the system of railroads and canals that were built in the Northeast. Ask in which direction these transportation systems were built (east-west). Tell students that by 1850 New Orleans had become the seventh largest city in the nation, and its rate of growth had declined. Have students discuss how the system of railroads and canals might have affected commerce on the Mississippi. (Commerce would decrease.) Ask how the increasing importance of the port of New York and the decline of the port of New Orleans might have affected the South. (The South would no longer be at the center of the nation's commerce.)

6. Conclude the lesson by having the class discuss the declining importance of the Mississippi River as an example of the differences between North and South and as an additional reason for sectional conflict.

TOPIC: The Constitutional Rights of Free African Americans
TIME: One class period
TIME PERIOD: During study of the South in the 1800s

BACKGROUND

This teaching strategy emphasizes the importance of the rights guaranteed in the first 10 amendments to the Constitution by asking students to determine whether free African Americans in the South enjoyed constitutionally guaranteed freedoms. By 1790 all southern states, with the exception of South Carolina, had passed manumission laws permitting slaveholders to free their slaves. Free African Americans (those who had been freed by owners and the considerable number who had simply escaped) rapidly became farmers, opened shops, entered trades, and became ministers, merchants, painters, and authors. By 1810 free blacks, numbering 108,000, were the fastest-growing population in the South.

Attitudes toward freeing slaves, however, changed with the invention of the cotton gin. As slavery became entrenched in the South, free African Americans became viewed as a threat to the institution of slavery. Whites feared that free blacks might encourage slaves to rebel or run away. Southerners were aware that Toussaint L'Ouverture, a slave who had been freed by the French in Santo Domingo, rebelled and declared himself master of the island. Furthermore, free blacks who worked successfully at the same occupations as whites challenged the view that African Americans were somehow "inferior" and needed to be "taken care of" by white masters. In the early 1800s southern states passed a variety of laws that not only segregated free African Americans from whites but sharply curtailed their freedom. In fact, free blacks lived in fear of either being treated as escaped slaves or of committing some petty offense that would result in enslavement.

MATERIALS

Copies of the handout

SUGGESTED PROCEDURE

1. Organize the class into groups of three or four, and distribute copies of the handout. Ask students to work together in their groups to read the handout.
2. As groups complete their reading of the material, ask them if they think these laws existed in the North. Then have students open their textbooks to the Bill of Rights. (You may have students recall previous study of the Constitution, reminding them that the first 10 amendments guarantee individual liberties.) Then have each group compare the list of laws on the handout with the rights guaranteed in the Bill of Rights. Ask them to make a list of the constitutional rights that were violated by the laws.
3. Ask a volunteer in each group to read the group's list. One student may go to the chalkboard and write down the items as they are read. Conclude the lesson by discussing as a class the following questions:
   a. Do you think that free African Americans in the South were in fact "free"? (Students should say no.)
   b. Why do you think that some later historical commentators have referred to free African American as "slaves without masters"? (Suggested response: Even though free African Americans were "free," they still did not have the rights of citizens; they were, in effect, still slaves.)

Laws Limiting the Rights of Free African Americans in the South

Free blacks had to register with the town clerk (or other government official) to show that they were free. They were also required to carry papers, which had to be renewed within a certain time. Blacks who were found without papers were considered escaped slaves and could be sold into slavery.

Free blacks could not testify against whites in court, although slaves could testify against free blacks.

In some states free blacks were not allowed a trial by jury.

Some cities required that free blacks be inside by a certain time of night. In Norfolk, Virginia, for example, slaves had to be indoors by 9:00 P.M. in winter and 8:00 P.M. in summer. Free blacks had to be indoors by 10:00 P.M.

Several cities did not permit free blacks to walk on the city square. In Richmond, Virginia, a law said, "A negro meeting, or overtaking, or being overtaken by a white person on the sidewalk shall pass on the outside; and if necessary to enable such a white person to pass, shall immediately get off the sidewalk."

Free blacks could not travel freely from one state to another.

Free blacks could not go to the same churches, schools, and even zoos as whites.

Free blacks who broke the law were whipped, just as if they were slaves.

Free blacks could be sold into slavery if they failed to pay even small debts, fines, and taxes.

In the southernmost states free blacks were required to have a white guardian who supervised them.

Free blacks were allowed to own property, but many jobs became closed to them. Jobs that blacks could not have varied from state to state and from city to city. For example, in Virginia and Georgia, free blacks were not allowed to become river captains and pilots. A large proportion of free black men throughout the South were either tailors and carpenters because these were the jobs most often open to them.

In many states free blacks could not meet or gather together if a white was not there to supervise.

In many states a free black could not marry a slave without paying the owner.

TOPIC: GEOGRAPHY—The Cotton and Slave Economy of the South
TIME: One class period
TIME PERIOD: During study of the South and slavery

BACKGROUND

The physical characteristics of the South, including its climate and landforms, made it more suitable for agriculture than the Northeast. Fertile soil, especially in the eastern part of the Interior Plains, relatively flat lands, and a subtropical climate encouraged agriculture, particularly the growing of cotton. Cotton growing, in turn, required a labor source working year-round.

This teaching strategy helps students develop the understanding that historical events have occurred in particular places and that there are generally reasons why the events have occurred where they did. It furthers an understanding of geography, including the significance of location, which is essential to the study of historical events.

MATERIALS

Copies of the four maps for each student: "Climate of the South," "Landforms of the South," "Southern and Border States, 1850," and "Proportion of Slaves in Slave States, 1850"

SUGGESTED PROCEDURE

1. Explain to students that we cannot understand events unless we look at the settings in which they took place. You might compare historians to detectives, who look for clues not only by investigating the people who took part in an event but also by investigating the setting in which the event took place. Organize the class into small groups and give each group copies of the maps "Climate of the South" and "Landforms of the South." Have the students list the states that have a climate with mild winters, warm summers, year-round rainfall, and land that is flat and mildly hilly. (Louisiana, Mississippi, Alabama, Georgia, Arkansas, South Carolina, North Carolina, Tennessee, Florida, although most of Florida was unsettled at the time, and part of Texas) Have students temporarily set aside their lists.

2. Now give each group copies of the other two maps. Ask them to look at the map "Southern and Border States, 1850" and list the main cotton-growing states (Louisiana, Mississippi, Alabama, Georgia, Arkansas, South Carolina, part of North Carolina, and part of Texas). Have students compare this list with the list that groups the states by climate and land. Have students determine what kind of climate and land is suitable for growing cotton. (mild winter, warm summers, year-round rainfall, and land that is flat and mildly hilly)

3. Ask students to look at the map "Proportion of Slaves in Slave States, 1850" and determine which states had the largest slave populations. (Louisiana, Alabama, Mississippi, South Carolina, part of Georgia, and Virginia)

4. In a class discussion have students explain why cotton was an important crop in the South. Then discuss the connection between cotton and slavery. Ask why cotton was not grown in the border states and why slavery was widespread in Virginia, which grew wheat and other crops. (Slavery had begun there early in the history of the United States and had become part of the culture.)

5. A wrap-up discussion may center around the question of the labor needed for growing cotton. Although year-round labor was needed in northern factories, slavery was outlawed in the North. (Students should take into consideration the available labor supply of the North, which included immigrants.) Ask students: What alternatives to slavery might southerners have considered?

Free States

St. Louis •

MO.

Ohio River

KY.

W. VA.

MD.

VA. • Richmond

Territories

N.C.

ARK.

Memphis •

TENN.

Mississippi River

S.C.

MISS.

ALA.

GA.

• Charleston

Savannah

TEX.

LA.

Mobile •

• New Orleans

FLA.

ATLANTIC OCEAN

GULF OF MEXICO

Climate of the South

Humid subtropical
Mild winter; warm summer;
rainy year round

Continental
Severe winter; short, cool
summer; year round
moisture

Steppe
Cool or cold winter;
warm summer; little rain

0 | 600 Miles
0 | 600 Kilometers

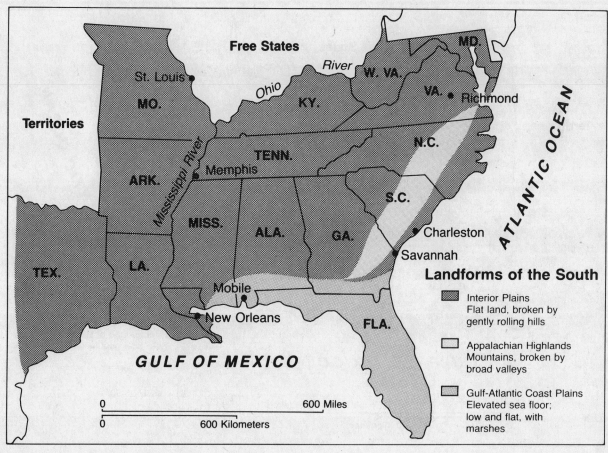

Free States

St. Louis •

Ohio River

KY.

W. VA.

MD.

MO.

VA. • Richmond

Territories

N.C.

ARK.

Memphis •

TENN.

Mississippi River

S.C.

MISS.

ALA.

GA.

• Charleston

Savannah

TEX.

LA.

Mobile •

• New Orleans

FLA.

ATLANTIC OCEAN

GULF OF MEXICO

Landforms of the South

Interior Plains
Flat land, broken by
gently rolling hills

Appalachian Highlands
Mountains, broken by
broad valleys

Gulf-Atlantic Coast Plains
Elevated sea floor;
low and flat, with
marshes

0 | 600 Miles
0 | 600 Kilometers

Southern and Border States, 1850

Free States

St. Louis

MO.

Territories

Ohio River

W. VA.

MD.

KY.

VA. • Richmond

N.C.

Mississippi River

TENN.

Memphis

ARK.

S.C.

MISS.

ALA.

GA.

• Charleston

• Savannah

TEX.

LA.

Mobile

• New Orleans

FLA.

Southern and Border States, 1850

☐ Primary cotton-growing states

ATLANTIC OCEAN

GULF OF MEXICO

0 ————— 600 Miles

0 ————— 600 Kilometers

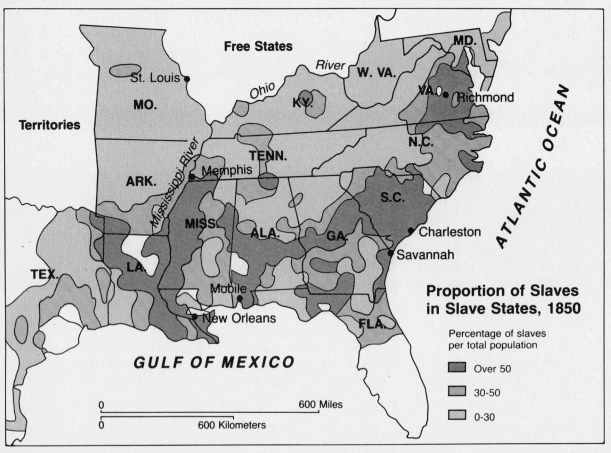

Free States

St. Louis •

MO.

Territories

Ohio River

W. VA.

MD.

KY.

VA. • Richmond

Mississippi River

TENN.

Memphis •

N.C.

ARK.

S.C.

MISS.

ALA.

GA.

• Charleston

• Savannah

TEX.

LA.

Mobile

• New Orleans

FLA.

Proportion of Slaves in Slave States, 1850

Percentage of slaves per total population

■ Over 50

▨ 30-50

▦ 0-30

ATLANTIC OCEAN

GULF OF MEXICO

0 ————— 600 Miles

0 ————— 600 Kilometers

TOPIC: The Impact of Slavery on the Southern Economy
TIME: One class period, with homework
TIME PERIOD: During study of the South and slavery

BACKGROUND

Scholars today still debate whether, in the long run, slavery proved to be economically sound for the South. Looked at from one perspective, slavery was indeed profitable: it provided cheap labor, ensured the survival of the South's most profitable crop, allowed people and their offspring to be treated as property and sold for a profit, and provided a comfortable standard of living for those able to benefit from it. On the other hand, slavery encouraged southerners to remain dependent on agriculture rather than diversifying by fostering industry, produced a large group of people (slaves) who were not allowed to develop skills and talent that could be used in a nonagricultural economy, and perpetuated an aristocratic system in which the majority of southerners had little incentive to invent or innovate because they had little chance of improving their economic position. This teaching strategy provides an opportunity for students to debate slavery as an economic as well as an ethical issue.

MATERIALS

Copies of the handouts. Separate the two debate topic sheets after you have copied them.

SUGGESTED PROCEDURE

1. At the end of the class period during which your class has read about or discussed this topic, ask students to prepare for debates that will be held during the next class. Tell students they will debate the issue: *Resolved:* Slavery Was Profitable for the South. Number students as "ones" and "twos." Give the first debate topic sheet to students numbered one. Ask them to study it and add at least three ideas of their own before the next class period. Then pass the second debate topic sheet to students who are numbered two. They will be arguing that slavery was *not* profitable for the South. They too should prepare for the debate by studying the handout and adding three of their own ideas.
2. At the beginning of the next class period, organize the class into small groups made up of equal numbers of students arguing each side. Then ask two volunteers from each group to debate. Following their debate other members of the group can comment and then choose two other debaters.
3. To conclude the lesson have the class discuss the arguments, explaining why some seemed more convincing than others. Ask students whether they think slavery should have been outlawed, regardless of its profitability. Encourage students to discuss ideals that take precedence over economic considerations, and have a volunteer list these on the chalkboard.

Slavery Was Profitable for the South

The South depended on agriculture, especially the growing of cotton, and slavery provided an inexpensive and steady supply of labor.

Plantation owners made profits from selling slaves, who were regarded as property.

Your ideas:

_____

_____

_____

_____

_____

_____

_____

- -

Slavery Was Not Profitable for the South

Because of slavery, the South chose to depend almost entirely on agriculture, especially the growing of cotton. If there had been no slavery, southerners might have built more factories.

Owners had to feed, clothe, and take care of slaves even when they became old and ill, because slaves were not allowed to learn the skills that would have allowed them to support themselves.

People who did not own slaves had few opportunities to become successful, because almost all wealth came from agriculture. Therefore, they were not encouraged to create new ways of working or invent new machines, as northerners were. The economy stayed dependent on cotton and a few other cash crops.

Your ideas:

_____

_____

_____

_____

_____

_____

_____

TOPIC: Spirituals as an Art Form Expressing the Inner Life of a People
TIME: Two class periods
TIME PERIOD: During discussion of the abolitionists and the Underground Railroad

BACKGROUND

Many blacks were familiar with the Bible and the Christian religion before they were enslaved and brought to America because of the teachings of missionaries. African American slaves, further exposed to Christianity, developed the spiritual, a musical form combining African rhythms and Judeo–Christian ideas. The spiritual, however, was rarely simply religious; it often made use of religious motifs to express the yearning for freedom.

The first spiritual, "Go Down Moses" is typical, drawing the parallel between the plight of slaves in America with that of the ancient Jews in Egypt. In the Old Testament, Moses, having finally received Pharaoh's consent, is leading the Hebrews to freedom when they are attacked by Pharaoh's army at the Red Sea. Moses raises his arm, the Red Sea parts and becomes dry land, and the Hebrews cross out of Egypt in safety. Walls of water then rise up, drowning the Egyptian pursuers. In the second spiritual, "The Gospel Train," the reference to "Gospel" expresses the slaves' hope for Christian salvation. More importantly, "train" undoubtedly refers to the Underground Railroad—the route to freedom. The third spiritual, "You Got a Right," is fairly straightforward, but it communicates on two levels—the level of Christian salvation and that of freedom from slavery. This teaching strategy will help students understand that music often reflects the inner life of a people.

MATERIALS

Copies of the three spirituals

SUGGESTED PROCEDURE

1. Ask students to read aloud as a group the words to "Go Down Moses." Write on the chalkboard unfamiliar words and usages, such as "smite" and "spoil." After you are sure that students understand the words, ask what story is told in the song. Some students may be familiar with the event described in the Old Testament, but you may want to explain it to the class. Then ask whether the slaves were really singing about Moses and the Hebrews. Have students discuss the similarities between the Hebrews' situation and that of African American slaves in the United States. Ask who the slaves might have considered their "Moses." (Different conductors on the Underground Railroad were referred to as "Moses," including Harriet Tubman, who sang some of these spirituals while leading slaves to freedom.) Point out, if necessary, that the Hebrews had originally chosen to go to Egypt, whereas blacks had been taken forcibly from Africa.

2. Have students read the words of the second spiritual, "The Gospel Train," and ask them the meaning of *gospel*. (the message concerning Christ, the kingdom of God, and salvation) Discuss particularly the second stanza in the refrain, beginning "The fare is cheap. . . ." Ask students whether the words might refer to something real in the slaves' lives. What might a train mean to slaves? Who might the "conductors" on such a "train" or "railroad" be? (Again, people like Harriet Tubman.)

3. After students have read the third spiritual, "You Got a Right," have them compare it to the other two. Discuss it in terms of religion, slavery, and human rights. Discuss the "tree of life" to which everyone has a right.

4. In a general discussion, ask students why slaves expressed their feelings in music. Make sure that the class understands not only that music has been a primary means of expression for all peoples but that slaves were not allowed to learn to read and write. Have the class discuss too why slaves did not simply sing about the pain of slavery, rather than singing about the Hebrews and a Gospel train. Ask why, in some Southern states, there were attempts to ban slaves from singing. Finally, ask why songs like these are called "spirituals," reminding students that there are different levels of meaning in the songs.

"Go Down Moses"

When Israel was in Egypt's land,
Let my people go!
Oppressed so hard they could not stand,
Let my people go!
Refrain: Go down, Moses, 'Way down in Egypt's land,
Tell old Pharaoh, Let my people go!
"Thus spoke the Lord," bold Moses said, Let my people go!
"If not I'll smite your first-born dead,"
Let my people go!
No more in bondage shall they toil, Let my people go!
Let them come out with Egypt's spoil, Let my people go!
Refrain: Go down, Moses, 'Way down in Egypt's land,
Tell old Pharaoh, Let my people go!

"The Gospel Train"

The Gospel train's a coming,
I see it close at hand,
I hear the car wheels rumbling,
And rolling through the land.

Refrain: Get on board, little children,
Get on board, little children,
Get on board, little children,
There's room for many more.

I hear the train a coming,
She's coming round the curve,
She's loosened all her steam and brakes,
And straining every nerve.

Refrain: Get on board, little children,
Get on board, little children,
Get on board, little children,
There's room for many more.

The fare is cheap and all can go,
The rich and poor are there,
No second class a board this train,
No difference in the fare.

Refrain: Get on board, little children,
Get on board, little children,
Get on board, little children,
There's room for many more.

"You Got a Right"

You got a right, I got a right,
We all got a right, to the tree of life.
The very first time I thought I was lost,
The dungeon shook and the chain fell off.
You may hinder me here, but you cannot there,
'Cause God in heaven gonna answer my prayer.
O brothers, O sisters, You got a right, I got a right,
We all got a right to the tree of life.

TOPIC: Workers on the Underground Railroad
TIME: One and one-half class periods, with homework
TIME PERIOD: During study of abolitionism and the Underground Railroad

BACKGROUND

The free African Americans in the South and the North and the white abolitionists who helped slaves escape did so at personal risk. The risk for blacks (those in the South and those who, like Harriet Tubman, returned to lead slaves to freedom) was great—they could be considered slaves and sold or, more likely, killed. White abolitionists faced the penalties of breaking fugitive slave laws.

The first reading is a letter from William Wells Brown, an African American abolitionist and fugitive slave, to the zealous abolitionist William Lloyd Garrison, who published it in *The Liberator*. The second reading is also a letter, from the fugitive slave J. H. Hill. Records of escapes on the Underground Railroad are relatively rare because it was necessary for all participants to maintain secrecy. This teaching strategy encourages students to examine how ethics and a commitment to democratic ideals influenced the behavior of those people who worked for the Underground Railroad.

MATERIALS

Copies of the two descriptions of escapes made by slaves on the Underground Railroad

SUGGESTED PROCEDURE

1. Divide the class into groups of three or four to read and discuss the letters.
2. In a class discussion, ask students why there is little detail in the Brown letter about the Crafts' introduction to abolitionists or about help or information they may have received from members of the Underground Railroad. Ask why J. H. Hill's letter contains few details about the people who helped him. (They did not want to get the people who helped them in trouble.) After establishing the risks encountered by escaping slaves and members of the Underground Railroad, have students discuss why people helped slaves to escape.
3. Conclude the lesson by having students imagine they are either an African American or a white abolitionist working on the Underground Railroad. Ask them to write a letter to a friend explaining the dangers they face and the reasons why they continue their work. Have students follow these five steps in writing their letters:

   Step 1: Prewriting
   Have students make two lists: one of dangers faced by members of the Underground Railroad and the other of reasons for working on it.
   Step 2: Writing a First Draft
   Ask students to write a first draft of their letters. They should include items from both of the lists they made in Step 1 and should also express their feelings about what they are doing and about slavery in general.
   Step 3: Revising
   Have students exchange letters with a partner, who will critique the letter and suggest improvements. Provide time for students to revise their letters.
   Step 4: Proofreading
   Ask students to proofread for errors in spelling, punctuation, grammar, and word usage.
   Step 5: Writing a Final Copy
   Have students write a final copy of their letters on clean paper. Ask volunteers to read their letters to the class or post them on the bulletin board.

The Flight of Ellen and William Craft
From *The Liberator*, January 12, 1849

One of the most interesting cases of the escape of fugitives from American slavery that have ever come before the American people, has just occurred, under the following circumstances:—William and Ellen Craft, man and wife, lived with different masters in the State of Georgia. Ellen is so near white, that she can pass without suspicion for a white woman. Her husband is much darker. He is a mechanic, and by working nights and Sundays he laid up money enough to bring himself and his wife out of slavery. Their plan was without precedent, and though novel, was the means of getting them their freedom. Ellen dressed in man's clothing and passed as the *master,* while her husband passed as the *servant.* In this way they travelled from Georgia to Philadelphia. They are now out of the reach of the blood-hounds of the South. On their journey, they put up at the best hotels where they stopped. Neither of them can read or write. And Ellen, knowing that she would be called upon to write her name at the hotels, etc., tied her right hand up as though it was lame, which proved of some service to her, as she was called upon several times at hotels to "register" her name. In Charleston, S.C., they put up at the hotel which Gov. M'Duffie and John C. Calhoun generally make their home, yet these distinguished advocates of the "peculiar institution" say that the slaves cannot take care of themselves. They arrived in Philadelphia, in four days from the time they started. Their history, especially that of their escape, is replete with interest. They will be at the meeting of the Massachusetts Anti-Slavery Society, in Boston, in the latter part of this month, where I know the history of their escape will be listened to with much interest. They are very intelligent. They are young, Ellen 22, and William 24 years of age. Ellen is truly a heroine.

Yours, truly,

William W. Brown

P.S. They are now hid away within 25 miles of Philadelphia, where they will remain until the 6th, when they will leave with me for New England.

The Escape of J. H. Hill from Virginia in 1853
From *The Underground Railroad,* by William Still, 1878

Nine months I was trying to get away. I was secreted for a long time in a kitchen of a merchant near the corner of Franklyn and 7th streets, at Richmond, where I was well taken care of, by a lady friend of my mother. When I got tired of staying in that place, I wrote myself a pass to pass myself to Petersburg, here I stopped with a very prominent colored person, who was a friend to freedom—stayed here until two white friends told other friends if I was in the city to tell me to go at once, and stand not upon the order of going, because they had heard a plot.

I wrote a pass, started for Richmond, reached Manchester, got off the cars, walked into Richmond, once more got back into the same old den, stayed here from the 16th of Aug. to 12th Sept. On the 11th of Sept. 8 o'clock P.M. a message came to me that there had been a state room taken on the steamer City of Richmond for my benefit, and I assured the party that it would be occupied if God be willing.

Before 10 o'clock the next morning, on the 12th, a beautiful Sept. day, I arose early, wrote my pass for Norfolk, left my old den with many a good bye, turned out the back way to 7th St., thence to Main, down Main behind 4 night watch to old Rockett's and after about 20 minutes of delay I succeeded in reaching the state room. My conductor was very much excited, but I felt as composed as I do at this moment, for I had started from my den that morning for liberty or for death providing myself with a brace of pistols.

Creative Strategies for Teaching American History

The Nation Divided
1850–1879

TOPIC: Images of the South on the Eve of the Civil War
TIME: Two or three class periods, with homework
TIME PERIOD: Following introductory readings on the causes of and prelude to the Civil War

BACKGROUND

This teaching strategy will guide students toward understanding that on the eve of the Civil War the North and South had in effect already become two separate nations. The focus is on the image of southern life and culture, as perceived by southerners and by northerners. By examining a series of illustrations of southern life, students will come to recognize how northerners, even those who were indifferent to the issue of slavery, could have come to view the South as an alien and contemptible place. Students will also come to recognize how white southerners, even those not directly involved in the slave system, could have come to view northern hostility as a threat to their independence and their way of life. Students will read and discuss a short excerpt from *Uncle Tom's Cabin* and engage in a discussion of the impact of Harriet Beecher Stowe's novel on northerners' views of the South and of slavery. Students will realize an appreciation for the way that images can shape our perception of events and issues.

MATERIALS

1. Transparencies or copies of the two illustrations
2. Copies of the handout with the excerpts from *Uncle Tom's Cabin*

SUGGESTED PROCEDURE

1. Review with students the growing division between the South and other regions of the country in the decades prior to 1850, particularly regarding the institution of slavery and its effect on the South's economy, politics, and culture. Also review northern opposition to the slave system as exemplified by the abolitionist movement. Emphasize that only about one-fourth to one-third of all white southern families owned slaves and that many northern whites were prejudiced against African Americans, indifferent to southern slavery, and hostile to the abolitionist movement.
2. Write on the chalkboard the names of several American cities and states (e.g., Chicago, Hollywood, Texas, Indiana) and several foreign cities, countries and regions (e.g., Paris, Beirut, Japan, Central America). Ask students the following questions:
   a. What words and ideas do these places bring to mind? (Very likely, the students' responses will be conditioned by media associations. They may relate "gangsters" to Chicago, for example.)
   b. How do you "know" such facts about these places? Have you ever been there? (In most cases students' associations will come from images in the media, particularly from television, and from popular stereotypes based on such images.)
   c. Can you depend on the accuracy of such images? (Most students will recognize that they cannot—that the images are conditioned by someone's personal opinion or prejudices, or by a deliberate effort to change someone's point of view.)
   d. What does the word *stereotype* mean? (a standardized mental image of someone or something) What are some examples of stereotypes prevalent in today's culture? (punk rockers, greasers, "red necks")
   e. Where do you think most Americans in 1850 got their ideas about other regions of the country? (from books, magazines, and newspapers) Do you think people at that time were any more or less likely than people of today to be swayed by such images?
3. Distribute copies of the two illustrations, or display the transparencies on an overhead projector. Explain that these illustrations show views of the South in the 1840s and 1850s. Have students identify some of the images they see in the illustrations and the emotional responses they raise. Ask students the following questions:

   a. Which illustration do you think was created by a southern artist? Which one appeared in an abolitionist magazine? (The peaceful plantation scene was done by a southern artist; the illustration of the lynching appeared in an abolitionist magazine.)

   b. How might northerners exposed continually to images such as those in the bottom illustration have come to regard the South? (as an evil place)

   c. How might white southerners with an image of their culture like the one conveyed in the top illustration have reacted to the image conveyed by the bottom illustration? (They would probably deny that the lynching situation existed.)

   d. Why might southern whites who did not own slaves have felt threatened by the images in the bottom illustration? (They may have thought that northerners thought that all southern people acted in the same way.)

4. Distribute copies of the reading selection from *Uncle Tom's Cabin*. Tell students that the book was published in 1852, that it sold 300,000 copies in its first year of publication alone, and in the years that followed was performed as a play all over the North. Have students read the selection as homework. Advise them that Harriet Beecher Stowe used spelling and expressions that attempted to reproduce the way uneducated southern people talked and that some of the characters' dialogue might be difficult to understand.

5. At the beginning of the next class period, organize students into groups of four. Allow about 15 minutes for them to discuss the excerpt with their groups to make sure they understand the dialogue. Discuss the excerpt with the entire class. Ask students the following questions:

   a. What words would you use to describe the three characters depicted in the scene? (uneducated; insensitive; prejudiced; crude; brutish)

   b. How might a northerner who was indifferent to the issue of slavery have changed his or her feelings as a result of reading *Uncle Tom's Cabin?* (Suggested response: the book would have horrified the reader and "educated" the person about slavery; the northerner would now probably be against slavery.)

   c. Have you ever had your opinion about an issue changed by a book, movie, or television program?

   d. Are there any current social concerns that are subjects of debate today but may be regarded by future generations of Americans to be as wrong and unethical as slavery? (Students may bring up some surprising issues. Encourage discussion of this question.)

Excerpts from *Uncle Tom's Cabin*

By Harriet Beecher Stowe

The setting of this selection is a tavern in Kentucky. Haley, a slave trader, has bought a young black child, George, planning to take him to New Orleans to sell him. But George's mother, Eliza, has escaped to the free state of Ohio, taking the child with her. Tom Loker and Marks are professional slave-catchers, a type familiar in northern states after the passage of the Fugitive Slave Act of 1850.

"This yer young-un business makes lots of trouble in the trade," said Haley, dolefully.

"If we could get a breed of gals that didn't care, now, for their young uns," said Marks; "tell ye, I think 'twould be bout the greatest mod'rn improvement I know on,"—and Marks patronized his joke by a quiet introductory sniggle.

"Jes so," said Haley; "I never could see into it; young uns is heaps of trouble to 'em; one would think, now, they'd be glad to get clar on 'em; but they arn't. And the more trouble a young un is, and the more good for nothing, as a gen'l thing, the tighter they sticks to 'em."

"Wal, Mr. Haley," said Marks, "jest pass the hot water. Yes sir; you say jest what I feel and all'us have. Now, I bought a gal once, when I was in the trade . . . and she had a young un that was mis'able sickly; it had a crooked back, or something or other; and I just gin't away to a man who thought he'd take his chance raising on't, being it didn't cost nothin'—never thought, yer know, of the gal's takin' on about it—but Lord, yer oughter seen how she went on. Why, re'lly, she did seem to me to valley the child more 'cause '*twas* sickly and cross, and plagued her; and she warn't making b'lieve, neither,—cried about it, she did, and lopped around, as if she'd lost every friend she had. It re'lly was droll to think on't. Lord, there an't no end to women's notions."

"Wal, jes so with me," said Haley. "Last summer, down on Red river, I got a gal traded on me, with a likely lookin' child enough, and his eyes looked as bright as yourn; but, come to look, I found him stone blind. Fact—he was stone blind. Wal, ye see, I thought there warn't no harm in my jest passing him along, and not saying nothin'; and I'd got him nicely swapped off for a keg of whiskey; but come to get him away from the gal, she was jest like a tiger. So t'was before we stared, and I hadn't got my gang chained up; so what should she do but ups on a cotton-bale, like a cat, ketches a knife from one of the deck hands, and I tell ye, she made all fly for a minit, till she saw 'twan't no use; and she jest turns round, and pitches head first, young un and all, into the river—went down plump, and never ris."

"Bah!" said Tom Loker, who had listened to these stories with ill-repressed disgust,—"shif'less, both on ye! my gals don't cut up no such shines, I tell ye!"

"Indeed! how do you help it?" said Marks, briskly.

"Help it? why I buys a gal, and if she's got a young un to be sold, I jest walks up and puts my fist to her face, and says, 'Look here, now, if you give me one word out of your head, I'll smash your face in. I won't hear one word—not the beginning of a word.' I says to 'em, 'This yer young un's mine, and not yourn, and you've got no kind o' business with it, I'm going to sell it, first chance; mind, you don't cut up none o' yer shines about it, or I'll make ye wish ye'd never been born.' I tell ye, they sees it ain't no play, when I gets hold. I makes 'em as whist as fishes; and if one on 'em begins and gives a yelp, why—" and Mr. Loker brought down his fist with a thump that fully explained the hiatus.

[The men bargain over shares of the reward they will get if Eliza and her child are caught.]

"I suppose you've got good dogs," said Haley.

"First rate," said Marks. "What's the use? you han't got nothing o' hers to smell on."

"Yes, I have," said Haley, triumphantly. "Here's her shawl she left on the bed in her hurry; she left her bonnet, too."

"That ar's lucky," said Loker; "fork over."

"Though the dogs might damage the gal, if they come on her unawars," said Haley.

"That ar's a consideration," said Marks. "Our dogs tore a feller half to pieces, once, down in Mobile, 'fore we could get 'em off."

"Well, ye see, for this sort that's to be sold for their looks, that ar won't answer, ye see," said Haley.

"I do see," said Marks. "Besides, if she's got took in, 'tant no go, neither. Dogs is no 'count in these yer up states where these critters gets carried; of course, ye can't get on their track. They only does down in plantations." . . .

If any of our refined and Christian readers object to the society into which this scene introduces them, let us beg them to begin and conquer their prejudices in time. The catching business, we beg to remind them, is rising to the dignity of a lawful and patriotic profession. If all the broad land between the Mississippi and the Pacific becomes one great market for bodies and souls, and human property retains the locomotive tendencies of this nineteenth century, the trader and catcher may yet be among our aristocracy.

TOPIC: The Fugitive Slave Act
TIME: One-half class period, with homework
TIME PERIOD: After discussion of the Fugitive Slave Act

BACKGROUND

The Fugitive Slave Act forced many northerners to consider for the first time the ethical implications of the slave system by forcing them to participate in it. To understand the issues raised by this law, students will simulate a town meeting held in response to a demand for aid in capturing runaway slaves. Then they will write an essay in the form of a journal entry in which they try to reconstruct what might actually have gone on at such a meeting. Students will be able to explain how the act changed northern attitudes by forcing them to take sides on an issue that had formerly been "someone else's problem." They will be able to relate this change to the split between the sections that developed over the next 10 years. This teaching strategy will also deepen students' awareness of the debate over civil disobedience, an ongoing issue throughout American history. Students will be able to relate resistance to the Fugitive Slave Act with later episodes in which individual conscience came into conflict with adherence to the law.

MATERIALS

Several copies of the "Reward Poster" to be circulated through the class

SUGGESTED PROCEDURE

1. Post one copy of the "Reward Poster" near the entrance to the classroom so that students can see it as they enter. Circulate five or six other copies through the class. Ask students where and when Americans were likely to have seen a poster like this. (in the free states; 1850 and after) Review the major points of the Compromise of 1850, highlighting the Fugitive Slave Act. Ask for students' emotional reactions to this poster.
2. Tell the class that they are going to participate in a town meeting to discuss the reward poster, just as citizens of northern cities and towns might really have held in 1851. Assign one student to chair the meeting. Organize the rest of the class into five groups. Try to form the groups so that each one includes students with good verbal skills. Assign each group to represent different points of view to be expressed at the meeting.
   a. One group approves of the Fugitive Slave Act and wants to help capture the runaway slaves. They agree that slaves are the property of their masters and that Mr. Rudman's property rights must be respected.
   b. One group disapproves of slavery but thinks the two runaways should be returned to their master because "it is the law."
   c. One group does not care one way or the other about slavery but wants to collect the reward.
   d. One group hates slavery and favors helping the two runaways to remain free even if it means breaking the law. They agree with Ralph Waldo Emerson statement concerning the Fugitive Slave Act: "This filthy enactment was made in the nineteenth century, by people who could read and write. I will not obey it, by God!"
   e. One group is ready to do violence against the slave catchers. They agree with Frederick Douglass that "The only way to make the Fugitive Slave Act a dead letter is to make a dozen or more dead kidnappers."
3. Tell the chairperson that his or her job is to keep order and to call upon others to speak. Remind students in each group that they should raise their hands if they want to speak but not to do so until they have been recognized by the chair.
4. Let students conduct their town meeting. Allow them to simulate the emotional climate of such a meeting as freely as seems reasonable in your classroom. The discussion could get lively as students representing the various points of view shout to be heard and refuse to wait for the chair's recognition. The chair might

tend to recognize speakers who agree with his or her personal views and fail to give other groups "equal time."

5. Stop the discussion after about 20 minutes. As homework, assign students to write an eyewitness account of such a meeting as it might have occurred in 1851. Have them write the accounts in the form of diary or journal entries. Their entries should:
   a. Describe what took place at the meeting
   b. Express their own point of view about the issue of compliance with the Fugitive Slave Act and their reasons for it
   c. Tell how the meeting changed their attitude toward this issue

$2,000   REWARD $2,000

Offered by Mr. Hughes Rudman of Wilcox County, Alabama,
for the return, **Alive** and in **Good Condition,** of his negroes:

Peter, 29 years of age, six feet, one inch tall, 190 pounds in weight. He has very dark skin, a knife scar shaped like a half moon on his left cheek, numerous whip scars on his back. He possesses the skills of a blacksmith and may have secured employment in that trade. $1,500 reward.

and

Lucy, his wife, 18 years of age, five feet, five inches tall, 140 pounds in weight. She has light skin and a very prominent chin. She can read and write, and may have forged freedom papers for the couple. $500 reward.

These two ran off April 21, 1851, and have been reported heading for this vicinity. Anyone having any knowledge of the whereabouts of either or both of these negroes is requested to contact the nearest sheriff or federal authorities. Reward will be paid upon comfirmation of identity.

Warning

Willful withholding of information pertaining to the apprehension of these fugitives is a violation of federal statute and is punishable by fine and imprisonment.

August 7, 1851

TOPIC: The Battle for Kansas
TIME: One to two class periods, with homework
TIME PERIOD: During study of the Kansas–Nebraska Act and its effects

BACKGROUND

In 1855 and 1856 a prelude to the Civil War was fought in the Kansas territory. In this teaching strategy students will explore the circumstances that led to the fighting, the role played by Stephen A. Douglas, and the significance of the struggle in deepening the divisions between North and South. This teaching strategy will help students understand that the battle for Kansas represented a departure from earlier sectional crises in that it could not be resolved by compromise. They will recognize that the "Bleeding Kansas" episode represented a prelude to the full-scale war that followed.

SUGGESTED PROCEDURE

1. On the day before you introduce the activity, tell the students that they are going to examine the issues and results of the Kansas controversy as Americans in the 1850s might have followed it in their newspapers. As preparation for the activity, have them review the material in their textbooks and to define the following terms as homework:

Kansas–Nebraska bill	Wilmot Proviso	popular sovereignty
Missouri compromise	Ostend Manifesto	free soilers
Beecher's Bibles	border ruffians	sack of Lawrence
Pottawatomie massacre	guerrillas	"Bleeding Kansas"

2. Organize the class into eight groups. Be sure to place students with the best verbal and writing skills among the various groups. Tell the students that each group is going to compose an article that might have appeared in a newspaper during the Kansas controversy.

   a. One group will compose an editorial *supporting* the Kansas–Nebraska bill that might have appeared in a Louisiana newspaper during the summer of 1854. They will give reasons for favoring the bill.

   b. One group will compose an editorial *supporting* the Kansas–Nebraska bill that might have appeared in a small-town Ohio newspaper during the summer of 1854. They will give reasons for favoring the bill.

   c. One group will compose an editorial *attacking* the Kansas–Nebraska bill that might have appeared in a Chicago newspaper during the summer of 1854. They will give reasons for opposing the bill.

   d. One group will compose an editorial *attacking* the Kansas–Nebraska bill that might have appeared in an abolitionist newspaper in Boston during the summer of 1854. They will give reasons for opposing the bill.

   e. One group will compose an article that might have been written by a Kansas free soiler about the territorial election in March, 1855.

   f. One group will compose an "eyewitness" account of a violent battle between free soilers and pro-slavery people in Kansas in May, 1856, as reported in a Canadian newspaper.

   g. One group will compose an article that might have been written by Stephen A. Douglas during the summer of 1856, defending his role in bringing about the Kansas–Nebraska Act.

   h. One group will compose an article explaining the results of the presidential election of 1856 and how Buchanan came to be elected, as might have appeared in a newspaper a month after the election.

3. Allow the groups one whole class period to discuss and compose their articles. Tell each group to follow this five-step procedure:

   Step 1: Prewriting
   Have students spend some time writing down and discussing the various points that will be made in their article and deciding how it will be structured. They may consult the textbook and/or other available references. If time permits, allow one or two students from each group to obtain information from library sources.

Step 2: Writing a First Draft
Using their prewriting notes as a guide, students should write a first draft of their article. The entire group may participate in verbally composing the article, with students taking turns doing the actual writing.

Step 3: Revising
Students should read over their article and suggest ways to make it stronger. Redundant, repetitive or irrelevant sections may be cut; new material may be added to strengthen or enhance a point.

Step 4: Proofreading
The entire group should participate in proofreading for errors in spelling, punctuation, grammar, or usage.

Step 5: Writing a Final Copy
Have students write a final copy on a clean sheet of paper.

4. The following day have one student from each group read their articles, in the order listed under the second procedural instruction. Have the class take notes on the oral presentations. Then call upon each student in turn to critique, challenge, or add to one of the articles prepared by another group.

TOPIC: Abe Lincoln, in His Own Words
TIME: One class period
TIME PERIOD: During study of the Lincoln–Douglas debates and/or the rise of
  Lincoln to national prominence.

BACKGROUND

Abraham Lincoln first achieved the stature of a national political figure during his debates with Stephen A. Douglas when both men were candidates for the United States Senate in Illinois in 1858. But Lincoln's views on the issue of slavery, its continued existence in the South, and its extention into new territories, had been developing throughout the 1850s.

In this teaching strategy students will gain some insights about Lincoln and his views on the slavery issue by reading two excerpts from his speeches and one from his personal correspondence. Students will be able to define and explain the significance of events such as the Kansas–Nebraska Act and the Dred Scott decision in altering the terms of the national debate over slavery. They will then use their understanding to explain Lincoln's views as expressed in the selections. Students will see how the ideas Lincoln expressed in the famous debates had been developing as a result of the events of the previous years. They will understand how Lincoln's election to the presidency in 1860 indicated that many northerners who had previously supported Douglas and compromise had by then come to share Lincoln's views.

MATERIALS

1. Copies of the excerpted material from Lincoln's writings
2. Copies of the question sheets

SUGGESTED PROCEDURE

1. Ask the class to share any impressions they may have about the life and ideas of Abraham Lincoln. Their responses will probably be based largely on the popular iconography of Lincoln: "He was born in a log cabin"; "He was called 'Honest Abe'"; "He freed the slaves"; and so on. Ask students the following questions:
   a. Can you explain just what Lincoln's views were about slavery? (Most students will probably say that he was against it.)
   b. How might the popular image of Lincoln be different if the South had won the Civil War? (He would probably not be as revered.)
   c. Do you think you could get a better idea of who Lincoln really was by reading his own words or by reading someone else's comments about him?
2. Tell the class that they are going to read two excerpts from Lincoln's speeches and one from a letter he wrote to a friend, all from the period between 1854 and 1857. Distribute copies of the three Lincoln excerpts. Ask for volunteers to read the three selections aloud. Call upon students to define the following terms as they occur: Kansas–Nebraska Act, Know-Nothings, Dred Scott decision. Explain, or call upon students to explain, any difficult or obscure terms encountered in the selections (e.g., Lincoln's references in his letter to "the progress in degeneracy" and the "base alloy of hypocrisy").
3. Organize the class work into groups of four. Distribute one copy of the question sheet to each student. Let them use the rest of the class period to answer the questions. They may discuss the questions and the three Lincoln excerpts among their groups, but each student should complete his or her own question sheet.

Answers to Worksheet (Page 209)

1. He thought it was unjust and hypocritical; he thought slavery went against the meaning of the phrase "all men are created equal" in the Declaration of Independence.
2. He disagreed with it. He said that taking slaves into new territories was the same as bringing them from Africa.
3. The personal letter used stronger language than the public speeches. He emphatically denounced the Know-Nothings.
4. He thought that the intention of the writers of the Declaration was to declare the right of equality so that the enforcement of the right would follow when circumstances would allow.
5. They degraded white people such as Catholics and foreigners as well as African Americans.
6. He disagreed with it. He thought the justices' arguments went against the wording of the Declaration of Independence.

Abraham Lincoln:
Excerpts from His Writings and Speeches
1854–1857

1. *From a speech opposing the Kansas–Nebraska Act, given at Peoria, Illinois, October 16, 1854*

This *declared* indifference, but, as I must think, covert *real zeal* for the spread of slavery, I can not but hate. I hate it because of the monstrous injustice of slavery itself. I hate it because it deprives our republican example of its just influence in the world—enables the enemies of free institutions, with plausibility, to taunt us as hypocrites—causes the real friends of freedom to doubt our sincerity, and especially because it forces so many really good men amongst ourselves into an open war with the very fundamental principles of civil liberty—criticizing the Declaration of Independence, and insisting that there is no right principle of action but *self-interest*.

Before proceeding, let me say that I have no prejudice against the Southern people. They are just what we would be like in their situation. If slavery did not now exist among them, they would not introduce it. If it did now exist among us, we should not instantly give it up.—This I believe of the masses north and south.—Doubtless there are individuals on both sides who would not hold slaves under any circumstances; and others who would gladly introduce slavery anew, if it were out of existence. We know that some southern men do free their slaves, go north, and become tip-top abolitionists; while some northern ones go south, and become most cruel slave-masters.

When southern people tell us they are no more responsible for the origin of slavery than we; I acknowledge the fact. When it is said that the institution exists, and that it is very difficult to get rid of it, in any satisfactory way, I can understand and appreciate the saying. I surely will not blame them for not doing what I should not know how to do myself. If all earthly power were given me, I should not know what to do, as to the existing institution. . . . It does seem to me that systems of gradual emancipation might be adopted; but for their tardiness in this, I will not undertake to judge our brethren of the south.

When they remind us of their constitutional rights, I acknowledge them, not grudgingly, but fully, and fairly; and I would give them any legislation for the reclaiming of their fugitives, which should not, in its stringency, be more likely to carry a free man into slavery, than our ordinary criminal laws are to hang an innocent one.

But all this, to my judgment, furnishes no more excuse for permitting slavery to go into our own free territory, than it would for reviving the African slave trade by law. The law which forbids the bringing of slaves *from* Africa; and that which has so long forbidden the taking of them *to Nebraska,* can hardly be distinguished on any moral principle.

2. *From a letter to Joshua F. Speed, dated August 24, 1855*

I am not a Know-Nothing; that is certain. How could I be? How can anyone who abhors the oppression of negroes be in favor of degrading classes of white people? Our progress in degeneracy appears to me to be pretty rapid. As a nation we began by declaring that *"all men are created equal."* We now practically read it *"all men are created equal, except negroes."* When the Know-Nothings get control, it will read, *"all men are created equal except negroes, and foreigners and Catholics."* When it comes to this, I shall prefer emigrating to some country where they make no pretense of loving liberty—to Russia, for instance, where despotism can be taken pure, and without the base alloy of hypocracy[*sic*].

3. *From a speech commenting on the Dred Scott decision, given at Springfield, Illinois, June 26, 1857*

Chief Justice Taney, in his opinion on the Dred Scott case, admits that the language of the Declaration is broad enough to include the whole human family, but he and Judge Douglas argue that the authors of that instrument did not intend to include negroes, by the fact that they did not at once, actually place them on an equality with the whites. Now this grave argument comes to just nothing at all, by the other fact, that they did not at once, *or ever afterwards,* actually place all white people on an equality with one another. And this is the staple argument of both the Chief Justice and the Senator, for doing this obvious violence to the plain, unmistakable language of the Declaration. I think the authors of that notable instrument intended to include *all* men, but they did not mean to declare all men equal *in all respects.* They defined with tolerable distinctness, in what respects they did consider all men created equal—equal in "certain inalienable rights, among which are life, liberty, and the pursuit of happiness." This they said, and this they meant. They did not mean to assert the obvious untruth, that all were then actually enjoying that equality, nor yet that they were about to confer it immediately upon them. In fact they had no power to confer such a boon. They meant simply to declare the *right,* so that the *enforcement* of it might follow as fast as circumstances should permit.

Abe Lincoln, in His Own Words

Directions: Answer the following questions. Use evidence from the three Lincoln excerpts to support your answers.

1. During the years 1854–1857, what were Lincoln's views about slavery in the South?

   _____

   _____

   _____

2. What were Lincoln's views about the extention of slavery into new territories?

   _____

   _____

   _____

3. Did Lincoln privately express different views on slavery than he did publicly?

   _____

   _____

   _____

4. What did Lincoln believe that the phrase "All men are created equal" meant in the Declaration of Independence?

   _____

   _____

   _____

5. Why was he opposed to the Know-Nothings?

   _____

   _____

   _____

6. How did Lincoln feel about the Dred Scott decision? How can you tell?

   _____

   _____

   _____

   _____

TOPIC: John Brown on Trial
TIME: Two to three class periods, with homework. The teacher may choose to allow half a period to introduce the lesson, give student groups time to prepare independently for the "trial" portion of the activity while teaching the rest of the unit, and then allocate one or two periods for the trial and follow-up activity.
TIME PERIOD: During study of the struggle for Kansas and John Brown's raid on Harpers Ferry

BACKGROUND

In this teaching strategy students will examine the way in which John Brown's raid on Harpers Ferry underscored the bitter, irreconcilable division between North and South. Upon completion of the activity, students will be able to express an understanding of how public reaction to Brown's raid was symbolic of the transition between the compromising spirit of earlier years and "the irrepressible conflict" that followed.

Students will use a modified courtroom setting to conduct a mock trial of John Brown. They will examine the facts of Brown's role in "Bleeding Kansas" in 1856 and his raid on the Harpers Ferry arsenal in 1859. Students will assume the roles of judge, prosecution and defense teams, witnesses, and John Brown. Other students representing the jury will take notes on the facts of the case and reach a verdict. Finally, students will write essays critiquing the activity and expressing their understanding of the issues and emotions raised by John Brown's raid. They will recognize that what might have been regarded 10 years earlier as the ineffectual gesture of a madman was seen in the North as a heroic blow for freedom and in the South as an act of treason that might have set off a race war.

MATERIALS

Copies of the "Trial Procedures Guide"

SUGGESTED PROCEDURE

1. Write on the chalkboard the words *terrorist* and *freedom fighter*. Ask students what these words mean. Ask the class: Was John Brown a terrorist or a freedom fighter? Allow students several minutes to discuss the question. (They will very likely come to the conclusion that the difference between the two concepts depends largely on one's personal point of view.)
2. Tell the class that they will be conducting a trial of John Brown for murder and treason against the United States. Ask students for their impressions of what goes on in a criminal-court trial. Explain that a trial has four essential elements:
   a. The judge, who conducts the trial, keeps order, and rules on matters of law
   b. The jury of citizens, who decide the guilt or innocence of the accused person
   c. The prosecuting attorney, who is a government lawyer and presents the case against the accused person
   d. The defense attorney, a lawyer who presents the case for the accused person. Both the prosecution and the defense may introduce witnesses to support their side of the case, and the attorneys for both sides have the right to question any witness.
3. Emphasize that the class will not be following authentic courtroom procedure in their mock trial, nor should they try to copy the proceedings of the real trial of John Brown. The goal is to understand the case and the issues and feelings it raised, not to reenact what actually happened. However, students in their various roles should try to observe their real courtroom functions as well as possible.
4. Assign students to various roles for the trial. Point out that in real trials there are often teams of lawyers handling each side of the case and a group of law clerks and other advisers assisting the judge; and so there will be in their mock trial. Let the number of students in the class guide you in determining the actual number of students for each group.
   a. Assign three or more students to the judicial team. One will act as the judge; the others will assist in gathering information necessary to conduct the trial and will advise the judge during the trial.

b. Assign five or more students to the prosecution team. Remind them that they will be trying to prove Brown guilty of murder and treason against the United States. One will act as the actual prosecuting attorney; others will assist him or her in preparing the case and providing advice during the trial. Two (or more, if time and class size permits) of the prosecution team will be assigned roles as witnesses. These witnesses should prepare testimony favorable to the prosecution. Students in the group may decide the specific roles these witnesses will assume. They may be actual historical figures, if appropriate.

c. Assign five or more students to the defense team. They will be trying to save Brown from the gallows. One will act as the actual defense attorney; others will assist him or her in preparing the case and providing advice during the trial. A student assuming the role of John Brown should also be part of the defense team. Two (or more, if time and class size permits) of the team will be assigned roles as witnesses. These witnesses should prepare testimony favorable to the defense. Students in the group may decide the specific roles these witnesses will assume. The team should also decide whether to allow Brown himself to testify. Tell them that in the actual trial the defense tried to prove that Brown was insane but that they need not follow the same strategy. Remind them also that the Constitution guarantees that no one may be compelled to testify against himself or herself.

d. The remaining students should form the jury. Tell students that in most real trials the jury consists of 12 citizens. The members of the jury should prepare for the trial by researching the circumstances of the jury that heard the actual case (where the trial was held; from what class(es) of citizens the jurors were drawn; what the attitude of people in that region of the country was toward slavery, and so on). During the trial they should pay close attention and take notes on the attorneys' statements and the witnesses' testimony.

5. Distribute copies of the "Trial Procedures Guide." Remind the judicial team that they will be responsible for making sure that the procedures are correctly followed. Have the groups find reference materials in the school or public library to research the case and prepare for their roles in the trial. Do not direct them toward specific conclusions, but suggest that they use information about the time and place in which the incident occurred, statements of well-known persons, maps, and so on, in preparing and presenting their cases. You may wish to allow about a week before scheduling the trial to give groups time to meet and plan strategies. Prosecution and defense teams must advise each other who they plan to present as witnesses to allow time for the teams to prepare cross-examinations.

6. Allow one class period for the trial. Allow students to proceed in a moderately open-ended fashion and do not be concerned about departures from real-world jurisprudence. Remind the judge that he or she is responsible for making sure the two sides present their cases according to the "Trial Procedures Guide." When both sides have given their closing summations, allow the jury about 10 minutes to vote on Brown's guilt or innocence. Tell students that in most real criminal trials, a unanimous ballot is necessary to convict the accused person, and that most juries deliberate for several hours and take several ballots.

7. As a closure activity have students write an evaluation addressing the following questions:

   a. How was the trial conducted? Did both sides present their cases well? Did the judge manage the trial competently and the jury decide fairly? Give reasons for your answer.

   b. What insights did this mock trial give you about Americans' feelings toward the slavery issue in 1859?

Trial Procedures Guide

1. The judge calls the court to order. One of the judge's assistants announces the business of the trial. The judge reminds the jury to take notes throughout the trial.

2. The prosecution gives its opening statement: what it intends to prove during the trial (that John Brown is guilty of murder and treason) and how it intends to do it.

3. The defense gives its opening statement: what it intends to prove during the trial and how it intends to do it.

4. The prosecution calls its first witness. The prosecuting attorney asks the witness questions about what he or she knows about the facts of the case. If the defense thinks the question is unfair or the witness is not qualified to answer, the defense attorney may object to the question. It is then up to the judge to decide whether to allow the question.

5. The defense may choose to cross-examine the witness: to ask questions calling into doubt the accuracy of the witness's testimony. The defense may only cross-examine the witness on issues raised by his or her original testimony. The same rules of objection apply as in Step 4.

6. The prosecution calls its other witnesses in order, and the same procedure is followed as in Steps 4 and 5. When the prosecution has presented all its witnesses, the prosecuting attorney announces, "The prosecution rests."

7. The defense presents its witnesses. The defense attorney asks each witness questions about what he or she knows about the facts of the case. Then the prosecution gets a chance to cross-examine the witness. The same rules of cross-examination and objection as stated in Steps 4 and 5 apply here. When the defense has presented all its witnesses, the defense attorney announces, "The defense rests."

8. The judge calls on each side to present its closing statement; defense first, then prosecution. These statements review the cases that the defense and prosecution have presented and ask the jury to rule in favor of their particular side on the basis of the facts.

9. The jury deliberates, votes on the guilt or innocence of the accused, and announces its verdict.

10. The judge dismisses the jury. If the accused was found innocent, he is set free. If he is found guilty, the judge passes sentence—in this case, death by hanging.

TOPIC: A Chain of Events—The Path to Civil War
TIME: One class period
TIME PERIOD: Toward the end of study of the causes of the Civil War

BACKGROUND

In this teaching strategy students will analyze the cause-and-effect relationships among the events most often cited as causes of the Civil War. As a whole-class activity, students will review the Kansas–Nebraska Act, the Dred Scott decision, the election of 1860, and other events. Then they will work in groups to create a chart showing how each event led to another. Students will be able to explain the various cause-and-effect relationships and conclude that the Civil War cannot be said to have had any single cause. Thus the teaching strategy reviews the complex chain of events that led to the war and guides students toward the understanding that any major historical event results from a complexity of causes.

MATERIALS

11″ x 14″ fan-fold computer paper (if available) or cellophane tape

SUGGESTED PROCEDURE

1. Before class begins, write on the chalkboard the following list:

Wilmot Proviso	Compromise of 1850
Ostend Manifesto	*Uncle Tom's Cabin*
Dred Scott case	Kansas–Nebraska Act
Lincoln-Douglas debates	John Brown's raid
"Bleeding Kansas"	Election of Lincoln as president

2. Ask the class: Which of these events was the cause of the Civil War? For any event that a student names, suggest a plausible alternative (or allow another student to offer one). Most students will quickly get the point that no single event can be said to have been the cause of the war.
3. Briefly review with the class the events listed above by calling on students in turn to define, explain, or summarize each of them.
4. Organize the class into groups of four. Have each group make a chart that shows the cause-and-effect relationships among the events leading to the Civil War. Instruct the students to use a flow chart to show the relationship between events. They are to use boxes to set off the terms that identify the events and draw an arrow from the box that identifies a cause to the box that identifies the effect of the cause. Tell them that they may use events other than those listed. Remind them that a cause may have more than one effect and an effect more than one cause. Draw a sample flow chart on the chalkboard to demonstrate how their charts might look. Tell students that beside each arrow showing a cause-and-effect relationship they should write a sentence or two explaining why one event was the cause of the other. Ask two students to help demonstrate how the chart you have drawn on the chalkboard will be filled in. Have one student write an event in one box on the chalkboard. Have the other student show its cause-and-effect relationship with another event and write a sentence explaining the relationship. Tell students in each group to work out and discuss a rough form for their chart before producing the final version. Advise them that they may need to attach two or more sheets of paper together to create enough space for their chart. Provide 11″ x 14″ fan-fold computer paper or cellophane tape and paper for students to construct their charts.
5. Allow students the rest of the class period to work on their charts. Use the completed charts for evaluation of the activity.

TOPIC: Why Did the South Secede?
TIME: One class period
TIME PERIOD: During study of the secession of the southern states

BACKGROUND

The Union ultimately broke apart in 1860 because southerners felt a stronger identity with their state and region than with the United States. This is a concept that twentieth-century Americans may find hard to comprehend. This teaching strategy will guide students in understanding that the value system of most southern Americans in 1860 included a different hierarchy of loyalties from what most Americans would adhere to today. Students will be able to explain how the election of Lincoln to the presidency put this traditional hierarchy of loyalties to the test. As students study the history of the post-Civil War period, they will recognize how one result of the North's victory in the war was the overturning of this prewar hierarchy of loyalties.

MATERIALS

Copies of the "Personal Loyalties" sheet

SUGGESTED PROCEDURE

1. Ask the class: Why did the southern states leave the Union? You will most likely get the usual variety of answers. Engage the class in a dialogue: "Yes, the southerners wanted to keep slavery, but Lincoln had promised not to interfere with slavery where it already existed. The Supreme Court had ruled in the Dred Scott case that the federal government couldn't keep slavery out of any territory. Why should the South have left the Union over that issue?" "Yes, the southerners believed in states' rights, but wasn't that just a legal justification for what they had already decided they had to do?" Let the dialogue go on for about five minutes. Then ask: Can you imagine enough Americans being so upset about [name a current political issue in your state] that it would make them seriously want to leave the United States and start a separate country?

2. Tell the class that the reason the South seceded may have to do with the difference between the way Americans thought and felt about their country then and the way we feel about it now. Now proceed in the following manner:

   a. Ask students: Suppose you made a list of the different ways in which you identify yourself. What are some of the things you would put on the list to describe how you think of yourself?

   b. Use the chalkboard to illustrate an example. Write the various categories of identification as you say: "Let's take Mary Smith, for example. She might put on her list that she's American (nationality), she's female (sex), she's a resident of California (state), a state on the Pacific Coast (region) of the United States." Ask students to name other categories (not the specifics of them) by which Mary might define herself. Write them on the board below the others. When you have written 10 or 12 categories on the board, tell the class: "Now, think about the categories on this list. Pick out the three for which you have the strongest personal feeling and loyalty—the three that best define what's important to you and how you feel about yourself. Because these feelings can be very personal, you don't have to share them with the class. But think about which three are the most important to you."

   c. Now ask for a show of hands: How many of you included "state" among your three categories? How many included "region"? (Very few are likely to have chosen either of these categories.) Ask students: Does it bother anyone that so few people feel loyalty toward their state or region? Do you think many people would be angry and question your patriotism if you said you weren't willing to fight for [your state]? Encourage students to discuss their responses. Emphasize again that some people might consider their choices personal and that no one is required to reveal them.

3. Now tell students: "You have been studying the way Americans of the 1850s thought, felt, and behaved. Now I want you to try to put yourselves in the position of a person of that time and try to answer the same question. What are the three categories for which you have the strongest personal feeling and loyalty—the

three that best define what's important to you and how you feel about yourself? Might they include any that are not even on this list?" Prompt students further by saying: "For example, it's not likely that anyone today would consider that he or she is a free person. But if you lived at a time when one American in eight was a slave, wouldn't you have a strong feeling about being or not being free?"

3. Distribute copies of the "Personal Loyalties" sheet. Have students answer the questions as an evaluation of the teaching strategy.

The United States, 1860:
Personal Loyalties

Which three categories of personal identification do you think would have been most important to you if you were each of the following people?

1. A white farmer in the North

_____   _____   _____

Why?
_____

2. A white farmer in the South who did not own slaves

_____   _____   _____

Why?
_____

3. A black slave on a Louisiana cotton plantation

_____   _____   _____

Why?
_____

4. A free black laborer in the North

_____   _____   _____

Why?
_____

5. A white laborer in the North

_____   _____   _____

Why?
_____

What does this activity suggest to you as an answer to the question, "Why did the southern states leave the Union?"

_____

_____

_____

_____

_____

TOPIC: African American Soldiers
TIME: One class period, with homework
TIME PERIOD: After students have begun study of the actual conduct of the war

BACKGROUND

Two hundred thousand African Americans served in the Union army during the Civil War. At the onset of the war, African American soldiers served almost exclusively as non-combatants: wagon drivers, cooks, laborers, and so on. President Lincoln was urged by Frederick Douglass and others to recruit free blacks as combat troops, but he was reluctant to do this. Lincoln was worried about political repercussions in the slave-holding "border states" should he put guns into the hands of black men. But he was also reflecting a prejudice on the part of the Union officer corps that African Americans were cowards and would not fight.

Major General Benjamin F. Butler was one officer who did not share this view. Butler had been active in the abolitionist movement before the war. While in command of Union forces in eastern Virginia early in the fighting, Butler freed the slaves in territory captured by his troops by declaring them "contraband of war." Butler thought that black soldiers "would fight more desperately than any white troops in order to prevent capture because they knew if they were captured, they would be returned to slavery." It was while in command of Union troops occupying New Orleans in 1862 that he got his opportunity to prove it.

In this teaching strategy students will read excerpts from a first-person account by General Butler of his recruitment of two black regiments, and of the insights he gained about African Americans from a conversation he had with an African American officer. Students will discuss the issues raised by Butler's account. The strategy reaches into American history in two directions. Students will recognize that the slurs against black soldiers during the Civil War were echoes of similar prejudices expressed during the War of Independence and continued to be expressed during America's twentieth-century wars.

MATERIALS

Copies of the reading for each student

SUGGESTED PROCEDURE

1. Ask the class for any facts they may know about the participation of African Americans in the Civil War. (Some students may know specific facts that they can cite.) Guide the discussion by asking the following questions:
   a. Did African Americans serve in the Union army? In what capacities? Were any of them officers? How about in the Confederate army? (Students may know about blacks in the Union army, but most will be surprised to learn that blacks served the Confederacy as soldiers, let alone as officers.)
   b. What does the phrase "contraband of war" mean? (Have a student look up *contraband* in a dictionary and allow the class to infer that *contraband of war* means goods that are useful to a country's war effort, such as guns and ammunition.)
   c. In the Civil War slaves in territory captured by Union troops were sometimes referred to as "contrabands." Can anyone explain why? (As slave labor, they were useful to the Confederate war effort. But designating them as "contraband" was also an excuse to set them free.)
   d. Does anyone know who first declared slaves to be contraband of war? (General Benjamin F. Butler)
2. Provide students with the background information on General Butler. Tell them that they are going to read Butler's own account of his first recruitment of African American soldiers. Distribute copies of the reading and have students read it aloud.
3. Discuss the selection with the class. Ask students to locate on a wall map the region Butler refers to in the first paragraph. As a locational hint, tell them that he was in charge of the Union troops occupying New Orleans at the time. Then ask students the following questions:
   a. Why do you think many white northerners believed that blacks would not make good soldiers? (Possible answer: they thought that blacks were cowards and would not fight.)

b. Can you think of any other reasons why President Lincoln would have been reluctant to employ black combat troops? (Try to lead students to infer the political reason discussed in the Background section.)

c. What point was the black officer making about why the slaves had not started an uprising? (Slaves would be killing their white masters.) What was the officer's reasoning? (It would then be the slaves' duty to kill all white people because they were the enemy.) Does his reasoning make sense to you? Why or why not? What do you think about the officer's contention that "the only cowardly blood in our veins is the white blood"?

d. What sort of person do you think General Butler was? How did he feel about slavery? (He was against it.)

4. Conclude the activity by distributing copies of the question sheet and assigning students to answer the questions as homework. Before students begin, call their attention to Questions 7 and 8. Ask students what further information they would need to answer these questions and where they could find such information. Encourage them to check other sources and answer these last two questions. (Question 7: Students might infer that the South hated Butler because of his use of black troops, when in fact the "Beast Butler" nickname predated the incident described in the account and refers to his harsh military rule in New Orleans. Question 8: The evidence of Butler's life and career suggests that he truly supported the abolition of slavery and full racial equality.)

General Butler's Black Regiments

Written after the war by Major General Benjamin F. Butler
From *A Civil War Treasury of Tales, Legends and Folklore,* edited by B.A. Botkin
Excerpted

I desired to organize a special brigade to capture and occupy all the western part of Louisiana and other places east of the Red River, and to control the mines of salt deposit in New Iberia. These mines could be approached by water, an advantage which Jefferson put forth as one of the reasons for the purchase of Louisiana.

I could get no reply from Washington that I could have any reinforcements whatever. . . . I sent a confidential message to Washington saying that if they could not do anything for me by sending troops, I would call upon Africa for assistance, i.e., I would enlist all the colored troops I could from the free Negroes.

While I was waiting . . . the rebel authorities in New Orleans had organized two regiments from the free Negroes, called "Native Guards, Colored." When Lovell ran away with his troops these men stayed at home. The rebels had allowed the company officers to be commissioned from colored men. . . .

I found out the names and residences of some twenty of these colored officers, and sent for them to call on me. They came, and a very intelligent-looking set of men they were. I asked them if they would like to be organized as part of the United States troops. They unanimously said they would. In all bodies of men there is always a spokesman, and while many of my guests were of a very light shade, that spokesman was a Negro nearly as dark as the ace of spades.

"General," he asked, "shall we be officers as we were before?"

"Yes; every one of you who is fit to be an officer shall be, and all the line officers shall be colored men."

"How soon do you want us to be ready?"

"How soon can you give me two regiments of a thousand men each?"

"In ten days."

"But," I said, "I want you to answer me one question. My officers, most of them, believe that Negroes won't fight."

"Oh, but we will," came from the whole of them.

"You seem to be an intelligent man," said I, to their spokesman; "answer me this question: I have found out that you know just as well what this war is about as I do, and if the United States should succeed in it, it will put an end to slavery." They all looked assent. "Then tell me why some Negroes have not in this war struck a good blow somewhere for their freedom? All over the South, the men have been conscripted and driven away to the armies, leaving ten Negroes in some districts to every white man, and the colored men have simply gone on raising crops and taking care of their women and children."

The man's countenance lighted up. He said: "You are General here, and I don't like to answer that question."

"Answer it exactly according as the matter lies in your mind, and I pledge you my honor, whatever the matter may be it shall harm no one of you."

"General, will you permit a question?"

"Yes."

"If we colored men had risen to make war on our masters, would not it have been our duty to ourselves, they being our enemies, to kill the enemy wherever we could find them? and all the white men would have been our enemies to be killed?"

"I don't know but what you are right," said I. "I think that would be a logical necessity of insurrection."

"If the colored men had begun such a war as that, General, which general of the United States army should we have called upon to help us fight our battles?"

That was unanswerable.

"Well," I said, "why do you think your men will fight?"

"General, we come from a fighting race. Our fathers were brought here as slaves because they were captured in war, and in hand-to-hand fights, too. We are willing to fight. Pardon me, General, but the only cowardly blood we have got in our veins is white blood."

"Very well," I said, "recruit your men and let them be mustered into the service at"—I mentioned a large public building—"in a fortnight from to-day, at ten o'clock in the morning. Report, and I will meet you there."

TOPIC: How Legend Can Disprove History
TIME: One-half class period, with optional homework
TIME PERIOD: During study of the Civil War, ideally after students have read about Lee's first invasion of the North and the Battle of Antietam

BACKGROUND

John Greenleaf Whittier's poem, "Barbara Frietchie," first appeared in 1863. It was a morale booster for the North for the rest of the war, and it has been a favorite in anthologies of American verse ever since. Whittier based the poem on a real incident that happened during Robert E. Lee's first invasion of the North in September 1862. There was a real Barbara Frietchie, and she did wave the Stars and Stripes at some passing Confederate troops. But at this point, "history" and fact diverge.

In this teaching strategy students will read Whittier's poem as an example of the literature of the Civil War. They will relate the event, location, and characters in the verse to the historical facts and discuss how the poem might have been received in the North. Then they will read a brief account of the actual event that inspired the poem—a rather different and less heroic story than the one Whittier told. Students will recognize that literature is not history; that indeed, "history" is sometimes not history. Legend and common memory often pass as history while the facts are forgotten; and it is always a good idea to be critical about one's sources. This is a lesson that students will find useful throughout their study of history.

MATERIALS

1. Copies of the handout with the poem "Barbara Frietchie"
2. Copies of the handout with the reading selection "Barbara Frietchie: What Really Happened"

SUGGESTED PROCEDURE

1. Ask students: How do we know what we know about history? Prompt them to think about who writes history and where they get their information. Review the differences between primary and secondary source material. Ask them to suggest examples of how legends and outright lies can become accepted as history. Ask if anyone knows of any specific examples of "historical facts" that are misinterpretations, embellishments, or just plain myth. (Some students will probably suggest George Washington chopping down the cherry tree, or Betsy Ross designing the American flag.)
2. Tell students that they are going to read a poem that was very popular during the last years of the Civil War. Tell them that the poem is based on a true incident, and that as they read the poem, they are to try to evaluate what might be true and what might be embellishment or fiction.
3. Distribute copies of "Barbara Frietchie." Have students read the poem aloud. Ask students the following questions:
   a. Where does the poem take place? (lines 3–4). Have students locate Frederick, Maryland, either on a classroom wall map or on a map in their textbooks.
   b. Who are the two Confederate generals named in the poem? (Robert E. Lee and Stonewall Jackson) What time of year does the event take place? (September). Tell them that the incident described in the poem happened when Lee was preparing to invade the North in September 1862.
   c. To what do the "forty flags" refer? (lines 13–14). Ask students to explain Barbara Frietchie's heroics and Stonewall Jackson's response to her.
   d. How can you tell that the poem could not have been written before the Battle of Chancellorsville, in May 1863? (Line 43 refers to "Stonewall's bier"; students may know that Jackson was killed at Chancellorsville.)
   e. Why would a poem have had a huge public impact in 1863? Is there such a thing as a "popular poem" today? (Before electronic media were developed, reading poetry aloud was a popular form of entertainment. Today, popular songs fill the same sort of cultural niche.) Why would "Barbara Frietchie" have been widely read? (It made Barbara Frietchie a heroine, and it glorified the Union.) What effect would it have had on people in the North? (It would have been a morale booster.)
   f. To what extent do you think the incident described in the poem was true?

4. Now distribute copies of the second reading selection. Have students read it aloud. Ask for students' comments on the quotation from the Richmond newspaper that closes the selection. Discuss with students the following items:
   a. Why might popular accounts "outlive and disprove all histories"? Why are people often more inclined to accept "popular ballad" as the truth? (It is usually more exciting and colorful.) Ask again whether students know of any other popular versions of historical events that may have been similarly embellished. Prompt them about the danger of accepting something as fact just because it has appeared on television or in a newspaper. (Students will recognize that dramatic presentations may be assumed to be largely fiction, but they may need reminding that even news stories may be distorted by rumor, misunderstanding, or deliberate falsification.)
   b. Ask students to list the stages a news item goes through between the time of the actual event and our hearing of it and how this process is reflected in the story of Barbara Frietchie. Write the stages on the chalkboard as students list them.
5. As a closure activity you might have students write a descriptive essay about a benign confrontation and how by repetition the story became one of heroic deed. Ask them to use an incident from their own experience or to make up a fictional one. Have students follow these steps in completing the activity:

   Step 1: Prewriting
   Students should make a list of the stages that their incident would go through from the time of the event to the time the public would finally hear of it.

   Step 2: Writing a First Draft
   Students should use their prewriting lists as a guide for the first draft of their essays. Remind students that their essays should have an introduction, a body, and a conclusion.

   Step 3: Revising
   Have students exchange essays with a partner who will critique the essay and offer improvements. Students should revise their essays.

   Step 4: Proofreading
   Students should proofread for errors in spelling, punctuation, grammar, and word usage.

   Step 5: Writing a Final Copy
   Have students write a final copy on clean paper. Collect the essays and display them in class so that students can read one another's work.

"Barbara Frietchie"
By John Greenleaf Whittier

Up from the meadows rich with corn,
Clear in the cool September morn,

The clustered spires of Frederick stand
Green-walled by the hills of Maryland.

Round about them orchards sweep,
Apple and peach tree fruited deep,

Fair as a garden of the Lord
To the eyes of the famished rebel horde,

On that pleasant morn of the early fall
When Lee marched over the mountain wall,

Over the mountains winding down,
Horse and foot, into Frederick town.

Forty flags with their silver stars,
Forty flags with their crimson bars,

Flapped in the morning wind: the sun
Of noon looked down and saw not one.

Up rose old Barbara Frietchie then,
Bowed with her fourscore years and ten;

Bravest of all in Frederick town,
She took up the flag the men hauled down;

In her attic window the staff she set,
To show that one heart was loyal yet.

Up the street came the rebel tread,
Stonewall Jackson riding ahead.

Under his slouched hat left and right
He glanced; the old flag met his sight.

"Halt!"—the dust-brown ranks stood fast,
"Fire!"—out blazed the rifle blast.

It shivered the window, pane and sash;
It rent the banner with seam and gash.

Quick, as it fell, from the broken staff
Dame Barbara snatched the silken scarf;

She leaned far out on the window-sill,
And shook it forth with a royal will.

"Shoot, if you must, this old gray head,
But spare your country's flag," she said.

A shade of sadness, a blush of shame,
Over the face of the leader came;

The nobler nature within him stirred
To life at that woman's deed and word.

"Who touches a hair on yon gray head
Dies like a dog! March on!" he said.

All day long through Frederick street
Sounded the tread of marching feet;

All day long that free flag tossed
Over the heads of the rebel host.

Ever its torn folds rose and fell
On the loyal winds that loved it well;

And through the hill-gaps sunset light
Shone over it with a warm good-night.

Barbara Frietchie's work is o'er
And the rebel rides on his raids no more.

Honor to her! and let a tear
Fall, for her sake, on Stonewall's bier.

Over Barbara Frietchie's grave,
Flag of Freedom and Union, wave!

Peace and order and beauty draw
Round thy symbol of light and law;

And ever the stars above look down
On thy stars below in Frederick town!

Barbara Frietchie: What Really Happened

The facts of what happened in Frederick, Maryland on September 10, 1862, will probably never be known. What is known, however, is that it did not happen the way Whittier's poem said it did. For one thing, Lee's army was not marching into Frederick that day, but out of it. They were setting forth on their campaign that would result a week later in the Battle of Antietam.

What historians believe happened that morning was this: 95-year-old Barbara Frietchie was at home when a child rushed in, shouting, "Look to your flag, the troops are coming!" As the Confederates had been in Frederick for several days, Frietchie thought the child was talking about Union troops. She went out onto her front porch and began waving an American flag. After some soldiers began threatening her, she realized her mistake. But even so, she went on waving her flag. A crowd of angry soldiers gathered. Then one of their officers (not Stonewall Jackson) ordered the soldiers to march on, saying, "Go on, Granny, wave your flag as much as you please."

Two days later Union troops did enter Frederick. By that time the story of Barbara Frietchie had been told and retold among the citizens. In the retelling the tale changed; then it changed again as word of the incident spread. By the time John Greenleaf Whittier published his poem in 1863, Frietchie was a national hero. The poem became such a favorite that it was known even in the South. As the Richmond *Examiner* put it, "History is powerless in competition with popular ballad. The uncultivated may pronounce the poem so much nonsense, but the wise know that it will outlive and disprove all histories."

TOPIC: Faces of Heroism
TIME: Two to three class periods, with homework
TIME PERIOD: Any time during study of the Civil War, ideally after completing the teaching strategy "How Legend Can Disprove History"

BACKGROUND

The idea of the hero is one that is familiar to all students. But what constitutes heroism is subject to value judgment, and in recent times the concept has been so debased by politicians that students may view with cynicism anyone so labeled. In this teaching strategy students will read excerpts from three true accounts of Civil War incidents that involved acts many people would call heroic. In the first account a Union officer risked his life and disobeyed his general to rescue some men wounded under his command. In the second account a slave gained freedom for his family and others by stealing a supply boat and piloting it to the Union blockade under the unsuspecting eyes of Confederate forces. In the third account a young Alabama woman helped a Confederate general and his men escape a "Yankee" trap.

Students will read and discuss the accounts, using map skills and their understanding of specialized vocabulary to visualize the events. Students will examine notions of heroism as conveyed by the three accounts, evaluate the reliability of the sources of the three accounts, and further explore the events described. In a final, optional, activity students will work in groups to create dramatized versions of the three events for presentation to the class.

MATERIALS

1. Copies of the handout with the "Three Tales of Heroism" readings
2. Copies of the question sheet

SUGGESTED PROCEDURE

1. The day before you introduce the teaching strategy, have students define the following words as homework. They should define the words as they were understood during the Civil War period:

infantry	cavalry	artillery	regiment
blockade	pilot	flag of truce	

2. At the beginning of the next class period, ask students to voice their ideas of what the word *hero* means. Tell students that they are going to read three true stories from the Civil War and answer some questions about them. Distribute copies of the reading selections. Tell students to be sure to notice where each account came from. Give students time to read the three accounts.
3. Ask students for a show of hands as you ask the following questions:
   a. Who thinks that Lieutenant Lemuel Crocker was a hero?
   b. Who thinks that Robert Smalls was a hero?
   c. Who thinks that Emma Sansom was a hero?
   Allow time for students to discuss their reasons.
4. Organize the class into groups of four. Distribute copies of the question sheets. Have students complete the answers. Tell them that they may discuss the questions with members of their group but that each of them is to complete his or her own question sheet.
5. As an optional activity have each group of students choose one of the three accounts and write a play based on the incident. Suggest that because all three involve action and motion, a video script might be the best way to dramatize one of the stories. Tell them not to worry about writing such a script exactly as a screenwriter would. They should simply think of each piece of action in terms of a camera "shot" and indicate in their script what the camera "sees." If time permits, make copies of the best of these student plays and have students volunteer to perform them for the class.

Three Tales of Heroism

From *A Civil War Treasury of Tales, Legends and Folklore,* edited by B.A. Botkin
Selections excerpted

1. *This story appeared in 1905, in the* History of the 118th Pennsylvania Volunteers: the Corn Exchange Regiment. *Such regimental histories, collected from the memories of survivors, were popular for decades after the war. The incident described here took place after the Union defeat at the Battle of Shepherdstown, West Virginia, on September 20, 1862. The inexperienced Pennsylvania regiment had been routed by a much larger Confederate force while attempting to retreat across the Potomac River, losing 269 of its 750 men.*

The sensibilities of Lieutenant Lemuel L. Crocker had been aroused by the necessary abandonment of the dead and wounded. . . . He entreated Colonel Barns so earnestly for permission to go and care for the foresaken ones, that the Colonel, fully comprehending the impropriety of the request, at last reluctantly consented to present it to General Fitz-John Porter, the corps commander. It was met with a flat, emphatic refusal. There was no communication with the enemy, and it was not proposed to open any. War was war, and this was neither the time nor the occasion for sentiment or sympathy. But Crocker was not to be deterred in his errand of mercy, and, fully accoutred with sword, belt and pistol, to cross the river at the breast of the dam. It was a novel spectacle for an officer, armed with all he was entitled to carry, to thus commence a lonesome advance against a whole army corps. Bound upon by an unauthorized mission of peace and humanity, a little experience might have taught him his reception would have been more cordial if he had left his weapons at home. Still, it was Crocker's heart at work, and its honest, manly beats bade him face the danger.

He found the bodies of Saunders, Ricketts and Moss, and Private Mishaw badly wounded but still alive. He was bearing them on his shoulders, one by one to the river-bank, when he was suddenly interrupted by an orderly from General Porter, who informed him that he was instructed to direct him to return at once or he would order a battery to shell him out. His reply was: "Shell and be damned!". . .

He had carried all the bodies to the bank, and was returning for the wounded Mishaw, when a Confederate general . . . accompanied by numerous staff, came upon the ground. An aide-de-camp rode up, inquiring with some asperity—explaining that no flag of truce was in operation—as to who and what he was, his purpose in being there, and by whose authority.

Crocker's work, which he had conducted wholly himself, had put him in a sorry plight. He was of large frame, muscular, and finely proportioned. He had carried the bodies over his left shoulder and was absolutely covered with blood and dirt, almost unrecognizable as a soldier. . . . His reply was prompt and ingenuous: he had been refused permission to cross by his corps commander, to whom he had made his purpose known; the dead and wounded of the regiment that fought on that ground yesterday were of the blood of Philadelphia's best citizens, and, regardless of the laws of war and the commands of his superiors, he of opinion that humanity and decency demanded that they be properly cared for. . . . The simplicity and earnestness of this reply prompted the further interrogation as to how long he had been in the service. "Twenty days," responded Crocker. The gentle "I thought so" from the lips of the veteran general showed that ingenuousness and sincerity had wholly captured him. He bade him continue his labors until they were fully completed, pointed out a boat on the shore that he could utilize to ferry his precious freight across the stream, and surrounded the field with a cordon of cavalry patrols to protect him from further molestation or interruption.

But Crocker had a host of troubles to face upon his return. He had openly violated the positive command of his superior; he had been shamefully insulting to the messenger who bore his superior's instructions, and had acted in utter disregard of well-known laws governing armies confronting each other. Still, there was something about the whole affair so honest, so earnest, and so true, that there was a disposition to temporize with the stern demands of discipline. And he had fully accomplished his purpose—all the bodies and the wounded man were safely landed on the Maryland side. However, he was promptly arrested.

Colonel Barnes, who had watched him through all his operations, was the first of his superiors who was prompted to leniency, and he accompanied him to headquarters to intercede in his behalf. They were ushered into the presence of General Porter, who, shocked at such a wholesale accumulation of improprieties, and angered to a high tension by such positive disobediences, proceeded, in short and telling phrases, to explain the law and regulations—all of which, if Crocker didn't know before he started, he had had full opportunity to gather in during his experiences. . . .

The General continued his reproof; but, considering his inexperience, unquestioned courage, and evident good intentions, he finally yielded, concluding that the reprimand was sufficient punishment, and released him from arrest and restored him to duty.

2. *This account appeared in a report of the U.S. House of Representatives. At the time the incident took place, Robert Smalls was a slave belonging to the port of Charleston, South Carolina. In 1886, when this account was published, Smalls was a member of Congress.*

On May 13, 1862, the Confederate steamboat *Planter,* the special dispatch boat of General Ripley, the Confederate post commander at Charleston, South Carolina, was taken by Robert Smalls under the following

circumstances from the wharf at which she was lying, carried safely out of Charleston Harbor, and delivered to one of the vessels of the Federal fleet then blockading that port.

On the day previous, May 12, the *Planter,* which had for two weeks been engaged in removing guns from Coles Island to James Island, returned to Charleston. That night all the officers went ashore and slept in the city, leaving on board a crew of eight men, all colored. Among them was Robert Smalls, who was virtually the pilot of the boat, though he was only called a wheelman, because at that time no colored man could have, in fact, been made a pilot. For some time previous, he had been watching for an opportunity to carry into execution a plan he had conceived to take the *Planter* to the Federal fleet. This, he saw, was about as good a chance as he would ever have to do so, and therefore, he determined not to lose it. Consulting with the balance of the crew, Smalls found that they were willing to cooperate with him, although two of them afterwards concluded to remain behind. The design was hazardous in the extreme. The boat would have to pass beneath the guns of the forts in the harbor. Failure and detection would have meant certain death. . . . Under the command of Robert Smalls, wood was taken aboard, steam was put on, and with her valuable cargo of guns and ammunition intended for Fort Ripley, a new fortification just constructed in the harbor, about two o'clock in the morning the *Planter* silently moved off from her dock, steamed up to North Atlantic Wharf, where Smalls's wife and two children, together with four other women and one other child, and also three men, were waiting to embark. All these were taken on board, and then at 3:25 A.M., May 13, the *Planter* started on her perilous adventure, carrying nine men, five women, and three children. Passing Fort Johnson, the *Planter's* steam whistle blew the usual salute and she proceeded down the bay. Approaching Fort Sumter, Smalls stood in the pilot-house leaning out of the window, after the manner of Captain Relay, the commander of the boat, and his head covered with the huge straw hat which Captain Relay commonly wore on such occasions.

The signal required to be given by all steamers passing out was blown as coolly as if General Ripley was on board. Sumter answered by signal, "All right," and the *Planter* headed toward Morris Island, then occupied by Hatch's light artillery, and passed beyond the range of Sumter's guns before anyone suspected anything was wrong. When at last the *Planter* was obviously going toward the Federal fleet off the bar, Sumter signalled toward Morris Island to stop her. But it was too late. As the *Planter* approached the Federal fleet, a white flag was displayed, but this was not at first discovered and the Federal steamers, supposing the Confederate rams were coming to attack them, stood out to deep water. But the ship *Onward,* Captain Nichols, which was not a steamer, remained, opened her ports, and was about to fire into the *Planter,* when she noticed the flag of truce. As soon as the vessels came within hailing distance of each other, the *Planter's* errand was explained. Captain Nichols then boarded her, and Smalls delivered the *Planter* to him.

3. *Emma Sansom wrote this account of her rescue of Confederate General Nathan B. Forrest several years after the war. It was not published until 1901, when it was quoted in a biography of Forrest. Emma was 16 years old at the time this incident took place near Gadsden, Alabama.*

When the war came on, there were three children—a brother and sister older than I. In August, 1861, my brother enlisted in the second company that left Gadsden and joined the Nineteenth Alabama Infantry. My sister and I lived with our mother on the farm.

We were at home on the morning of May 2, 1863, when about eight or nine o'clock a company of men wearing blue uniforms and riding mules and horses galloped past the house and went on towards the bridge. Pretty soon a great crowd of them came along, and some of them stopped at the gate and asked us to bring them some water.

Sister and I each took a bucket of water, and gave it to them at the gate. One of them asked me where my father was. I told them he was dead. He asked me if I had any brothers. I told him I had *six.* He asked where they were, and I said they were in the Confederate Army.

"Do they think the South will whip?"

"They do."

"What do you think about it?"

"I think God is on our side and we will win."

"You do? Well, if you had seen us whip Colonel Roddey the other day and run him across the Tennessee River, you would have thought God was on the side of the best artillery."

By this time some of them had begun to dismount, and we went into the house. They came in and began to search for firearms and men's saddles. They did not find anything but a side-saddle, and one of them cut the skirts off that. Just then some one from the road said in a loud tone: "You men bring a chunk of fire with you, and get out of that house." The men got the fire in the kitchen and started out and an officer put a guard around the house, saying, "This guard is for your protection." They all soon hurried down to the bridge, and in a few minutes we saw the smoke rising and knew they were burning the bridge. As our fence extended up to the railing of the bridge, Mother said, "Come with me and we will pull our rails away so they will not be destroyed." As we got to the top of the hill we saw the rails were already piled on the bridge and were on fire, and the Yankees were in line on the other side guarding it.

We turned back toward the house, and had not gone but a few steps before we saw a Yankee coming at full speed, and behind were some more men on horses. I heard them shout, "Halt! and surrender!" The man stopped, threw up his hands, and handed over his gun. The officer to whom the soldier surrendered said: "Ladies, do not be alarmed, I am General Forrest; I and my men will protect you from harm." He inquired: "Where are the Yankees?"

Mother said, "They have set the bridge on fire and are standing in line on the other side, and if you go down that hill they will kill the last one of you."

By this time our men had come up, and some went out into the field, and both sides commenced shooting. We ran to the house, and I got there ahead of all. General Forrest dashed up to the gate and said to me, "Can you tell me where I can get across that creek?"

I told him there was an unsafe bridge two miles farther down the stream, but that I knew of a trail about two hundred yards above the bridge on our farm, where our cows used to cross in low water, and I believed he could get his men over there, and that if he would have my saddle put on a horse I would show him the way.

He said, "There is no time to saddle a horse; get up here behind me." As he said this he rode close to the bank on the side of the road, and I jumped up behind him.

Just as we started off, Mother came up about out of breath and gasped out, "Emma, what do you mean?"

General Forrest said: "She is going to show me a ford where I can get my men over in time to catch those Yankees before they get to Rome. Don't be uneasy; I will bring her back safe."

We rode out into a field through which ran a branch or small ravine, and along which there was a thick undergrowth that protected us for a while from being seen by the Yankees at the bridge or on the other side of the creek. This branch emptied into the creek just above the ford. When we got close to the creek, I said, "General Forrest, I think we had better get off the horse, as we are now where we may be seen."

We both got down and crept through the bushes, and when we were right at the ford I happened to be in front. He stepped quickly between me and the Yankees, saying: "I am glad to have you for a pilot, but I am not going to make breastworks of you."

The cannon and the other guns were firing fast by this time, as I pointed out to him where to go into the water and out on the other bank, and then we went back towards the house. He asked me my name, and he asked me to give him a lock of my hair. The cannon-balls were screaming over us so loud that we were told to leave and hide in some place out of danger, which we did. Soon all the firing stopped, and I started back home. On the way I met General Forrest again, and he told me that he had written a note for me and left it on the bureau. He asked me again for a lock of my hair, and as we went into the house, he said: "One of my bravest men has been killed, and he is laid out in the house. His name is Robert Turner. I want you to see that he is buried in some graveyard near here." He then told me good-by and got on his horse, and he and his men rode away and left us all alone.

My sister and I sat up all night watching over the dead soldier, who had lost his life fighting for our rights, in which we were overpowered but never conquered.

Three Tales of Heroism

Answer these questions about the three accounts that you have just read.

1. Show on the map where each of the three incidents took place. Use your classroom wall map, your textbook, or other reference materials to help you locate the three places. Use the letter A to show the location of Colonel Crocker's story, B for the location of Robert Smalls' story, and C for the location of Emma Sansom's story.

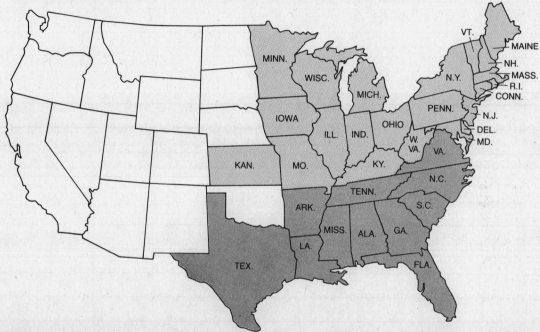

2. Which of the three accounts would you say is most likely to be an accurate representation of what really happened? Which would you say is the least likely? Give reasons for your answers.

_____

_____

_____

3. Would you call Lemuel Crocker a hero? Why, or why not?

_____

_____

_____

4. Would you call Robert Smalls a hero? Why, or why not?

_____

_____

_____

5. Would you call Emma Sansom a hero? Why, or why not?

_____

_____

_____

6. On a separate sheet of paper, draw a map of the Sansom farm based on Emma Sansom's story. Show the location of the creek and its branch, the road, the fence, the house, where the Union soldiers were stationed, and the place where Emma showed General Forrest to cross the creek.

7. Write your own story of heroism with a Civil War setting. Use another sheet of paper if you need more space.

_____
_____
_____
_____
_____
_____
_____
_____
_____
_____
_____
_____
_____
_____
_____
_____
_____
_____
_____
_____
_____
_____
_____
_____
_____
_____
_____
_____
_____

TOPIC: Behind the Scenes—Faces Among the Blue and Gray
TIME: One-half class period to introduce the lesson, with research and writing time. This teaching strategy should continue as an ongoing project throughout the unit.
TIME PERIOD: Near the beginning of the instructional sequence on the Civil War

BACKGROUND

Any United States history textbook will introduce students to biographical facts about the major historical figures of the Civil War era: Abraham Lincoln, Ulysses S. Grant, Robert E. Lee, Harriet Beecher Stowe, John Brown, and so on. This teaching strategy provides a framework within which students may conduct their own research projects into the lives of interesting "footnote" persons in Civil War history. Students may select their subjects from a list of names and brief descriptions—men and women, soldiers and civilians, "Yanks" and "Rebs"—or they may choose a subject not on the list. They will use as wide a variety of reference sources as possible to find information on the individuals they have chosen. Then they will write a short biographical paper highlighting the individual's role in the Civil War within the context of his or her life. Students should be allowed some class time to conduct their research and work on their papers, but most of their work on this project will be completed as homework. Through this teaching strategy students will reinforce their basic study skills and gain insights into how the war changed the lives of ordinary Americans.

MATERIALS

Copies of the list of suggested subjects

SUGGESTED PROCEDURE

1. Introduce the activity by asking students to name some people they have heard of in connection with the Civil War. They will probably be able to name Lincoln, Grant, Lee, and a few others. Ask students if they recognize any of these names: James Andrews, Mathew Brady, Sarah Edmonds, Thaddeus Lowe, Mary Walker. It is unlikely that any of these names will be familiar. Remind students that when we study history we too often focus on the famous and ignore the lives and contributions of millions of ordinary men and women.

2. Introduce the concept of the Civil War as a watershed event. Have a student look up the definition of *watershed* in the dictionary and let the class discuss how the term applies to the Civil War. (a crucial dividing point; a turning point) Tell them that many people's lives took odd turns as a result of the Civil War. Have the class suggest ways that the war would have changed people's lives. Ask them to name other watershed events in history and how they changed the lives of individuals.

3. Tell the class that as part of their study of the Civil War, they will do a research project on a "footnote" person in the history of the period—someone who made a special or unusual contribution to the war effort or whose life was changed in an unexpected way by his or her participation in the war effort. They will use various sources to find information about the person they choose and the role he or she played in the Civil War. Special attention should be paid to how the war changed the direction of the individual's life.

4. Distribute copies of the list of subjects to the class. Direct students' attention to the paragraph at the top of the list. Emphasize that the names on the list are only suggestions; that their research may turn up the names of other people about whom they may want to write. Review with the class various sources where they may find information about the people they choose. Tell them that they will be given some class time to work on their projects, but that they will be expected to do most of their research and writing as homework. Assign a date on which students will be required to submit the name of their subject, and assign a due date for the assignment. Length of the completed reports will vary, but suggest that five pages should be an average length for which to aim.

5. Have students follow these steps in completing their research project:

Step 1: Prewriting
Students should gather information from various sources, write down notes, and organize and structure their paper.

Step 2: Writing a First Draft
Using their prewriting notes as a guide, students should write a first draft of their paper.

Step 3: Revising
Have students exchange papers with a partner. The two partners should critique each other's essays and suggest ways to make them stronger. Redundant, repetitive, or irrelevant sections may be cut; new material may be added to strengthen or enhance a point.

Step 4: Proofreading
Students should proofread for errors in spelling, punctuation, grammar, and usage.

Step 5: Writing a Final Copy
Have students write a final copy on clean paper. If time permits, volunteers may read their papers to the class.

Faces Among the Blue and Gray

The names on this list are only suggestions to get you started. You may choose to do your report on an individual not named on this list.

James J. Andrews: This Union spy is best known for leading a daring raid that almost won the war for the North in April 1862.

Mary Ann Bickerdyke: When "Mother" Bickerdyke spoke, generals listened. This dedicated nurse became a legend among Union troops.

Belle Boyd: Though she was only 17 years old when war broke out, she became the Confederacy's most famous spy.

Mathew Brady: The Civil War was the first war to be extensively photographed, and Brady was the war's leading photographer.

Martin R. Delaney: A graduate of the Harvard medical school, he became the highest ranking African American in the Union army.

Sarah Edmonds: She served in the Union army disguised as a man, one of many disguises she assumed during her career as a soldier and spy.

John Ericsson: This Swedish-born inventor helped the Union Navy and changed forever the way sea battles were fought.

David G. Farragut: He was the greatest naval hero of the war, and a southerner who chose to fight for the Union. His father was a Spaniard who had fought against the British in the Revolutionary War.

John Hay: This young man from Illinois had a most unusual job during the war—private secretary to Abraham Lincoln.

Mary Todd Lincoln: There may be no better representative of the "brother against brother" aspect of the war than President Lincoln's southern-born wife.

Thaddeus Lowe: He devised a most unusual way of discovering what the Confederates were up to—sending men up in hot-air balloons.

Carl Schurz: This German-born immigrant probably helped the Union cause in more varied ways than anyone.

John Slidell: This Confederate diplomat was involved in an incident that almost brought England into the war on the side of the South.

Mary E. Walker: The Congressional Medal of Honor is our nation's highest military award. Mary Walker is the only woman ever to have won it.

Lew Wallace: This Union general is most famous for writing a best-selling historical novel—which had nothing to do with the Civil War.

Stand Watie: He was a Cherokee Indian tribal leader who became a general in the Confederate army.

The Unknown Hero: This man or woman from your own community was one of the millions of unknowns who contributed to the war effort. If your local library or newspaper office has information on such people, consider using one as your subject.

TOPIC: Images of War in Paintings, Drawings, and Photographs
TIME: One to two class periods
TIME PERIOD: Toward the end of the instructional sequence on the Civil War

BACKGROUND

When studying great events, the decisions of leaders, and their results, it is all too easy to lose sight of the fact that history is about people. This oversight is particularly true of students who typically have trouble grasping the fact that people of past times were not essentially different in their physical and psychological wants, needs, and aspirations from people of today. In this teaching strategy students will examine a set of paintings, drawings, and photographs of the Civil War era that show various aspects of camp life, combat, and the aftermath of battle. Students will discuss the images and make inferences about the lives of the people depicted and how they were affected by their wartime experiences. The insights gained from this teaching strategy will help students interpret any and all historical material. It will also promote their appreciation for history as a continuum of human experience.

MATERIALS

One copy of the set of seven illustrations for each group of students

SUGGESTED PROCEDURE

1. Ask students for any insights they may have gained from their study of the Civil War period about the lives of ordinary soldiers and civilians during the war. Ask them for personal feelings about what their lives might have been like if they had lived during that time.

2. Organize the class into groups of four. Distribute to each group a copy of the set of seven illustrations. Tell the class that they are going to look at a series of paintings, drawings, and photographs from the Civil War and try to gain some ideas about the people shown in them. Discuss each illustration in turn. (If possible, make transparencies of the illustrations and display them on an overhead projector as you discuss each one.)

   a. Illustration 1, a painting by Conrad Wise Chapman, shows a Confederate sentry in camp near Richmond during the winter of 1862–1863. What does his face tell you about the war he has seen? (Students may relate such questions to their knowledge of the fighting in northern Virginia.) What is he thinking about? How are he and his comrades faring with the weather? Where are they getting their food? (You may want to ask students where they think this man might be from in an attempt to guide them to the conclusion that many of the people in camp would have been from states such as Louisiana and Florida and never before experienced snow.)

   b. Illustration 2 shows a Union soldier in camp with a woman and children; other soldiers pose in the background. Prompt students' discussion: Who is the woman and who are the children posing with the soldier? What are they doing in camp? (They are the soldier's family. His wife is a laundress for the regiment. Union regulations allowed each regiment to employ four washerwomen when in camp—in the field, soldiers had to do their own laundry—and the women hired for this job were typically soldiers' wives.) What do you think her life was like before the war? What do you think she could tell you about the war and the job of soldiering? Why do you think she decided to take the job?

   c. Illustration 3 shows a scene from the Battle of Ball's Bluff (Virginia), October 21, 1861. Ask students to interpret what is happening in the picture. (The Union forces at the right are charging the Confederate position at the edge of the woods.) Ask students what they think might be going through the minds of the men in the picture.

   d. Illustration 4 shows wounded Union soldiers resting after the end of the big battle at Chancellorsville that took place May 3–5, 1863. Ask students: What could any of these men tell you about the battle that has just been fought?

   e. Illustration 5 shows the burning and looting of the Orphan Asylum for Colored Children in New York City during the draft riots of 1863. Review the causes and circumstances of the draft riots. (They were sparked by the institution of military conscription by the United States government; most of the rioters were poor Irish immigrant laborers; most of the violence was directed toward the free African American community.) Ask why the people who are burning and stealing from the orphanage are behaving as they are. What are their lives like? What were the reasons that they went after the free blacks? How did the people in the orphanage feel while the riots were happening? (Point out that the rioters in New York killed hundreds of people but that no one in this orphans' home was killed.) Discuss the ethics of the all too common occurrence that results when people feel powerless and their true enemies are too strong: they choose some weaker group as a convenient enemy on whom they can take out their frustrations.

f. Illustration 6 is a photograph showing the aftermath of the Battle of Antietam, September 17, 1862. Ask students to identify the elements in the picture. (Dead soldiers and horses, a wrecked cart, the building pocked with holes, a pair of boots in the foreground.) Ask students if they can tell whether the dead men are northerners or southerners. (The men are Confederates, but there is no way of telling.) Ask for students' emotional responses to the picture. Ask: Why might these men have joined the army? What might their last thoughts have been?

g. Illustration 7 is a photograph taken in Richmond during the last days of the war. Tell students that most of the damage in Richmond was caused by the Confederates, who blew up the city when they left. Ask students: Why would the southerners have done this to their own capital? (To prevent the Union army from using its resources.) Who do you think are the women in the foreground? (female relatives of dead soldiers) What do their black dresses signify? (They are dressed in mourning clothes.) Ask students to discuss how they might cope with a similar destruction of their own town or city. Ask: How would you find food? How would you find out information about what was happening? As a guide to understanding the technology of the period, ask students at this point to consider why there are no photographs showing combat or other action. (Students will be used to seeing televised news footage of military action and may not understand that cameras of the 1860s could not photograph people in motion.)

3. Instruct students to select one of the people in any of the illustrations and write a first-person story about the event shown in the picture. Students should attempt to convey the reality of the situation depicted as they understand it and as they themselves might have experienced it. Even the "responses" of the dead soldiers might be considered. If time permits, allow students to read their stories to the class.

1.

2.

3.

THE CIVIL WAR IN AMERICA : THE FIGHT AT BALL'S BLUFF, UPPER POTOMAC—DESPERATE EFFORT MADE BY THE 15TH MASSACHUSETTS REGIMENT TO CLEAR THE WOODS BY A BAYONET CHARGE.—FROM A SKETCH BY OUR SPECIAL ARTIST.—SEE PAGE 514.

4.

5.

THE RIOTS IN NEW YORK : DESTRUCTION OF THE COLOURED ORPHAN ASYLUM. 1863.

6.

7.

TOPIC: "This Reminds Me of a Little Joke"—Views of Lincoln
TIME: One-half to one class period
TIME PERIOD: After students have studied the election of 1864

BACKGROUND

Abraham Lincoln is such an icon in American history that students may have trouble understanding that during his lifetime he was a figure of controversy, vilified not only in the South but by many northerners as well. This teaching strategy will aid students in appreciating how our image of Lincoln was formed and how this image differs from the way he was viewed by his contemporaries. Students will read and discuss Lincoln's Gettysburg Address, one of the most famous speeches ever given by an American president, as a starting point for considering their image of Lincoln. Then they will examine two political cartoons about Lincoln—one praising him and one making fun of him—and discuss the issues that made him a figure of controversy. Through this teaching strategy students will come to appreciate the function of image-making in history and will gain some insight into the lively tradition of the American political cartoon.

MATERIALS

1. One copy of the Gettysburg Address for each student
2. One copy of the two political cartoons for each group
3. Drawing pencils for each student, if available

SUGGESTED PROCEDURE

1. Organize the class into groups of four. Distribute copies of the Gettysburg Address. Have students read the speech aloud. Discuss the circumstances under which Lincoln gave the speech. (The dedication of a national cemetery at Gettysburg, several months after the greatest battle of the war took place at the site.) Call on volunteers to summarize the content of the speech. Then ask the following questions:
   a. Why do you think the Gettysburg Address is considered such a great speech?
   b. What are your impressions concerning who Lincoln was and how the speech relates to your image of him? How do you think such a speech would be received by a modern audience? How would Lincoln have fared as a politician had he lived in the age of television?
   c. How was Lincoln viewed by his contemporaries? How does the way in which Lincoln was viewed by his contemporaries compare with the historical image of Lincoln? Extend this discussion in a general direction: How does the image of a well-known person change and become "fixed" in people's minds after he or she is dead?
2. Distribute copies of the two cartoons to each group. Have students examine the cartoons. Ask them to identify which one is favorable to Lincoln and which one is unfavorable. Students should be able to make this distinction quickly. Now proceed in the following manner:
   a. Have students consider the unfavorable cartoon. Ask: On what issue is it critical of Lincoln? (the severe human losses suffered by Union forces at the Battle of Fredericksburg) Who is the woman on the left supposed to represent? ("Columbia," a symbol of the American people) What does the sign on the ground mean? (It refers to the often-repeated and always-broken promise that the Union's Army of the Potomac would soon capture Richmond and to Lincoln's placing of one commanding general after another at its head. The cartoon is presented in the style of a poster advertising a theatrical performance.) How does the cartoon portray Lincoln? (It ridicules his fondness for telling jokes and portrays him as a theater comedian.)
   b. Have students consider the favorable cartoon. Ask: Can you identify the little man in Lincoln's palm? (If students do not know who the little man is, hint that the cartoon appeared during the election campaign of 1864. The man is George B. McClellan, Lincoln's opponent.) What is the cartoonist trying to say about the election? (Lincoln, the giant, will easily defeat McClellan.) What is the spade in McClellan's hand supposed to represent? (It is a slur on McClellan's record as a general, implying

that his army did more gravedigging than fighting.) Which aspect of Lincoln's image is used as a take-off point for both cartoons? (his fondness for telling jokes)

3. Discuss political cartoons in general. Ask students: What makes political cartoons effective in delivering a political message? Ask students to describe memorable political cartoons they might have seen about contemporary issues.

4. Instruct students to draw their own political cartoons about Lincoln as they might have appeared in American newspapers during the Civil War period. (Encourage all students to complete the assignment, but those students who are easily embarrassed about their drawing ability should be allowed to do a written "editorial" instead.) Tell them that their cartoons might represent any time or issue during the period. Examples include the Emancipation Proclamation, the draft, and Lincoln's appointment of Grant as commander of the Army of the Potomac. Guide students in suggesting different points of view that they could take. Examples include a northern, pro-Union newspaper, a northern newspaper critical of Lincoln and wanting to abandon the war, a newspaper in a Confederate city, a magazine published by and for free African Americans, a magazine published by and for the immigrant community in the North.

5. Post some of the better cartoons on a bulletin board or elsewhere in the classroom for student viewing and informal discussion.

The Gettysburg Address

President Lincoln's speech at the dedication of the national cemetery at Gettysburg, November 19, 1863

Four score and seven years ago our fathers brought forth on this continent a new nation, conceived in liberty, and dedicated to the proposition that all men are created equal.

Now we are engaged in a great civil war, testing whether that nation, or any nation so conceived and so dedicated, can long endure. We are met on a great battlefield of that war. We have come to dedicate a portion of that field as a final resting place for those who here gave their lives that that nation might live. It is altogether fitting and proper that we should do this.

But in a larger sense, we cannot dedicate—we cannot consecrate—we cannot hallow—this ground. The brave men, living and dead, who struggled here, have consecrated it far above our poor power to add or detract. The world will little note nor long remember what we say here, but it can never forget what they did here. It is for us, the living, rather, to be dedicated here to the unfinished work for which they who fought here have thus far so nobly advanced. It is rather for us to be here dedicated to the great task remaining before us—that from these honored dead we take increased devotion to that cause for which they gave the last full measure of devotion; that we here highly resolve that these dead shall not have died in vain; that this nation, under God, shall have a new birth of freedom; and that government of the people, by the people, for the people, shall not perish from the earth.

COLUMBIA. "Where are my 15,000 Sons—murdered at Fredericksburg?"   LINCOLN. "This reminds me of a little Joke—"   COLUMBIA. "Go tell your Joke AT SPRINGFIELD!!"

TOPIC: A New Birth of Freedom
TIME: One to two class periods
TIME PERIOD: Early in the study of the Reconstruction period

BACKGROUND

During the first years after the Civil War, the ex-slaves of the South had good reason to hope that freedom would be real and permanent. The establishment of the Freedmen's Bureau in 1865 led to the opening of more than 4,300 schools for blacks around the South. The Civil Rights and Reconstruction Acts passed by the radical Congress gave blacks the rights of citizenship and backed them with military force. The federal government seemed prepared to enforce not only emancipation but true freedom for the former slaves.

In this teaching strategy students will consider the early effects of emancipation and Reconstruction on the freed slaves. Students will gain insights into their thoughts and feelings by reading and discussing a letter dictated by one freedman to his former master. From two illustrations, students will draw conclusions about the importance of education and voting rights in securing freedom.

MATERIALS

1. One copy of the Jourdon Anderson letter for each student
2. One copy of the two illustrations for each group

SUGGESTED PROCEDURE

1. Ask the class: What do you think life must have been like in 1865 for the newly freed slaves? Remind students of the devastation of the South by the Union troops, the worthlessness of Confederate money after the war, and the abandonment of land. To prompt students' responses, read this statement by Union General Carl Schurz, sent by President Johnson in 1865 to report on conditions in the South:

   [The land] looked for miles like a broad black streak of ruin and desolation—the fences all gone; lonesome smoke stacks, surrounded by dark heaps of ashes and cinders, marking the spots where human habitations had stood; the fields along the roads wildly overgrown by weeds, with here and there a sickly patch of cotton and corn cultivated by Negro squatters.

   Now read this statement of a former slave:

   They turned us loose like a bunch of stray dogs. No homes, no clothing, no nothing. All we had to farm with were sharp sticks. We'd stick holes and plant corn.

2. Distribute copies of the Jourdon Anderson letter to each student. Tell the class that this letter was dictated by Anderson to be sent to his former master. Have them read the letter aloud. Ask students the following questions:
   a. What do you think were the circumstances under which this letter was written? (Anderson's former master in Tennessee had written to him in Ohio, where he had gone after emancipation, asking him to come back and work for him for wages.)
   b. Why would Anderson have the same last name as his former master? (Slaves were typically given the names of their masters.) Have students discuss the various points made in the letter and the ironic tone of Anderson's reply.
   c. Have students compare Anderson's situation to that of the freedman quoted above. Ask: Which of the two do you think was more typical of ex-slaves in 1865? Do you think many slaves would have been willing to give up their new freedom for guarantees of food and a place to live? (Remind them of the government's promise to give every freedman "forty acres and a mule.")
3. Read the following quotation to the class, written by Benjamin Franklin in 1759: "They that can give up essential liberty to obtain a little temporary safety deserve neither liberty nor safety." Ask students: Do

you agree or disagree with this statement? Why? To what extent does the statement apply to the freed slaves in 1865?

4. Review briefly the events that took place during the first few years after the war: the "Black Codes," the Thirteenth, Fourteenth, and Fifteenth amendments, the Civil Rights Act of 1866, and the Reconstruction acts. Have volunteers record these events on the chalkboard in timeline form. Then ask students the following questions:

   a. Why was it important to have a constitutional amendment that expressly made black Americans citizens of the United States and of the states in which they lived? (Because in the Dred Scott case, the Supreme Court had ruled that blacks could not be citizens.)

   b. How did the situation of the freed slaves in 1865 compare with their situation in 1868? Which aspects of freedom do you think were most prized by the ex-slaves?

5. Organize the class into groups of four. Distribute copies of the two illustrations to each group. Ask the class: What is represented in each drawing? (In one, black people of all ages and both sexes are being taught in a classroom presided over by a white teacher. In the other, a black politician is addressing a plantation meeting.) Prompt students to suggest ideas about what is being talked about in each of the two scenes. For further information about the mood of black Southerners during the early years of Reconstruction, read to students the following reminiscence of Booker T. Washington:

   It was a whole race trying to go to school. Few were too young, and none too old, to make the attempt to learn. As fast as any teachers could be secured, not only were day schools filled, but night schools as well. The great ambition of older people was to try to learn to read the Bible before they died. Men and women who were 50 and 75 years old would be found in night schools. Sunday schools were formed shortly after freedom, but the principal book studied in Sunday school was the spelling book. Day school, night school, and Sunday school were always crowded, and many had to be turned away for want of room.

Read this statement from Radical Congressman Thaddeus Stevens on the new political order in the South:

   [Some politicians] proclaim that "this is the white man's government." What is implied by this? That one race of men are to have the exclusive rights forever to rule this nation while all other races and nations and colors are to have no voice in making the laws and choosing the rulers by whom they are to be governed? This is not a white man's government, in the exclusive sense in which it is used. This is the government of all men alike. Equal rights to all the privileges of the government is innate in every immortal being, no matter what the shape or color of the tabernacle which it inhabits.

Discuss the impact that land, education, and voting rights had on the freed slaves. Point out to students that before the Civil War, some southern states did not have public schools, not even for white students. Ask: How do you think children in those states received an education? (Rich children were sent to privately run schools; poor children received no education at all.) Have students express their views on whether land, education, or voting rights was what the freed slaves most needed. Guide students in recognizing that even when freed slaves were given land, they needed capital for seed and equipment.

6. Allow students to use the rest of the class period to complete one of the following written assignments. Write the assignments on the chalkboard.

   a. Compare the lives of Jourdon Anderson and his family after emancipation to what they experienced under slavery.

   b. Imagine yourself as one of the people in either of the two drawings. Describe the scene shown in the drawing as if you were writing it from your own experience.

   Students are to complete their work independently, but they may share ideas and insights with members of their group. Students should write two to three paragraphs.

This letter, said to have been dictated by Jourdon Anderson, was published soon after the end of the war in The Freedmen's Book, *edited by the abolitionist writer Lydia Maria Child.*
Excerpted

Dayton, Ohio, August 7, 1865

To my old Master, Colonel P. H. Anderson, Big Spring, Tenn.

SIR: I got your letter, and was glad that you had not forgotten Jourdon, and that you wanted me to come back and live with you again, promising to do better for me than anybody else can. I have often felt uneasy about you. I thought the Yankees would have hung you long before this, for harboring Rebs they found at your house. I suppose they never heard about your going to Colonel Martin's to kill the Union soldier that was left by his company in their stable. Although you shot at me twice before I left you, I did not want to hear of your being hurt, and I am glad you are still living. It would do me good to go back to the dear old home again, and see Miss Mary and Miss Martha and Allen, Esther, Green and Lee. Give my love to them all, and tell them I hope we will meet in the better world, if not in this. I would have gone back to see you all when I was working in the Nashville hospital, but one of the neighbors told me that Henry intended to shoot me if he ever got a chance.

I want to know particularly what the good chance is you propose to give me. I am doing tolerably well here. I get twenty-five dollars a month, with victuals and clothing; have a comfortable home for Mandy . . . and the children . . . go to school and are learning well. . . . They go to Sunday school, and Mandy and me attend church regularly. We are kindly treated. Sometimes we overhear others saying, "Those colored people were slaves" down in Tennessee. The children feel hurt when they hear such remarks; but I tell them it was no disgrace in Tennessee to belong to Colonel Anderson. Many darkeys would have been proud, as I used to be, to call you master. Now if you will write and say what wages you will give me, I will be better able to decide whether it would be to my advantage to move back again.

As to my freedom, which you say I can have, there is nothing to be gained on that score, as I got my free papers in 1864. . . . Mandy says she would be afraid to go back without some proof that you were disposed to treat us justly and kindly; and we have concluded to test your sincerity by asking you to send us our wages for the time we served you. This will make us forget and forgive old scores, and rely on your justice and friendship in the future. I served you faithfully for thirty-two years, and Mandy for twenty years. At twenty-five dollars a month for me, and two dollars a week for Mandy, our wages would amount to eleven thousand six hundred and eighty dollars. Add to this the interest for the time our wages have been kept back, and deduct what you paid for our clothing, and three doctor's visits to me, and pulling a tooth for Mandy, and the balance will show what we are in justice entitled to. Please send the money by Adams' Express, in care of V. Winders, Esq., Dayton, Ohio. If you fail to pay us for faithful labors in the past, we can have little faith in your promises in the future. We trust the good Maker has opened your eyes to the wrongs which you and your fathers have done to me and my fathers, in making us toil for you for generations without recompense. Here I draw my wages every Saturday night; but in Tennessee there was never any pay-day for the Negroes any more than for the horses and cows. Surely there will be a day of reckoning for those who defraud the laborer of his hire.

In answering this letter . . . please state if there has been any schools opened for the colored children in your neighborhood. The great desire of my life now is to give my children an education, and have them form virtuous habits.

Say howdy to George Carter, and thank him for taking the pistol from you when you were shooting at me.

From your old servant,
—JOURDON ANDERSON

ELECTIONEERING AT THE SOUTH.—Sketched by W. L. Sheppard.—[See Page 467.]

TOPIC: The (Cotton) Empire Strikes Back—White Resistance to Reconstruction
TIME: One class period
TIME PERIOD: During study of the events of the Reconstruction period

---

BACKGROUND

As long as Reconstruction was in effect, the white South resisted government by northern conquerers and freed slaves. In this teaching strategy students will explore the means, legal and otherwise, through which white southerners fought the northern occupation and disenfranchised the region's black population in the decades following the Civil War. Students will see that for every measure instituted by the United States government to secure equal rights for African Americans, there was a countermeasure on the part of the South's "old regime." They will read and discuss excerpts from two of the "Black Codes" imposed by southern states after emancipation and will identify similar countermeasures that were made against each attempt to enforce racial equality. Students will be able to explain how Reconstruction ended when northerners eventually became bored with the "Negro problem," and how white southerners installed the system of racial oppression that characterized the region for the next three-quarters of a century. In their subsequent study of history students will be able to explain the connection between the constitutional and legislative guarantees of equal rights instituted during the Reconstruction period and the civil rights advances of the 1960s.

MATERIALS

1. One copy of the Black Code excerpts for each student
2. One copy of the Ku Klux Klan newspaper cartoon and drawing of hooded Klansmen for each group

SUGGESTED PROCEDURE

1. Organize the class into groups of four. Review with students the stages in the abolition of slavery:
   a. President Lincoln issued the Emancipation Proclamation.
   b. As the Union army conquered southern territory, slaves ran away to freedom.
   c. The Thirteenth Amendment to the Constitution was passed.
2. Ask students: How did the southern state governments respond to the end of slavery? Did they give in to the idea of full equality for blacks and whites? (Students may know that the South's immediate response was the imposition of Black Codes in most southern states.) Tell the class that they will read some excerpts from two states' Black Codes. Distribute copies of the excerpts to each student. Give the class 5 to 10 minutes to read them. Discuss the excerpts with the class. Ask students: What rights and freedoms to which United States citizens are supposed to be entitled were denied under the Black Codes? How did the codes represent a situation little different from slavery?
3. Ask students the following questions:
   a. How did the victorious North respond to the Black Codes? (The response was Radical Reconstruction, the occupation of the South by Union troops to enforce equal rights.)
   b. Who governed the southern states during Radical Reconstruction? (Northern Republicans, blacks, and those white southerners who were willing to go along with the Reconstruction program.)
   c. What did most white southerners call these northern occupiers and those southerners who cooperated with them? (Carpetbaggers and Scalawags)
4. Now ask students these questions about the South:
   a. What was the South's response to the order imposed by Radical Reconstruction? (terror and violence directed against black politicians, black voters, Carpetbaggers, and Scalawags.)
   b. Can you name any groups that were responsible for the violence and terror? (Some students will be able to name the Ku Klux Klan.)
5. Distribute copies of the Ku Klux Klan newspaper cartoon and drawing of hooded Klansmen. Ask students to examine the two illustrations and to read the caption below the cartoon. Tell them that the Klansmen

often dressed in costumes like this when they conducted their activities. Ask students to infer the Klan's program and activities from the two illustrations and the caption. Ask students: Why do you think so many poor white people in the South joined the Klan or supported its activities? Prompt students: What had been the position of poor whites under the old slave system? What were their expectations now that the war was over? Who benefited when poor whites and blacks were fighting each other? How did the Reconstruction government respond to the Klan and its activities, and how effective was its response? Ask students to generalize about the South's responses to every new constitutional amendment and civil rights act instituted under Reconstruction. How did the end of Reconstruction come about? Extend this discussion. Why did northerners allow Reconstruction to end?

Excerpts from the Black Code of Mississippi (1865)

All freedmen, free negroes, or mulattoes who do now and have herebefore lived and cohabitated together as husband and wife shall be taken and held in law as legally married . . . it shall not be lawful for any freedman, free negro, or mulatto to intermarry with any white person; nor for any white person to intermarry with any freedman, free negro, or mulatto; and any person who shall so intermarry, shall be deemed guilty of felony, and on conviction thereof shall be confined in the State penitentiary for life. . . .

All contracts for labor made with freedmen, free negroes, and mulattoes for a longer period than one month shall be in writing and if the laborer shall quit the service of the employer before the expiration of his term of service, without good cause, he shall forfeit his wages for that year up to the time of quitting.

Every civil officer shall, and every person may, arrest and carry back to his or her legal employer any freedman, free negro, or mulatto who shall have quit the service of his or her employer before the expiration of his or her term of service without good cause; and said officer and person shall be entitled to receive for arresting and carrying back every deserting employee aforesaid the sum of five dollars, and ten cents per mile from the place of arrest to the place of delivery; and the same shall be paid by the employer, and held as a set-off for so much against the wages of said deserting employee.

All freedmen, free negroes and mulattoes in this State, over the age of eighteen years . . . with no lawful employment or business, or found unlawfully assembling themselves together, either in the day or night time, and all white persons so assembling themselves with freedmen, free negroes, or mulattoes . . . on terms of equality shall be deemed vagrants, and on conviction shall be fined. . . .

No freedman, free negro or mulatto, not in the military service of the United States government, and not licensed so to do by the board of police of his or her county, shall keep or carry fire-arms of any kind, or ammunition, dirk or bowie knife. . . .

Any freedman, free negro, or mulatto committing riots, routs, affrays, trespasses, malicious mischief, cruel treatment to animals, seditious speeches, insulting gestures, language, or acts, or assaults on any person, disturbance of the peace, exercising the function of a minister of the Gospel without a license from some regularly organized church; vending spiritous or intoxicating liquors . . . shall . . . be fined . . . and may be imprisoned. . . .

If any freedman, free negro or mulatto convicted of any of the misdemeanors provided against in this act, shall fail . . . to pay the fine and costs imposed, such person shall be hired out by the sheriff or other officer, at public outcry, to any white person who will pay said fine and all costs, and take said convict for the shortest time.

Excerpts from the Black Code of Louisiana (1865)

Every laborer shall have full and perfect liberty to choose his employer, but when once chosen, he shall not be allowed to leave his place of employment until the fulfillment of his contract . . . and if they do so leave, without cause or permission, they shall forfeit all wages earned to the time of abandonment. . . .

In case of sickness of the laborer, wages for the time lost shall be deducted, and where the sickness is feigned for purposes of idleness, and also on refusal to work according to contract, double the amount of wages shall be deducted for the time lost . . . and should the refusal to work continue beyond three days, the offender . . . shall be forced to labor on roads, levees, and other public works, without pay, until the offender consents to return to his labor.

Failing to obey reasonable orders, neglect of duty, and leaving home without permission shall be deemed disobedience; impudence, swearing, or indecent language or quarreling or fighting with one another, shall be deemed disobedience. For any disobedience a fine of one dollar shall be imposed on and paid by the offender.... For all absence from home without leave, he will be fined at the rate of two dollars per day.

A Newspaper Cutting put in Evidence before the Congressional Committee

TWO MEMBERS OF THE KU-KLUX KLAN IN THEIR DISGUISES.

TOPIC: Leaders of the Reconstructed South—An Informational Scavenger Hunt
TIME: One to two class periods, with homework
TIME PERIOD: During study of the Reconstruction governments established in the southern states

BACKGROUND

Between the establishment of Radical Reconstruction in 1867 and the imposition of the Jim Crow system toward the end of the century, black southerners experienced a generation of political participation and representation in government. African Americans in several southern states were elected to Congress, state and local offices, and judgeships. In this teaching strategy students will follow a game format to research and compile biographical data on some of these black political leaders. Through this activity, students will gain insights into the varied backgrounds of these figures—some were former slaves, some free persons of color who had been educated in the North or in Europe, and others were northern blacks who saw opportunities for success in the South. Students will conclude from their research that these people hardly fit the stereotype that has often presented these Reconstruction leaders as ignorant and incompetent opportunists. From compiling and comparing information on these individuals and their careers, students will learn something of the situation of free blacks in the period before the Civil War and of the process by which black southerners were once again disenfranchised after Reconstruction.

MATERIALS

One copy of the list "Leaders of the Reconstructed South" for each group

SUGGESTED PROCEDURE

1. Organize the class into groups of four. Tell the class that they are going to participate in an informational scavenger hunt. Each group will constitute a team. They will be given a list of names of people who became prominent in the politics of the South during the Reconstruction period, and they will find information about the life and political career of each person. Each team will decide among its members how they will go about finding the information and writing about it. Decide on some reward or recognition for the winning team. Conduct the activity in either of two ways, as time and situation permit:
   a. Allow students one class period to find the information, using classroom references and the school library. The team that has recorded data on the most names by the end of that time is the winner.
   b. Allow the class several days to find the information, giving them time to access public-library material and other resources. The team that submits the most complete information by the end of the allotted time is the winner.
2. Distribute copies of the list to each group. Ask if students can identify any of the people on the list. Some names may be familiar to them. Tell the class that all the people on the list were African Americans who were elected to political office in the South during Reconstruction. Ask the class to speculate on the backgrounds of these people: how they might have become qualified for government service, considering that most southern blacks had been slaves and even northern blacks were forced into subservience and social inferiority.
3. Ask for suggestions from the class as to where they will find information on the people on the list. Give them additional ideas concerning where to look. Depending on the availability of resources, suggest encyclopedias, biographical dictionaries, books on black American history, general United States history books, and so on.
4. Allow students time to complete the scavenger hunt. To close the activity after all groups have completed their scavenger hunts, ask the following questions for discussion:
   a. Were the black leaders during Reconstruction representative of all parts of the South, or did more of them tend to come from some states than from others? What might account for this finding?
   b. Can you make a generalization about when and why the political careers of these leaders ended?

Answers to "Leaders of the Reconstructed South" (Pages 261–262)

Bruce, Blanche Kelso: (1841–1848) Born in Virginia; originally a slave, he became a planter and politician in Mississippi; U.S. senator (1875–1881); U.S. register of treasury (1881–89, 1895–98); recorder of deeds for District of Columbia (1889–95)

Cain, Richard Harvey: (1825–1887) Born in Virginia; ordained as minister in the African Methodist Episcopal Church in 1862; member of the U.S. House of Representatives (1873–75, 1877–79); bishop of Louisiana and Texas diocese (1880)

Dunn, Oscar James: (1826–1871) Born in New Orleans; worked with the Freedman's Bureau at the close of the Civil War; served as Louisiana's lieutenant governor, the highest elective office held by an African American to that time; attended the Louisiana Constitutional Convention (1867–1868)

Elliott, Robert Brown: (1842–1884) Speaker of the House in South Carolina (1874); educated at Eton; could read French, German, Spanish, and Latin; served in 42nd and 43rd U.S. Congresses but resigned in 1871

Lynch, John Roy: (1847–1939) Born in Louisiana; a former slave who became a lawyer, politician, and army officer; represented Mississippi in U.S. House of Representatives (1873–1877, 1882–1883); first African American to preside over a national convention of the Republican party (1884); author of *The Facts of Reconstruction*

Menard, John Willis: (1838–1893) Born in Illinois; clerk in U.S. Department of the Interior (1861–65); first African American elected to fill an unexpired term in the House of Representatives (1868); denied seat in challenge; active in Republican party of New Orleans and later of Florida Republican party

Pinchback, Pinckney Benton Stewart: (1837–1921) Born in Georgia; son of a white planter and an African American slave; raised a volunteer African American company for service with the Union army in the Civil War; lieutenant governor of Louisiana (1871); acting governor of Louisiana (1872–1873); elected to U.S. House of Representatives (1872) but not seated; elected to U.S. Senate (1873), again not seated

Rainey, Joseph Hayne: (1832–1887) Born in South Carolina; barber by trade; first African American to serve in the U.S. House of Representatives (1870–1879); defender of civil rights; special agent for the Treasury Department for South Carolina (1879–1881)

Revels, Hiram Rhoades: (1822–1901) Born in North Carolina; clergyman, educator, and politician; first African American elected to the U.S. Senate (1870–1871); president of Alcorn College in Mississippi (1871–1874, 1876–1883)

Smalls, Robert: (1839–1915) Born a slave in South Carolina; American naval hero (see Strategy 10); highest ranking African American officer in Union navy; member of U.S. House of Representatives (1875–79, 1881–87); civil rights advocate; port collector of Beaufort (1889–93, 1897–1913)

Leaders of the Reconstructed South

Bruce, Blanche Kelso

    Birth date _____ Death date _____ State(s) _____

    Political office(s) and years held: _____

    _____

    Facts about life and career: _____

    _____

    _____

Cain, Richard Harvey

    Birth date _____ Death date _____ State(s) _____

    Political office(s) and years held: _____

    _____

    Facts about life and career: _____

    _____

    _____

Dunn, Oscar James

    Birth date _____ Death date _____ State(s) _____

    Political office(s) and years held: _____

    _____

    Facts about life and career: _____

    _____

    _____

Elliott, Robert Brown

    Birth date _____ Death date _____ State(s) _____

    Political office(s) and years held: _____

    _____

    Facts about life and career: _____

    _____

    _____

Lynch, John Roy

    Birth date _____ Death date _____ State(s) _____

    Political office(s) and years held: _____

    _____

    Facts about life and career: _____

    _____

    _____

Menard, John Willis

    Birth date _____ Death date _____ State(s) _____

    Political office(s) and years held: _____

    _____

    Facts about life and career: _____

    _____

    _____

Pinchback, Pinckney Benton Stewart

    Birth date _____ Death date _____ State(s) _____

    Political office(s) and years held: _____

    _____

    Facts about life and career: _____

    _____

    _____

Rainey, Joseph Hayne

    Birth date _____ Death date _____ State(s) _____

    Political office(s) and years held: _____

    _____

    Facts about life and career: _____

    _____

    _____

Revels, Hiram Rhoades

    Birth date _____ Death date _____ State(s) _____

    Political office(s) and years held: _____

    _____

    Facts about life and career: _____

    _____

    _____

Smalls, Robert

    Birth date _____ Death date _____ State(s) _____

    Political office(s) and years held: _____

    _____

    Facts about life and career: _____

    _____

    _____

TOPIC: Andrew Johnson Versus the Radicals
TIME: Two class periods
TIME PERIOD: After students have read about the impeachment of Andrew Johnson

BACKGROUND

Was the defeated South to be restored to the Union "with malice toward none," or was it to be treated as a conquered enemy? Was control of the South to be returned to the same men who had been responsible for secession, or was a new social order to be established? Were African Americans to be second-class citizens, or was the United States government prepared to enforce true equality under the law? These questions were at the heart of the political struggle between President Andrew Johnson and the Radical Republicans in the years following the Civil War. But there was a fundamental constitutional question at issue as well: could a president of the United States be removed from office merely for political reasons?

In this teaching strategy students will examine the issues involved in the impeachment and trial of Andrew Johnson. They will recognize the debate over Reconstruction as an extention of the old question of whether the war was fought to preserve the Union or to free the slaves. As they continue their study of history, students will recognize how the outcome of the Reconstruction debate affected the history of the South well into the next century. They also will recognize how the Senate's failure to convict Johnson helped to establish the precedent that a president cannot be removed from office simply because of political differences with Congress.

SUGGESTED PROCEDURE

1. Review with the class the facts of the three-year period between the assassination of Lincoln and the impeachment of Johnson.
   a. Review the major points at issue in the United States over restoration of the South in the years 1865–1868: the conditions under which the former Confederate states would be readmitted to the Union, the status of the freed slaves, and the broader question of who would hold power in the postwar South.
   b. Review the sequence of the major events related to those issues: Johnson's granting of amnesty to most former Confederates, Thaddeus Stevens' plan for the redistribution of land; the Freedman's Bureau and Civil Rights Acts of 1866 and the various Reconstruction acts, all passed by Congress over presidential veto; Johnson's defiance of the Tenure of Office Act.
2. Discuss with the class the issues relating to Johnson's impeachment. Ask students the following questions:
   a. Should Johnson have been impeached? (Remind students that the grounds the Constitution specifies for impeachment of a president are "Treason, bribery, or other high crimes and misdemeanors.") Discuss whether Johnson had committed an impeachable offense under the Constitution. Guide students toward the recognition that Congress's dispute with Johnson was political: the Radicals had one plan for dealing with the defeated South, and Johnson had another.
   b. What was Johnson's plan for Reconstruction of the South? Ask what population group he came from and what his attitude had been toward the leaders of the South during the war. (He was a "poor white" from Tennessee who hated the planter aristocracy and their great wealth and who wished to punish them. You might tell students that while he was vice president, Johnson told a Washington crowd that he would hang Jeff Davis and all the "diabolical" leaders of the Confederacy if he got the chance.)
   c. What was Johnson's attitude toward African Americans? (He opposed slavery, but only because it put poor whites at a disadvantage; he did not favor political or social equality for blacks.)
   d. Were Johnson's policies as president consistent with these positions? (He continued to favor white supremacy, but he was ready to pardon most of the Confederate leaders and restore them to power in the southern states.) Why might Johnson have had such a change in attitude?
   e. Who were the leaders of Congress and what had their attitude been toward the South before the war? (Men like Thaddeus Stevens and Charles Sumner had been part of the abolitionist movement.) What was the Radicals' plan for Reconstruction of the South? (To punish the leaders of the Confederacy; to enforce political and social equality for blacks.) Read this quotation from Thaddeus Stevens as an example of his attitude toward the defeated South:

*I have never desired bloody punishments to any great extent, but there are
punishments quite as appalling and longer remembered than death. They are
more advisable, because they would reach a greater number. Strip a proud
nobility of their bloated estates; reduce them to a level with [ordinary people];
send them forth to labor and teach their children to enter the workshops or handle
a plow, and you will thus humble the proud traitors.*

    f. Why did the Radicals have such a large majority in Congress? (Discuss the extent to which their majority reflected the balance of opinion in the country in 1868. Point out that with the exception of Tennessee, none of the former Confederate states were represented in Congress. The war was only recently over, and many northerners were in a mood for revenge. The Radicals' majority may well have reflected public opinion in the North.)

    g. Which approach to Reconstruction would Lincoln have taken had he lived? (Based on his record and his speeches, Lincoln would have followed a moderate approach.) Read this excerpt from Lincoln's second inaugural address:

*With malice toward none; with charity for all; with firmness in the right, as God
gives us to see the right, let us strive on to finish the work we are in; to bind up the
nation's wounds to do all which may achieve and cherish a just and lasting peace.*

    h. Discuss Johnson's defiance of Congress over the Tenure of Office Act. (This law, passed over Johnson's veto, prohibited the president from removing appointed officials without the consent of Congress. Johnson tried to remove Secretary of War Edwin M. Stanton, a member of the Administration who supported the Radicals.)

3. Tell the class that they are going to assume the roles of members of Congress to decide whether President Johnson should be removed from office. "Radicals" will argue in support of their program of Reconstruction and attempt to prove that Johnson should be removed. "Moderates" will argue in support of their program of Reconstruction and attempt to prove that Johnson has done nothing to constitutionally justify his removal.

4. Organize the class into groups of four. Assign two groups of every three to represent "Radicals" and one group in three to be "Moderates." (This ratio approximates the actual balance of the two sides in Congress.) Allow the class the rest of the period to discuss the debate with their groups. They should work together to familiarize themselves with the issues of the debate. Remind students to be sure to anticipate what the other side will argue and to have their own arguments ready to refute them.

5. Hold the debate during the next class period. Allow students five minutes to meet with their groups and review the issues. Assign one of the "Radical" students to be the chairperson and to recognize other students to speak. Do not attempt to direct this activity under formal debate procedure. Instead, have the chairperson call upon other students in turn to speak. Allow the debate to proceed for about 20 to 30 minutes. Have the chairperson take a vote by a show of hands on the question of whether Johnson should be removed from office. Remind the class that they are not obligated to vote according to their assigned roles but should vote for the side that presented the more persuasive argument.

6. As an evaluation of the activity, have students write informal papers answering the following questions:
    a. If you had been a voter in 1868, would you have favored the Radicals' plan for Reconstruction, the Moderates' plan, or a different plan altogether? Give reasons for your answer.
    b. If you had been a senator at President Johnson's impeachment trial, would you or would you not have voted to remove him from office? Give reasons for your answer.

7. Allow students the rest of the class period to write their papers. Have them complete the assignment as homework, if necessary.

Creative Strategies for Teaching American History

The Transforming Nation
1877–1914

TOPIC: Causes of Immigration, 1820–1930
TIME: One class period
TIME PERIOD: During study of immigration and the growth of cities during the late
1800s and early 1900s

BACKGROUND

As part of the American history curriculum, students will be learning about the enormous influx of people who immigrated to the United States between 1820 and 1930. During the period of 1820 through 1860 the majority of the immigrants came from northern and western Europe. After 1860 more and more people from southern and eastern Europe immigrated to the United States.

This teaching strategy will provide students with an opportunity to discover the reasons that these waves of immigrants sought refuge in the United States. Students will use a chronological lists of events and a table of immigration statistics to uncover the underlying causes of immigration between 1820 and 1930. Students will also learn about the reactions of people in the United States to the influx of immigrants.

MATERIALS

1. Copies of "Immigration and World Events" and "Immigration and United States History" chronological lists
2. Copies of the table "Immigrants to the U.S. by Region of Origin, 1820–1930"
3. Copies of the "Immigration to the United States" question sheet

SUGGESTED PROCEDURE

1. Explain to students that they will be studying two chronological lists of events and a table of immigration statistics in order to discover why people from various parts of the world came to the United States during the mid- to late-1800s and early 1900s. Organize the class into groups of four or five. Distribute to each student the chronological lists and table. Give one task sheet to each group and assign one student to be the recorder.
2. Lead students into the activity by asking them to study the table. Use a wall map to locate countries in each of the seven regions listed on the table and graphs. Ask students during which time period they first see a considerable increase in immigration from Mexico and South America. Then direct their attention to the "World Events" chronological list. Ask students to determine what happened in the world during that time period that would help to explain the rise in immigration from Mexico and South America. Briefly discuss why people might want to leave a country during or after a revolution.
3. Instruct the groups to complete the group task sheet. Circulate among groups to make sure that all students are participating and that students are on the right track. When the groups have completed the task sheet, discuss the answers as a class. Ask students the following questions:
   a. Which events found on the chronological lists were factors in the immigration of your own ancestors to the United States?
   b. What events occurring around the world today are influencing people to leave their homelands?

Immigrants to the United States by Region of Origin, 1820–1930

REGION	1820–1869		1861–1900		1901–1930	
	Number	Percent	Number	Percent	Number	Percent
Northern, Central, and Western Europe	4,616,000	94.67	9,524,000	67.90	4,208,000	22.65
Southern and Eastern Europe	36,000	.74	3,108,000	22.16	10,751,000	57.89
Canada, Newfoundland, and West Indies	157,000	3.22	1,019,000	7.27	2,152,000	11.59
Mexico, Central, and South America	25,000	.51	17,000	.12	870,000	4.68
Asia	42,000	.86	336,000	2.40	536,000	2.89
Africa	—	—	2,000	.01	22,000	.12
Australia and New Zealand	—	—	20,000	.14	33,000	.18
TOTALS	4,876,000	100.00	14,026,000	100.00	18,572,000	100.00

Source: *Historical Statistics of the United States*, U.S. Department of the Census, 1975

Immigration and World Events

1845–49	Potato famine in Ireland
1846	Crop failures in Germany and Holland
1848	German revolution is put down; Germany experiences severe depression and unemployment
1854	End of Japanese isolation; Japan opens several ports over next few years
1860–90	Crop failures in Germany and Holland
1870s	Introduction of steamship decreases cost, time, and danger of ocean travel
1880–1914	Religious persecution of Jews in eastern Europe
1894–95	Japan and China fight a war; Japan defeats China
1900–20	Overpopulation on southern and eastern European farms
1904–5	Japan and Russia fight a war; Japan defeats Russia
1905–6	Economic problems, expanding population, and epidemics in Italy
1910–20	Revolution in Mexico
1914–18	World War I
1917	Russian Revolution

Immigration and United States History

1848	Gold is discovered in California
1850	Order of Star Spangled Banner is founded; eventually becomes the Know-Nothing party, formed to control immigration
1860s	Chinese immigration to work on railroads and in gold mines
1861–65	Civil War
1862	Homestead Act offers free land to citizens and to immigrants who intend to become citizens
1865	Construction begins on transcontinental railroad
1877	Workingman's party opposes immigration of Chinese laborers
1882	Chinese Exclusion Act keeps Chinese from entering the U.S.
1907	"Gentlemen's agreement" between U.S. and Japan denies passports to laborers from Japan
1917	Immigration Act says immigrants must read English; excludes anarchists and those with certain diseases; excludes most Asians and Pacific Islanders
1919–20	"Red Scare" promotes the idea that communists are plotting to overthrow the U.S. government
1920–25	Ku Klux Klan resurfaces as an anti-foreign, anti-Semitic, anti-Catholic force
1921	Emergency Quota Act reduces number of immigrants from eastern and southern Europe allowed to enter the U.S.
1924	Immigration Act creates a permanent quota system called the national-origins system; designed to prevent any major change in the racial and ethnic makeup of the U.S. population

Immigration to the United States

Directions: Use the lists and table to complete the items below.

1. In the appropriate column below, list those events that led either to an increase or a decrease in immigration.

Increased Immigration	Decreased Immigration

2. Use the information on the chart above to write a general statement identifying those types of events that cause people to leave their homelands.

_____

_____

3. Between 1861 and 1900 the greatest number of immigrants came from northern and western Europe. From where did most immigrants come between 1900 and 1930?

_____

_____

4. The shift of immigration mentioned in Question 3 actually began during the 1880s. What event or events caused this migration?

_____

_____

5. What are some possible explanations for the increase in Asian immigration between 1820 and 1930?

_____

_____

6. What factors caused immigration to reach its highest point in the United States in the early 1900s?

_____

_____

7. What steps did the government take to respond to a demand by many Americans to control or stop immigrants from entering the country?

_____

_____

TOPIC: Transcontinental Railroad Newspaper
TIME: Five class periods
TIME PERIOD: During study of the expansion of railroads to the west and the building of the transcontinental railroad

BACKGROUND

In this teaching strategy groups of students will use their historical imaginations and research skills to create a page for a newspaper that might have appeared during the building of the transcontinental railroad. You will assign a newspaper section to each group. All newspaper items must pertain to a group's section. (For example, one group's newspaper page will be about travel on the transcontinental railroad.) Arrange with the librarian to have your class spend time in the library or bring in a large supply of books for students to use for their research.

MATERIALS

1. One copy of the appropriate section sheet for each person in the group to which the section has been assigned. Separate the sections after you copy them.
   a. Railroad Workers and Daily Life (Life Style)
   b. Financing the Railroad (Business)
   c. Laborers on the Transcontinental Railroad (Labor)
   d. The Transcontinental Railroad and the Settlement of the Plains (Settlement)
   e. Construction of the Transcontinental Railroad (Construction)
   f. Travel on the Transcontinental Railroad (Travel)
2. One copy of the "Group Task Sheet" for each student
3. One copy of the "Responsibility Sheet" for each group
4. Six copies of the "Newspaper Page Evaluations" for each group (36, if you have six groups)
5. Books with information about the transcontinental railroads, settlement of the plains, Chinese immigration, travel by train, and so on
6. Supplies
   a. Glue or paste
   b. Paper the size of a newspaper page
   c. Paper cut into strips for newspaper columns
   d. Black fine-line, felt-tip markers and black pens
   e. Envelopes or folders for the groups' news items
7. Before you begin the activity, prepare a packet for each group. Include enough "Group Task Sheets" and topic sheets for each person in each group and one "Responsibility Sheet" per group.

SUGGESTED PROCEDURE

1. Show students a daily newspaper. Point out the parts of the newspaper (masthead, headline, byline, dateline, and so on). Show students the various newspaper sections. Tell students that they will be working in groups to create a newspaper page that might have been published after the building of the transcontinental railroad.
2. Organize the class into six groups. Distribute the packets to each group. Describe the newspaper activity, focusing on each of the sections and how they should contain important information about the building and the effects of the transcontinental railroad. Students may come up with their own topics for a section, but you should approve all topic ideas. Have students follow along on the "Group Task Sheet" as you explain the activity.
3. Have the groups select their copy editors, supply sargeants and layout artists. If groups have more than four students each, two students may perform one job. Each student should be assigned a job. Group members should then decide which topics they will each take and what type of items they will create. Have them complete the "Responsibility Sheets." (If any changes are made in responsibilities after the

sheets have been handed in, make sure you approve the changes.) Remind the groups that their pages are to have a variety of items but that each person must do at least one straight news story. Collect the sheets and check for duplication and variety.

4. Allow students all of the next class period to research and take notes for their newspaper pages. On the third day of the activity students should write their news items. If they do not complete their three items, they should complete them as homework.

5. On the fourth day of the activity, students should have their three news items checked by the copy editor(s) and make any necessary revisions. The layout artists should begin the process of putting the news item on the strips of paper. Tell them to be sure they make an attractive section title to be placed at the top of the page. The layout artists should then place items for the best fit. Once all items are in place, they should begin to paste them on the page. Meanwhile others in the group should be finishing any leftover work and helping to create items to fill in any empty places. Students' newspaper pages should be completed by the end of this class period.

6. On the fifth day of the activity distribute the "Newspaper Page Evaluation Sheets" (six sheets per group, one for each groups' newspaper page). Instruct the groups to pass their newspaper page clockwise to the nearest group (or use instructions that suit your classroom arrangement). Allow five minutes for the groups to evaluate the page of the paper that they have received. One person from each group should fill in the evaluation sheet, but all students should comment, and students should try and agree on a number rating for each part of the evaluation. For the next round have the group pass the newspaper page they have just evaluated clockwise to the next group, take a fresh copy of the "Newspaper Page Evaluation," and complete it for the newspaper page they receive. Continue until all pages have been evaluated by all groups. You can reduce the time after the first or second page. At the end of the period collect all evaluation sheets from each group.

7. Return to the respective groups their own newspaper pages with your comments. Ask them how they might have done things differently. You may wish to have them complete a self-evaluation of their own work on the paper.

Railroad Workers and Daily Life

TOPICS

1. Buffalo hunts provide entertainment for adventuresome workers.

2. The Chinese laborers bring in their own cooks.

3. A daily bath is routine for the Chinese laborers.

4. Bunkcars are used as mobile hotels for railroad construction crews.

5. Construction workers complain about service at mealtime.

6. Chinese workers travel to America after signing labor agreements in China.

7. Hoodlums attack the newly arrived Chinese railroad workers in San Francisco.

8. The Chinese crews' camps are different from the camps of the Irish crews.

9. Mormon railroad construction workers prove to have a way of life all their own.

10. Fashion on the railroad: what laborers wear for work and play.

11. Up-and-at-'em: the typical daily schedule of a railroad worker.

12. American Indians not always happy with railroad crews.

13. Telegraph message, three dots, sends news east that the lines have met.

Section: Construction

Construction of the Transcontinental Railroad

TOPICS

1. Crews blast their way through the mountains.

2. Crews forge their way through the snows of 1866–67.

3. Trusses are used to span the canyons.

4. Theodore Judah and Grenville Dodge map the route of the first transcontinental railroad.

5. Crews build trestles to span rivers for the transcontinental railroad.

6. Ties made of wood are laid for the transcontinental railroad to cross the treeless plains.

7. The roadbeds for the transcontinental railroad are graded.

8. The Chinese show great skill in blasting through the mountains by working "Cape Horn," a treacherous ledge.

9. The "rolling factory town" provides for the needs of contruction crews.

10. James Howden manufactures nitroglycerin for blasting at the site of the Summit Tunnel.

11. Telegraph lines are strung along the tracks.

12. The Summit Tunnel is built through Donner Pass.

13. The Central Pacific and Union Pacific crews race to lay the most track.

14. A track-laying record is set by the Central Pacific.

Financing the Transcontinental Railroad

TOPICS

1. Congress passes the Pacific Railway Act in 1862.

2. One hundred million dollars is needed to build the transcontinental railroad.

3. The Credit Mobilier scandal offends the decency of Washington, D.C.

4. The California legislature agrees to pay $10,000 for every mile of track laid within California.

5. "The Great Dutch Flats Swindle" creates distrust of the Central Pacific's "Big Four."

6. Durant makes an offer no one can refuse and raises stock subscriptions of $2,180,000.

7. Collis Huntington lobbies for money for the Central Pacific.

8. Congress enacts second Pacific Railway Act in 1864.

9. The Central Pacific's Contract and Finance Company scandal brings no indictment.

10. Durant throws a one-hundredth meridian celebration in hopes of raising money from private investors.

Section: Labor

Laborers on the Transcontinental Railroad

TOPICS

1. Irish workers make up construction crews for the Union Pacific.

2. Chinese workers prove to be exemplary railroad laborers for the Central Pacific.

3. Civil War veterans join the railroad labor force.

4. Charlie Crocker is the Central Pacific's construction boss.

5. Harvey Strobridge, Central Pacific's chief of staff, is nicknamed the "One Eye Bossy Man" by Chinese laborers.

6. John Stephen Casement is the Union Pacific's construction boss.

7. Crocker and Strobridge dispute the use of Chinese labor.

8. The recruitment of Chinese farm boys from Canton saves the day for the Central Pacific.

9. Negotiators talk to Brigham Young to get his permission to recruit Mormon laborers.

10. The Irish strike the Union Pacific.

11. Durant is kidnapped by unpaid workers and is delayed in reaching Promontory, Utah.

Settlement of the Plains and the Transcontinental Railroad

TOPICS

1. The railroads sell off their land grant acreage to the new settlers.

2. The Mussel Slough Tragedy is a lesson in "Buyer Beware."

3. Railroads use propaganda and false advertising in order to lure western settlers.

4. Railroads establish "bonanza farms" in order to lure settlers.

5. The railroads sell land at $2 an acre with 10 cents down and payments over 6 years.

6. The more settlers the railroads can attract, the more income there will be on railroad freight in the future.

7. The railroads develop the practice of settling immigrants in nationality groups.

8. Castle Gardens is the first stop for immigrants headed west.

9. Immigrant sleeping cars are nicknamed the "Zulu cars."

10. Carl Schmidt and other railroad agents attract Mennonites to western lands.

11. High railroad rates hurt western farmers.

Section: Travel

Travel on the Railroads

TOPICS

1. What was the 84-hour trip from New York to San Francisco like?

2. What does it cost to travel west on the transcontinental railroad?

3. The Eight-Car Pullman Express puts elegance on rails, but only for the wealthy.

4. Frank Leslie's *Illustrated Newspaper* chronicles the ride west.

5. Traveling west in first class is a treat.

6. Dining at railroad stations is not first class.

7. The Boston Board of Trade takes a trip west on the railroad.

8. Sites along the route are advertised in railroad brochures.

9. Robert Lewis Stevenson takes a trip west in "emigrant class."

10. American Indians disrupt trains with derailments.

11. Travel through the snow in the mountains proves to be an adventure.

12. Canada Bill and Three-Card Monte raise the risks of train travel.

13. Sam Bass, notorious train robber, terrorizes passengers.

14. Helen Hunt Jackson travels west on the train.

TRANSCONTINENTAL RAILROAD
GROUP TASK SHEET

1. Your group's task is to prepare one page of a class newspaper. You have been assigned one of the following sections: Life Style, Business, Construction, Settlement, Labor, or Travel. Each group will be completing a different section.

2. Each person in your group will prepare three items for the page. No more than two of these and at least one will be a news story. Other types of items are listed at the end of this task sheet. Regardless of what type of item a person chooses to do, that item should relate to the section your group has been assigned and should also be about a specific topic on your group's topic list. (While researching you may find another topic of interest that fits your section. Be sure to get that topic approved.) Each group should plan to have a variety of items on its page of the newspaper. Your group must work together in deciding on what topic and type of item each person will work.

3. Each group should choose at least one copy editor, a supply sargeant, and two layout artists. Every person in your group should have a job.
   a. The copy editor(s) will check all items for grammar, spelling, capitalization, correct form, and clarity.
   b. The supply sargeant will pick up the group's folder at the beginning of each period, collect the work at the end of the period, place it in the folder, and return the folder to the teacher or to its proper place in the classroom. The supply sargeant will also distribute any necessary supplies (pens, paper) to the group.
   c. The layout artists will take all items written or drawn on the paper strips and lay them out on your newspaper in columns. After fitting items the layout artists will paste the items on the newspaper page.

4. A rough draft of all items should be submitted to the copy editor(s) for checking. After being checked the items should be revised and written on strips of paper for pasting into newspaper columns by the layout editors.

5. All articles should be written as if you were living at the time of the railroad's completion or while it was the most reasonable means of traveling west. The newspaper will be prepared as an "anniversary edition" and look back at the important events in the building of the transcontinental railroad (except for the Travel section, which will use information about travel on the railroad after it was completed).

6. Your news articles can, and in most cases should, use real people and describe real events. In some cases it might be more appropriate to make up characters and events, but make sure you place them in the correct historical setting.

7. A news story should have the following characteristics:
   a. A headline that catches the reader's eye and clearly tells about the story that follows
   b. The 5 Ws lead—the first paragraph (only one or two sentences) that tells who, what, where, when, why and/or how
   c. Inverted pyramid structure—the organization of an article in which the most important information comes first and the least important comes last
   d. Information that does not express the opinion of the writer
   e. A dateline at the beginning of the story that states where the story took place
   f. A byline that gives the name of the journalist who prepared the story

8. Other types of items you may include are:

a. Feature story—much like a news story but does not have to have a 5-Ws lead or inverted pyramid structure. It usually focuses on something that has human interest rather than on "hard news." It may focus on an on-going situation. It must include a headline, dateline, and byline, and it should relate to a topic on your list.

b. Political cartoon or comic strip—focuses on a controversial issue whereas a comic strip tells a story. Both types of illustrations must have a title and/or a caption, an artist's signature, and it should relate to a topic on your list.

c. Editorial article—focuses on a controversial opinion and expresses one person's point of view. It should have a headline and a byline, and it should relate to a topic on your list.

d. Letter to the editor—focuses on a controversial issue. A reader writes a letter to the newspaper to express an opinion. It is about one subject or issue. Appropriate background information should be given in the letter so that a reader can understand the issue. The letter must have a signature, and it should relate to a topic on your list.

e. Advertisements—several small advertisements such as those found in the classified section of the newspaper count as one item. A display advertisement should be eye-catching and make a product seem appealing. It should have some type of illustration of the product. If it is for a mail-order item, the price and address for ordering should be given. A display advertisement counts as one item. All advertisements should give complete information about where to get the product or how to contact the seller. Advertisements should relate to the time period, not necessarily to a topic on your list.

f. Advice column—should contain questions and answers. Letters should relate to the time period, and if possible, to a topic on your list.

g. Obituaries—several obituaries will count as one item. An obituary is an announcemnt of someone's death. It should include the full name of the person, his or her age, the circumstances of the death, the person's importance in the community, and where interested parties can contact the family or attend the funeral. Obituaries should relate to the time period, and if possible, to a topic on your list.

h. Crossword puzzle—must relate to the transcontinental railroad and the section of the paper on which you are working.

TRANSCONTINENTAL RAILROAD
RESPONSIBILITY SHEET

Directions: Each member of your group must commit to complete three items for your group's section of the class newspaper. Hand in this sheet during the second class period of this activity.

Newspaper section: _____

Name	Item	Topic
_____	_____	_____
	_____	_____
	_____	_____
_____	_____	_____
	_____	_____
	_____	_____
_____	_____	_____
	_____	_____
	_____	_____
_____	_____	_____
	_____	_____
	_____	_____
_____	_____	_____
	_____	_____
	_____	_____
_____	_____	_____
	_____	_____
	_____	_____

NEWSPAPER PAGE EVALUATION

Page or Section Title: _____

Evaluating Group's Section: _____

Directions: Circle the number that most closely describes your group's reactions to each of the following statements concerning this page of the newspaper.

5 = Strongly agree

4 = Agree

3 = Slightly agree

2 = Slightly disagree

1 = Strongly disagree

STYLE

1. Headlines for articles stand out and are clear, readable, and to the point.

    5   4   3   2   1

2. News articles are written in appropriate newspaper style (who, what, where, when, why, or how in the lead with the most important information first).

    5   4   3   2   1

3. Advertisements and cartoons are completed as described on the "Group Task Sheet."

    5   4   3   2   1

4. Page is written as if it really appeared in the historical time period.

    5   4   3   2   1

HISTORIC AUTHENTICITY

5. Articles, advertisements, cartoons, and columns relate to actual historic events and situtions.

    5   4   3   2   1

6. The articles, advertisements, cartoons, and columns are interesting and informative.

    5   4   3   2   1

CREATIVITY

7. Original drawings are used where appropriate.

    5   4   3   2   1

8. There are a variety of things to read and see on the page.

    5   4   3   2   1

9. News stories and columns show imagination but are still realistic and believable.

    5   4   3   2   1

10. Drawings, lettering, printing, and placement of all items appeal to the eye.

    5   4   3   2   1

TOPIC: Chief Joseph—Writing a Biopoem
TIME: One class period
TIME PERIOD: During study of the removal of American Indians to reservations in the late 1800s

BACKGROUND

The search for gold in the mid-1800s drew miners to Indian lands in the mountains where the present states of Oregon, Washington, and Idaho meet. The whites called the Native Americans of this region the Nez Perce, or "pierced nose," because they wore nose ornaments made of shell. They were a peace-loving people. They claimed that no member of their tribe had ever killed a white. When Lewis and Clark traveled through Nez Perce lands on their expedition to the Pacific Coast, the explorers were treated as honored guests.

The Nez Perce chief was a man the whites called Joseph. His real name was Hinmaton–Yalaktit, which means "Thunder coming out of the water and over the land." Like Tecumseh, the great Shawnee leader, Joseph believed that Indians had no right to sell the land on which they lived.

In 1877 the government demanded that Joseph make way for the white miners and settlers and move his band from the Wallowa Valley in Oregon to the Lapwai Reservation in Idaho. Joseph had only 55 men of fighting age. He decided to yield, and he selected land on the reservation in May 1877. The government gave Joseph only one month in which to move his people and their possessions to the reservation.

While on the march to Idaho, a few angry Nez Perce killed some white settlers. Troops were sent to capture them. Chief Joseph decided that he must escape with his people to Canada instead of to Idaho. For months the band slipped away from thousands of pursuing troops in the rugged country along the border between Oregon and Montana. In September 1877 the Indians reached the Bear Paw Mountains, only 30 miles (48 kilometers) from Canada.

Joseph thought the mountains would make them safe at last. He stopped to rest, for many of his people were starving and the children were dying. Suddenly army cavalry units attacked the tribe. Joseph and his warriors held out for four days but finally surrendered after recognizing the futility of the fight.

Joseph's surrender speech is one of the most famous and admired of all such speeches. The Nez Perce were settled on a barren reservation in Oklahoma. Far from the mountains of Oregon, this land was "the malarial bottom of the Indian Territory." Joseph, however, was sent to a reservation in Washington state. There he lived in exile, separated from his people and removed from the land he loved. When Joseph died in 1904, the official cause of death was listed as a broken heart. In this teaching strategy students will use primary source material to write a "biopoem" (biographical poem) that reflects the character, emotions, and events in the life of Chief Joseph.

MATERIALS

1. Copies of the source sheet "I Will Fight No More Forever"
2. Copies of biopoem worksheet
3. Transparency or copies of model biopoem "Sitting Bull"

SUGGESTED PROCEDURE

1. Provide students with background information on Chief Joseph and the Nez Perce Indians. Tell students that they will be reading some material that will reflect many of the emotions Chief Joseph felt upon losing the land of his people in the Wallowa Valley and about the decision he made at his surrender to the United States Army in the Bear Paw Mountains. They will also read a statement made by Joseph's doctor upon Joseph's death that details the circumstances of that death. Distribute the source sheet. Allow students time to read and absorb the information.
2. Distribute the biopoem worksheet. Explain that the purpose of writing the poem is to portray Joseph's character as well as his beliefs and emotions. Tell students that they will follow the format on the worksheet to write their poems.

3. Display the transparency or distribute copies of the model biopoem "Sitting Bull." Use the worksheet to go through the model biopoem line by line. Remind students about rules for capitalization and organization of lines in a poem. Explain that the "things" required can be expressed in single words or in phrases but that within a line it is best not to mix the two. Encourage students to think about how their biopoem will sound when read aloud.

4. Instruct students to complete the worksheet. Circulate among students, making sure that they understand the procedure. When students are satisfied with their biopoems, have them copy the poems onto clean paper. Students may illustrate their poems if they wish. Ask volunteers to read their poems aloud to the rest of the class. Some students may wish to post their poems on the bulletin board.

I Will Fight No More Forever

Selections excerpted

Expelled from their home and given only 30 days to move from the Wallowa Valley to the Lapwai Reservation in Idaho, Chief Joseph and his people faced the sad news that a small band of their warriors with hot tempers and hearts full of revenge had killed some white soldiers and settlers. In fear of the white man's punishment and knowing he had to protect his people, Chief Joseph decided his people should flee into Canada. Avoiding General Howard and his troops until they were near collapse from hunger and the cold, Joseph and his people reached the Bear Paw Mountains, about 30 miles from the Canadian border. There Howard had them trapped. After four days of fighting Chief Looking Glass was killed. On the fifth day Chief Joseph made this speech of surrender, the most quoted of all Indian speeches:

> Tell General Howard I know his heart. What he told me before, I have it in my heart. I am tired of fighting. Our chiefs are killed. Looking Glass is dead. Too-hool-hool-zote is dead. The old men are all dead. It is the young men who say, "Yes" or "No." He who led the young men is dead. It is cold, and we have no blankets. The little children are freezing to death. I want to have time to look for my children, and see how many of them I can find. Maybe I shall find them among the dead. Hear me, my chiefs! I am tired. My heart is sick and sad. From where the sun now stands I will fight no more forever.

Before surrendering Joseph had been assured by Colonel Nelson A. Miles that Joseph and his people would be allowed to return to their home in the northwest. The government did not stand behind the promise. From his place of exile on the Coleville Reservation in Washington, Joseph continued to plead for a place for his people in the beloved Wallowa Valley. In April of 1879 Joseph published his argument in "An Indian's View of Indian Affairs" in *The North American Review*.

> [On his deathbed my father said:] "My son, never forget my dying words. This country holds your father's body. Never sell the bones of your father and mother." I pressed my father's hand and told him that I would protect his grave with my life. My father smiled and passed away to the spiritland.
>
> I buried him in that beautiful valley of winding waters. I love that land more than all the rest of the world. A man who would not love his father's grave is worse than a wild animal. . . .
>
> I cannot understand how the Government sends a man out to fight us, as it did General Miles, and then breaks his word. Such a government has something wrong about it. . . . It makes my heart sick when I remember all the good words and all the broken promises. There has been too much talking by men who had no right to talk. Too many misrepresentations have been made, too many misunderstandings have come up between the white men about the Indians. If the white man wants to live in peace with the Indian he can live in peace. There need be no trouble. Treat all men alike. All men were made by the Great Spirit Chief. They are all brothers. The earth is the mother of all people, and all people should have equal rights upon it. You might as well expect the rivers to run backward as that any man who was born a free man should be contented penned up and denied liberty to go where he pleases. If you tie a horse to a stake, do you expect he will grow fat? If you pen an Indian on a small spot of earth, and

compel him to stay there, he will not be contented nor will he grow and prosper. . . .

Whenever the white man treats the Indian as they treat each other, then we shall have no more wars. We shall be all alike—brothers of one father and one mother, with one sky above us and one country around us, and one government for all. Then the Great Spirit Chief who rules above will smile upon this land, and send rain to wash out the bloody spots made by brothers' hands upon the face of the earth. For this time the Indian race are waiting and praying. I hope that no more groans of wounded men and women will ever go to the ear of the Great Spirit Chief above, and that all people may be one people. . . .

Chief Joseph died on September 21, 1904. Dr. Latham, the doctor for the Indians at Nespelem where Joseph lived on the Coleville Reservation, was quoted in the newspaper:

Chief Joseph's End Due to His Grief
Broken Heart Said to Have Caused Death
Thwarted Desire for Power and Longing for His Old Home at Wallowa
Believed by His Physician to Have Broken His Spirit

WILBUR, Sept. 26.--(Special.)—"Chief Joseph died of a broken heart, following the conviction that in his old age he was unable to accomplish the desire for power that had been nourished throughout his lifetime," said Dr. E.G. Latham, physician for the Indians at Nespelem, who for fourteen years was the medical advisor of Chief Joseph. Continuing, Dr. Latham said:

"Four years ago Joseph was attacked by a strange illness. I examined, studied him, and decided that grief was all that ailed him. In vain I tried to console him. His low spirits was followed by a real illness from pneumonia, but the magnificent physique of the man brought him through.

"From that time Joseph was never the same man. He brooded constantly over the fact that Wallowa, the country of his youth and of his dreams, was going farther and farther from him, and that the region about his new home at Nespelem was year by year growing smaller and smaller through the encroachment of the prospector and the settler. In recent months this grief has resulted in a bent form, in a listless life, which ended in death.". . .

Biopoem Worksheet

Line 1: First name _____

Line 2: Four traits that describe the character _____

_____

Line 3: Position or job _____

Line 4: Longing for (list three things) _____

_____

Line 5: Who feels (list three things) _____

_____

Line 6: Who needs (list three things) _____

_____

Line 7: Who fears (list three things) _____

_____

Line 8: Who gives (list three things) _____

_____

Line 9: Who would like to see (list three things) _____

_____

Line 10: Resident of _____

Line 11: Indian name _____ Hinmaton–Yalaktit _____

Alternate for last line: Kopet ("That is all" in Joseph's language)

Model Biopoem

Sitting Bull

Sitting Bull
Powerful, wise, stubborn, and courageous.
Medicine man and Hunkpapa Sioux leader.
Longing for justice, freedom, and peace for his people.
Who feels hatred, hostility, and distrust toward whites.
Who needs many warriors, good ponies, and victory over Long Hair, Three
*   Star Crook, and the Great White Father.*
Who fears no victory is in sight, no end to the wars, and no return of the
*   buffalo.*
Who gives sacrifices to the Wakantanka, cures to the sick, and counsel to the
*   chiefs.*
Who would like to see the defeat of the Cavalry, reservations disappear, and
*   the Sioux free to return to their traditional hunting grounds.*
Resident of the buffalo country.
Tatanka Iyotake.

TOPIC: John D. Rockefeller—Business Practices in the Gilded Age
TIME: One-half class period
TIME PERIOD: During study of the muckrakers, the antitrust movement, and antitrust legislation, such as the Interstate Commerce Act of 1887 and the Sherman Antitrust Act of 1890

BACKGROUND

John D. Rockefeller, both a revered and hated figure in his own time, remains a center of historical controversy today. In 1870 Rockefeller formed Standard Oil of Ohio, which consolidated the oil industry by forcing railroads to give it rebates and to raise rates for rival refiners. Rockefeller was then able to cut prices, forcing competitors out of business. In the 1873 depression Rockefeller bought bankrupt companies, and throughout the 1870s, extended his reach into all areas of the oil industry until he owned ships, docks, barrel companies, and even the pipelines that carried oil. The result was an absolute monopoly, in which Standard Oil controlled all steps of the production of oil, from refining to delivery. In 1876 Rockefeller said, "The oil industry belongs to us."

The muckraker Ida Tarbell, journalist Henry Demarest Lloyd, and later historians such as Matthew Josephson and Chester M. Destler deplored Rockefeller's business practices, but other commentators, such as the historian Allan Nevins, took a more balanced view. Rockefeller's detractors argued that monopoly destroyed competition—the basis of our market economy. They emphasized human values, pointing to the competitors forced into bankruptcy and ruin. Rockefeller, they said, may have been a philanthropist, but he also exemplified greed and threatened the nation's political and social institutions because of the power given to him by his wealth.

Allan Nevins, a twentieth-century spokesperson for the opposing point of view, portrayed Rockefeller as neither villain nor hero. Business combinations, said Nevins, were essential to transform the fragmented and chaotic business markets of the 1860s and 1870s. Although commenting that no American should ever again become as wealthy as Rockefeller, Nevins wrote,

> The prime significance of Rockefeller's career lies in the fact that he was a bold innovator in both industry and philanthropy; that he brought to the first a great unifying idea, which he insisted should be thoroughly tested, and to the second a stronger, more expert, and more enduring type of organization.

This teaching strategy gives students an opportunity to examine controversies among historians, which will lead to the understanding that the historical record is open to debate, revision, and conflicting interpretations. It also asks students to examine governmental policies in the light of national economic goals.

MATERIALS

Copies of the handout "Rockefeller: Captain of Industry or Robber Baron?"

SUGGESTED PROCEDURE

1. Give each student a copy of the handout. Discuss with the class the titles "Captain of Industry" and "Robber Baron," making sure students understand the meaning of *baron*. Allow students about five minutes to complete the handout.
2. In a class discussion, have volunteers comment on the classifications they have made. Then ask whether both points of view concerning Rockefeller may be valid. Explain that historians have argued in favor of both, depending on the time in which they lived and their own values. Provide students with the background information. Ask how a historian's own values might affect his or her view of Rockefeller. (Historians emphasizing social equality, distribution of wealth, fair treatment of workers, and so on, would be likely to view him as a robber baron. Those historians emphasizing the value of free enterprise, the capability of industry to promote economic growth and raise the standard of living for all, and the overall benefits provided by industrialization would be likely to hold the opposing point of view.)

3. Conclude the activity by asking students to point out the main provisions of the Sherman Antitrust Act. (The act banned combinations, whether or not they were trusts, which restricted interstate trade or commerce. Any monopoly or attempt to form a monopoly that restricted trade thus was outlawed. Although the act proved mainly ineffective, it reflected the growing antitrust sentiment in the nation.) Then ask them to write down the arguments that members of Congress might have used in debating passage of this act. Finally, have volunteers argue either for or against passage of the Sherman Antitrust Act, using the points covered in their work on Rockefeller.

Suggested Responses to Worksheet (Page 289)

1. Captain of Industry
2. Robber Baron
3. Captain of Industry
4. Robber Baron
5. Captain of Industry
6. Captain of Industry
7. Captain of Industry
8. Robber Baron
9. Captain of Industry
10. Robber Baron

Rockefeller: Captain of Industry or Robber Baron?

Directions: For each situation listed below, decide if you think Rockefeller was a Captain of Industry or a Robber Baron. Write your answer in the space provided.

_____ 1. Rockefeller cut waste in the oil industry and thus was able to lower production costs. Lower production costs led to lower prices and higher wages for workers.

_____ 2. Rockefeller forced railroads to give Standard Oil rebates, or kickbacks. In other words, owners had to pay him for using their railroads.

_____ 3. Before Rockefeller built his trust, there were dozens of small companies competing against each other in the oil industry. In this confusing situation companies could not provide the oil needed to meet the nation's needs.

_____ 4. Rockefeller owned not only companies that refined oil but also ships, barrels, and pipelines that carried oil. He had a complete monopoly of the oil industry.

_____ 5. Rockefeller gave $500,000,000 to charity, the largest amount of money even given by one person.

_____ 6. During Rockefeller's time, many people thought the United States was still a nation of small businesses. They failed to see that Americans were no longer completely independent and self-sufficient. To build and manage the great empires of railroads, oil, and steel, Americans had to form large groups. In other words, they had to realize that they were becoming increasingly interdependent.

_____ 7. Rockefeller lived during a time of change. There were no laws or established business practices. He used the tools available to him as well as his own original ideas.

_____ 8. Rockefeller used the rebates he received from railroads to lower prices and destroy competitors.

_____ 9. Rockefeller was a hero of the age of industry, similar to the heroes of the age of exploration. Drake, Hawkins, Cavendish, and Cabot pursued new opportunities boldly and confidently, and some of them were good businessmen, too.

_____ 10. Rockefeller was worth $1,000,000,000 at a time when the most able factory workers made $14 to $16 a week.

TOPIC: Our Multicultural Background—Mexican Americans
TIME: Two class periods, with homework
TIME PERIOD: After study of the settlement of the Southwest from 1848 to the 1880s and Mexican immigration to the United States during the Mexican Revolution in 1910

BACKGROUND

Mexican Americans have faced the same problems as other immigrant groups. Yet there is a difference—many Chicanos did not immigrate to this nation but already lived on the lands that became part of the United States in 1848. After the war between Mexico and the United States, Mexico signed the Treaty of Guadalupe Hidalgo, in which it gave up its claims to Texas and was paid $15 million for all the rest of its territory west to the Pacific. These lands included New Mexico, Arizona, California, Utah, Nevada, and the southern part of Colorado. Lands long held by the descendants of the original Spanish now became the subject of dispute. Passage of the Federal Land Law in 1851, designed to separate worthless claims from valid claims, led to lawsuits, cheating, financial manipulation, and, in some cases, violence. In all but a few instances the original landholders lost their lands simply because it was too difficult for them to establish claims. By the 1880s *Californios* (native Californians) owned one-fourth of the land they had held before the Treaty of Guadalupe Hidalgo.

Today, however, the majority of Mexican Americans are not natives but rather are the descendants of immigrants who came to this country after 1848. The first large wave of immigration began in 1910, at the beginning of the Mexican Revolution. From that time on, successive waves of immigrants have traveled north, stamping their culture on our nation and providing the labor essential to the development of the Southwest and West.

The two readings in this teaching strategy provide glimpses of Mexican Americans from both these groups—natives and immigrants. The excerpts from *Ramona* involve a *Californio* family that is in the process of losing its lands. Published in 1884, *Ramona* was Helen Hunt Jackson's attempt to obtain justice by evoking the kind of response Stowe did in *Uncle Tom's Cabin*.

Ramona was a runaway best seller—a far more popular book than her factual treatment of Indians in *A Century of Dishonor*. In this reading she portrays *Californios*—a portrait that is idealized but not imaginary, for Jackson had visited California *ranchos* like the one she describes.

The reading from Ernesto Galarza's *Barrio Boy* presents a very different picture. Galarza, who holds a Ph.D. from Columbia University, has written several books on Mexican Americans. In *Barrio Boy,* however, Galarza writes of his own boyhood and of his family, who came to the United States to escape the Mexican Revolution—to flee the devastation, find work, and to keep the family together. In the excerpts he writes of an incident that took place in Matzatlán during the Revolution and then of his introduction to Sacramento, the city in which his family settled.

This teaching strategy provides an opportunity for students to broaden their multicultural perspective of the United States. American language and food, as well as architecture and place names, reflect the contributions of people of Spanish background. The development of the South and Southwest—particularly mining and agriculture—depended on, and continues to depend on, the labor of Mexican Americans.

SUGGESTED PROCEDURE

1. Provide students with the background information on Mexican-Americans who helped to settle the Southwest and West and on Mexican American immigrants. Also provide some background for the excerpts the students are to read.
2. Explain that the word *barrio*, when used in Mexico, describes a particular district or area of a town. When used in the United States, *barrio* describes the Spanish-speaking area of a town or city. Have students work with partners to read the excerpts.
3. Ask students to discuss with their partners how life was different for Mexicans who immigrated to the United States than it had been for the original Mexicans who lived on lands before they became part of the nation. Tell the partners to write journal entries. One student should write a journal entry from the point of view of a *Californio,* and the other student should write an entry from the point of view of a Mexican immigrant. Then have partners switch and write journal entries from the other perspective. Students

should include details such as why they are losing their land (for the *Californio* entry) and why they have left Mexico (for the Mexican immigrant entry).

4. To extend the teaching strategy, you may wish to have the partners prepare a biographical profile. Ask them to choose from the following list of people, conduct library research on that person, and write a biographical profile.

Mariano Vallejo, who argued for California statehood but eventually became disillusioned with the treatment of Mexican Americans in California

Andrés Pico, who in 1859 argued that California should be divided into two states—north and south—in the hope that the southern part would be able to retain its Spanish traditions

Benito Juárez, who led the fight for Mexican independence, helping to defeat Maximilian and the French

Emiliano Zapata, the leader of the revolution that began in 1910

Tell partners to follow this five-step procedure in writing their biographical profiles:

Step 1: Prewriting
Have the partners list details about the person's life.

Step 2: Writing a First Draft
Instruct the partners to write a first draft of their profile, using the lists that they made in Step 1.

Step 3: Revising
Have the partners exchange their profile with another set of partners. Each set of partners should criticize the profile and suggest improvements. Suggested improvements should include those that give interesting and informative details. Then have students revise their profiles.

Step 4: Proofreading
Partners should proofread for errors in spelling, punctuation, grammar, and word usage.

Step 5: Writing a Final Copy
Have partners write a final copy of their profile on clean paper. Collect the profiles and display them in class so that students can read one another's work.

Excerpts from *Ramona*
By Helen Hunt Jackson

The Señora Moreno's house was one of the best specimens to be found in California of the representative house of the half barbaric, half elegant, wholly generous free-handed life led there by Mexican men and women of degree in the early part of this century, under the rule of the Spanish and Mexican viceroys, when the laws of the Indies were still the law of the land, and its old name, "New Spain," was an everpresent link and stimulus to the warmest memories and deepest patriotisms of its people. . . .

When the house was built, General Moreno owned all the land within a radius of forty miles,—forty miles westward, down the valley to the sea; forty miles eastward, into the San Fernando Mountains; and good forty miles more or less along the coast. The boundaries were not very strictly defined; there was no occasion, in those happy days, to reckon land by inches. It might be asked, perhaps, just how General Moreno owned all this land, and the question might not be easy to answer. It was not and could not be answered to the satisfaction of the United States Land Commission, which, after the surrender of California, undertook to sift and adjust Mexican land titles; and that was the way it had come about that the Señora Moreno now called herself a poor woman. Tract after tract, her lands had been taken away from her; it looked for a time as if nothing would be left. Every one of the claims based on deeds of gift from Governor Pio Pico, her husband's most intimate friend, was disallowed. They all went by the board in one batch, and took away from the Señora in a day the greater part of her best pasture-lands. They were lands which had belonged to the Bonaventura Mission, and lay along the coast at the mouth of the valley down which the little stream which ran past her house went to the sea; and it had been a great pride and delight to the Señora, when she was young, to ride that forty miles by her husband's side, all the way on their own lands, straight from their house to their own strip of shore. No wonder she believed the Americans thieves, and spoke of them always as hounds. The people of the United States have never in the least realized that the taking possession of California was not only a conquering of Mexico, but a conquering of California as well; that the real bitterness of the surrender was not so much to the empire which gave up the country, as to the country itself which was given up.

Excerpts from *Barrio Boy*
By Ernesto Galarza

In Matzatlán, Mexico:
Everyone in the *barrio* came out to watch the entry of the victorious troops. They went by on foot and on horseback, old men and young men in work clothes, shoes or huaraches or boots or in bare feet. Some wore bandoliers and others ammunition belts, carrying their rifles this way and that on their shoulders or resting them across their saddles. Many wore pieces of green-white-and-red ribbons stuck in their hats. We joined the mob and followed it to the plaza where a revolutionary general spoke from a balcony. At the end of the speech the men raised their rifles and fired into the air, yelling "viva's" I couldn't make out. Standing in the doorway of a shop facing the plaza we cheered as the revolution took possession of Matzatlán. I never saw the captain of the rurales again, or the picture of Don Porfirio Díaz.

But this great event was not the end of hard times. José told us that shops and factories that hired people were closing. Ships were not putting into port as usual, which meant that the jobs we had depended on—loading, warehousing, and delivering—were scarce. My mother had pawned the ring and we were waiting for the mails to start again, sure that Gustavo would send us enough to get by. From all the rumors that José gathered and that the neighbors picked up about town, there seemed as much trouble ahead as there had been behind. . . .

At the table José ate in silence. When he had finished we waited for the story. The two men had walked two days to the place where they were to work. Together they had built four markers of the kind called *mojoneras,* hauling the stones from the quarry. They started to walk back to Mazatlán to report to the *patrón* and collect their wages—one peso a day for each man for two weeks work. Late in the afternoon of the first day they were shot at as they were tramping through a stretch of brush. Jose and his companion dived into the bushes. My uncle recognized one of the attackers as the foreman of the *patrón.* José told the story with a quiet rage that made his lips quiver, as if he were ready to cry, and I was already old enough to know the signs of terror and anger in my mother—a slow shaking of the head and a slight tremor, as if she felt a chill.

"Why?" she asked José.

"So they wouldn't have to pay us the wages."

In Sacramento, California:
In a corner of the musty lobby of the Hotel Español, we waited until it was our turn to talk with the manager. The place was filled with people stacking and moving luggage, some talking in Spanish, others in English and other strange tongues. The manager wore a long white apron and a blue beret and spoke *gachupín* like the Spaniards of Mazatlán. He led us to a back room, took our baggage claim check, showed us the dining room and returned later with our tin trunk.

The hotel was a prison, even more confining than the alley in Tucson. We were frightened by the traffic of mule teams, wagons, and the honking automobiles that passed by continuously. From our view in the lobby the street was a jumble. Up and down from the doorway of the hotel all we could see were shops and stores, warehouses and saloons, hotels and restaurants, few ladies and no children. Sacramento, I decided, was an ugly place, not like the vineyards and eucalyptus trees with pastel colored trunks we had seen from the train. . . .

Mostly with blinks and hand motions and a great many ceremonial smiles, we were introduced to Mrs. Dodson, who led us into the house, down some narrow, dark stairs and to the back of the first floor where she left us in our new apartment.

It consisted of one large room, a kitchen and a closet that had been a bathroom from which all the fixtures had been removed except the bathtub. Directly behind the kitchen was a cramped back yard enclosed on three sides by a board fence like all the other American fences I had already seen—dirty gray planks, streaked and cracked. Rising from the yard there was a steep wooden stairway resting on cement blocks. It made a right angle at the second story and turned back toward the house, continuing to the third floor. The stairway had panels on each side and a landing on the floor. From the yard the fire escape looked like a ladder into the wild blue yonder. Since people rarely used it, and the panels made private cubicles of the landings, I discovered that I could use them as private crow's nests from which I could survey the *barrio's* back yards for blocks around.

TOPIC: The Spanish–American War
TIME: Two class periods
TIME PERIOD: Before students are tested on the Spanish–American War and the
Treaty of Paris

BACKGROUND

The war with Spain, which lasted only a few weeks in the spring and summer of 1898, marked a turning point in American history. Before the war the only lands the United States owned beyond its immediate boundaries were Alaska and the Midway Islands. The United States had acquired the Midway Islands in the central Pacific in 1867. Within a few years after the Spanish–American War ended, however, the American flag flew over several islands in the Pacific.

In this teaching strategy students will work in home groups and expert groups to study the Spanish–American War. You will be assigning each member of a home group a particular topic about the war. All students who have the same topic will then work in expert groups to learn their topic and discuss how best to teach the concepts to their home groups. After students teach their topics to their home groups, students will take a quiz on the concepts and material studied. The quiz score will be a home-group score. Thus all students will be motivated to work hard in their expert groups so that they can help their home groups perform well on the quiz.

MATERIALS

1. Copies of the six topic "Expert Sheets"
2. Copies of the "Concept Quiz"

SUGGESTED PROCEDURE

1. Ask for student volunteers to locate the following places on a world map: Spain, Cuba, the Philippines, Puerto Rico, and Guam. Remind students that each of these nations played a role in the Spanish–American War and its aftermath.
2. Organize the class into home groups of six students each. (Materials are organized for six groups, but if you have a small class the expert sheets for the "Cuban Revolution" and "Reasons for American Involvement with Spain in Cuba" can be completed by one group.) Have students number off from one to six. Then assign a different topic to each number. Explain that each student will become an expert on his or her topic and then return to the home group to teach the information. Explain that the responsibility to home groups is very important because everyone in the home group will have to take a quiz on all of the material.
3. Instruct students to move to their expert groups. Allow students the remainder of the class period to work in their expert groups. They should reread the information about their topic in their textbooks (and other resources, if possible), complete their "Expert Sheets," and discuss with the rest of the group how they should teach the topic to members of their home groups. During this time you should circulate to make sure that students' answers to the questions are correct. Be especially careful about checking their examples of the concepts.
4. At the beginning of the next class period, have students return to their home groups and begin their instruction. Suggest that members of the home groups take notes to help them remember the ideas and examples that are being shared. Remind them that they are not to simply pass their "Expert Sheets" to be read by the other members of the group. (You may with to collect the "Expert Sheets" so that they do not become a crutch.) Allow 30 minutes for this phase of the activity.
5. Have students arrange themselves for a test. Distribute copies of the "Concept Quiz." Reward the home group that has the highest score with an announcement on the bulletin board.

Answers to Concept Quiz (Pages 304–305)

1. Exaggerated stories about Spanish cruelty and brutality caused many Americans to begin calling for intervention in Cuba.

2. Americans demanded Cuba's independence; they demanded that the islands of Puerto Rico and Guam be given up as reparations; they demanded American occupation of the Philippines.

3. The army had more volunteers than it could efficiently supply and train. Trainloads of uniforms, weapons, and supplies were backed up in Tampa while troops went into Cuba's heat in wool uniforms. Disease seriously weakened the effectiveness of the recruits' early efforts.

4. Some people favored expansion but opposed imperialism on the grounds that imperialism was annexation without the consent of the people whose country was being annexed. Other people thought that expansion and imperialism were the same thing.

5. Americans voted against William Jennings Bryan in 1900 partly because of his anti-imperialistic stand and his opposition to the annexation of the Philippines.

6. Newspaper owners Hearst and Pulitzer favored war because it would sell newspapers.

7. As a result of the Spanish–American War, the United States acquired Puerto Rico and Guam and, with the payment of $20 million, the Philippines as well.

8. "Remember the Maine!" became a battle cry for the Spanish–American War.

9. The widely circulated story of Theodore Roosevelt's leadership at San Juan Hill in Cuba had much to do with his being called upon to support the Republican presidential ticket as the vice presidential nominee in the election of 1900.

10. The first American objective in the Spanish–American War was to close off Santiago Harbor and destroy the Spanish fleet there.

CUBAN REVOLUTION

Directions: Carefully reread the material in your textbook about the Cuban Revolution in 1895 and then complete the expert sheet.

1. What did the revolutionaries in Cuba hope to accomplish?

_____

_____

_____

2. What were the causes of the Cuban Revolution?

_____

_____

_____

3. Describe the tactics used by both sides during the revolution.

_____

_____

_____

4. Why and how did the United States become involved in the revolution?

_____

_____

_____

5. What are some examples of the United States becoming involved in the internal affairs in foreign countries in the recent past?

_____

_____

_____

Concept: The following concept is important to this part of the activity. Find an example of the concept in your reading and record it in the space provided.

Pressures from the media and from people within a country can affect that country's relationships with other countries.

_____

_____

REASONS FOR AMERICAN INVOLVEMENT WITH SPAIN IN CUBA

Directions: Carefully reread the material in your textbook about American involvement with Spain in Cuba and then complete the expert sheet.

1. Why did the United States send a battleship to Cuba?

   _____

   _____

   _____

2. What event turned the Cuban revolution into armed conflict between Spain and the United States?

   _____

   _____

   _____

3. How did Spain and the United States react to this event?

   _____

   _____

   _____

Concepts: The following concepts are important to this part of the activity. Find an example of each concept in your reading and record it in the space provided.

1. Pressures from the media and from people within a country can affect that country's relationships with other countries.

   _____

   _____

2. The desire for revenge, whether ill-placed or not, can lead to war.

   _____

   _____

YELLOW JOURNALISM LEADS TO WAR

Directions: Carefully reread the material in your textbook about yellow journalism and then complete the expert sheet.

1. Why do you think that the phrase "Remember the Maine!" became a battle cry?

_____

_____

2. What is yellow journalism and how did its focus on events in Cuba play a role in involving the United States in a war with Spain?

_____

_____

_____

3. Why did newspaper owners Hearst and Pulitzer favor war with Spain and why did they use the type of reporting they did in their newspapers?

_____

_____

_____

4. List some examples of yellow journalism.

_____

_____

_____

Concepts: The following concepts are important to this part of the activity. Find an example of each concept in your reading and record it in the space provided.

1. Pressures from the media and from people within a country can affect that country's relationships with other countries.

_____

_____

2. The desire for revenge, whether ill-placed or not, can lead to war.

_____

_____

3. Economic considerations can affect how people view events or the sides they take on issues.

_____

_____

WAR IS DECLARED AND THE FIRST BATTLE WON

Directions: Carefully reread the material in your textbook about war being declared and the Battle of Manila Bay and then complete the expert sheet.

1. Why wouldn't Spain agree to complete independence for Cuba?

   _____

   _____

   _____

2. What procedures were followed by Congress and the president before war was declared on Spain?

   _____

   _____

   _____

3. How did the United States try to keep itself from looking like an imperialistic nation when it declared war on Spain?

   _____

   _____

   _____

4. Why did the first battle of the Spanish–American War take place in the Philippines in the Pacific Ocean rather than in Cuba in the Atlantic Ocean?

   _____

   _____

   _____

5. Who emerged as a naval hero as a result of the Battle of Manila Bay?

   _____

   _____

   _____

Concepts: The following concepts are important to this part of the activity. Find an example of each concept in your reading and record it in the space provided.

1. Pressures from the media and from people within a country can affect that country's relationships with other countries.

   _____

   _____

2. Military preparedness is important to success in war.

   _____

   _____

3. The desire for revenge, whether ill-placed or not, can lead to war.

   _____

   _____

4. Wars create heroes.

   _____

   _____

THE WAR IN THE CARIBBEAN

Directions: Carefully reread the material in your textbook about the war in the Caribbean and then complete the expert sheet.

1. Theodore Roosevelt's actions at the outset of the Spanish–American War are an example of how a well-known person can have a great effect on the actions of large numbers of people. What position did Theodore Roosevelt hold at the time, what did he do at the beginning of the war, and how did this action influence other people?

   _____

   _____

   _____

2. The first several weeks of the war drew attention to some serious shortcomings in America's state of military preparedness. What were these shortcomings, and how did they become apparent?

   _____

   _____

   _____

3. What was the main military objective of the United States in Cuba? Why was this objective important?

   _____

   _____

   _____

4. Why do you think the United States was interested in taking the island of Puerto Rico before the end of the war?

   _____

   _____

   _____

Concepts: The following concepts are important to this part of the activity. Find an example of each concept in your reading and record it in the space provided.

1. Military preparedness is important to success in war.

   _____

   _____

2. Military strategy in war includes an effort to cut off the enemy's ability to reinforce itself with fresh troops and supplies.

   _____

   _____

3. War usually results in the acquisition of territory by the winning nation(s).

   _____

   _____

4. The winning side in a war can determine the terms of the peace treaty.

   _____

   _____

THE TREATY OF PARIS

Directions: Carefully reread the material in your textbook about the Treaty of Paris and then complete the expert sheet.

1. What were the terms of the peace treaty?

_____

_____

_____

2. Why might some people consider United States involvement in the Spanish–American War as being imperialistic?

_____

_____

_____

3. Why did many people consider United States action to take over the Philippines un-American? Some people distinguished between expansionism and imperialism. On what basis did they make that distinction?

_____

_____

_____

4. How did the Spanish-American War affect the outcome of the election of 1900?

_____

_____

_____

5. War creates heroes. What important political figure became a hero in the Spanish–American War? What evidence can you provide of the esteem with which people held this person?

_____

_____

_____

6. What were the effects of the Treaty of Paris on the Philippines?

_____

_____

_____

Concepts: The following concepts are important to this part of the activity. Find an example of each concept in your reading and record it in the space provided.

1. The winning side of a war can determine the terms of the peace treaty.

_____

_____

2. Imperialism is defined differently by different people.

_____

_____

3. The state of war can influence the outcome of political elections.

_____

_____

4. War usually results in the acquisition of territory by the winning nation(s).

_____

_____

5. Wars create heroes.

_____

_____

CONCEPT QUIZ

Directions: Below is a list of the important concepts you should have learned in studying the Spanish–American War. In the space provided give one significant example of each concept. To receive full credit for an answer it must be correct, clearly stated, and contain supporting detail. Write your answers in complete sentences.

1. Pressures from the media and from people within a country can affect that country's relationships with other countries.

   _____

   _____

   _____

   _____

2. The winning side in a war can determine the terms of the peace treaty.

   _____

   _____

   _____

   _____

3. Military preparedness is important to success in a war.

   _____

   _____

   _____

   _____

4. Imperialism is defined differently by different people.

   _____

   _____

   _____

   _____

5. The state of war can influence the outcomes of political elections.

   _____

   _____

   _____

   _____

6. Economic considerations can affect how people view events or the sides they take on issues.

   _____

   _____

   _____

   _____

7. War usually results in the acquisition of territory by the winning nation(s).

_____

_____

_____

_____

8. The desire for revenge, whether ill-placed or not, can lead to war.

_____

_____

_____

_____

9. Wars create heroes.

_____

_____

_____

_____

10. Military strategy in war includes an effort to cut off the enemy's ability to reinforce itself with fresh troops and supplies.

_____

_____

_____

_____

TOPIC: Literature as a Reflection of Societal Concerns
TIME: One class period
TIME PERIOD: After study of the lack of equality for African Americans during the Progressive Era, growing violence against blacks, and the formation of the NAACP. It is also appropriate for use in connection with vigilantism in the West.

BACKGROUND

A representative of the frontier and of the egalitarian West, Mark Twain ended New England's domination of American literature and influenced, as Ernest Hemingway pointed out, all American writers who came after him. In his first novel, Twain gave the time period during which he lived its name—the Gilded Age. Contemptuous of wealthy industrialists and dishonest politicians, Twain satirized all that did not match his ideals about America. In his later years he was as bitterly sardonic about American expansionism as he had earlier been about venality in American society. In his fiction and non-fiction alike, Twain served as his society's critic, and sometimes as its conscience.

The two handouts concern Twain's view of lynching, a topic of increasing concern to Americans in the late 1800s and early 1900s as the lynching of blacks increased dramatically. In the first excerpt, Twain the essayist speaks of a lynching that took place in his native Missouri, using the incident as a springboard for a general discussion. In the second excerpt, Twain the novelist provides us with Huck Finn's description of the attempted lynching of Colonel Sherburn, a white southerner. Sherburn killed one of the town's "characters," a man who rode drunk into town every month and accused someone of having cheated him. The townspeople, accustomed to this spectacle, were stunned when the man's threats provoked violence.

This teaching strategy serves a variety of purposes. It asks students to examine the artist (in this case, the writer) as a social critic and social commentator. It may also serve to provoke a discussion of human rights, personal ethics, and the willingless to stand up against the group. Finally, the strategy touches upon constitutional issues, such as due process and respect for the law.

MATERIALS

Copies of the two reading selections

SUGGESTED PROCEDURE

1. Organize the class into small groups, and distribute the first handout to each group. Before the students begin reading, you may want to write *Savonarola* on the chalkboard, and explain that Savonarola was a fifteenth-century Italian priest who openly attacked the powerful Medici family of Florence and eventually even the pope. In 1498 he was found quilty of heresy and was executed.
2. Have students read the handout, and write the following questions on the chalkboard for the groups to discuss:
   a. Why did the violence against African Americans occur? (A white woman was found murdered.)
   b. Is there anything in the reading that tells who was responsible for the murder of the young white woman? (No one was sure who killed the woman.) Why might African Americans have been blamed? (racial prejudice)
   c. What does Twain think of people in a lynch mob? Does he think that they are mean and vicious? (No, he speaks of a fire in which these same people were heroic.)
   d. Why does he think people join such a mob? (group psychology, peer pressure, conformity)
   e. According to Twain, what does courage have to do with the people in the mob? (He says that the people lack courage because they do not really want to do what they are doing.)
3. Pass out the second handout, and provide as much background as you think necessary for students to understand the episode. Write on the chalkboard the following questions for groups to discuss:
   a. Why would it have been easier for someone like Sherburn to face a lynch mob than for blacks to have done so? (Sherburn was white and thus not the target of racial prejudice.)

    b. Is Twain's attitude toward lynch mobs the same in both readings? (Yes; in both readings, members of the mob are presented as cowards.)

    c. What does Twain have Sherburn say that is similar to what Twain says directly in his piece on lynching? (Sherburn's references to the men in the mob as not really being "men" indicates his contempt for their lack of courage.)

    d. Why is it significant that Sherburn is a southerner? (He is familiar with lynching, and his words about men who come in the "dark" and wear masks conjures up images of the lynchings of African Americans by violent groups, such as the Klu Klux Klan.)

4. In a class discussion, compare the people in lynch mobs with people today who take the law into their own hands. (Examples might include movies with vigilante heroes, newspaper reports of citizens who use weapons against others when their lives may not be in jeopardy, and so on.) Help students to arrive at an understanding of the importance of due process of law.

5. Have students work in their groups to discuss times when they have had to take a stand that is different from a group's stand or the stand of their friends. Ask them to discuss their thoughts in these situations and their reasons for not doing what everyone else is doing. Have interested groups reenact a few of these situations, with the class as a whole discussing the issues involved in the reenactments.

Excerpts from "The United States of Lyncherdom"

From *In Europe and Elsewhere,* by Mark Twain

Oh, Missouri!

The tragedy occurred near Pierce City, down in the southwestern corner of the state. On a Sunday afternoon a young white woman who had started alone from church was found murdered. . . . Although it was a region of churches and schools the people rose, lynched three Negroes—two of them very aged ones—burned out five Negro households, and drove thirty Negro families into the woods. . . .

It is thought, as I have said, that a lynching crowd enjoys a lynching. It certainly is not true; it is impossible of belief. . . . If that were so, the crowds that saw the Windsor Hotel burn down would have enjoyed the horrors that fell under their eyes. Did they? No one will think that of them, no one will make that charge. Many risked their lives to save the men and women who were in peril. Why did they do that? Because *none would disapprove*. There was no restraint; they could follow their natural impulse. Why does a crowd of the same kind of people in Texas, Colorado, Indiana, stand by smitten to the heart and miserable, and by ostentatious outward signs pretend to enjoy a lynching? Why does it lift no hand or voice in protest? Only because it would be unpopular to do it, I think; each man is afraid of his neighbor's disapproval, a thing which, to the general run of the race, is more dreaded than wounds and death. . . . We are not any better nor braver than anybody else and we must not try to creep out of it.

A Savonarola can quell and scatter a mob of lynchers with a mere glance of his eye. . . . For no mob has any sand in the presence of a man known to be splendidly brave. Besides a lynching mob would *like* to be scattered, for of a certainty there are never ten men in it would not prefer to be somewhere else—and would be if they but had the courage to go.

Excerpts from "Why the Lynching Bee Failed"

Chapter 22, in *Huckleberry Finn,* by Mark Twain

They swarmed up towards Sherburn's house, a-whooping and raging like Injuns, and everything had to clear the way or get run over and tromped to mush, and it was awful to see. . . .

They swarmed up in front of Sherburn's palings as thick as they could jam together, and you couldn't hear yourself think for the noise. It was a little twenty-foot yard. Some sung out "Tear down the fence! tear down the fence!" Then there was a racket of ripping and tearing and smashing, and down she goes, and the front wall of the crowd begins to roll in like a wave.

Just then Sherburn steps out onto the roof of his little front porch with a double-barrel gun in his hand, and takes his stand perfectly ca'm and deliberate, not saying a word. The racket stopped and the wave sucked back.

Sherburn never said a word—just stood there, looking down. The stillness was awful creepy and uncomfortable. Sherburn run his eye slow along the crowd and wherever it struck the people tried a little to outgaze him but they couldn't, they dropped their eyes and looked sneaky. Then pretty soon Sherburn sort of laughed; not the pleasant kind but the kind that makes you feel like when you are eating bread that's got sand in it.

Then he says, slow and scornful:

"The idea of *you* lynching anybody! It's amusing. The idea of you thinking you had pluck enough to lynch a *man!* . . .

"You didn't want to come. The average man don't like trouble and danger. *You* don't like trouble and danger. But if only *half* a man—like Buck Harkness there—shouts

'Lynch him! lynch him!' you're afraid to back down—afraid you'll be found out to be what you are—*cowards*—and so you raise a yell and hang yourselves onto that half-a-man's coat- tail and come raging up here, swearing what big things you're gong to do. The pitifulest thing out is a mob. . . . If any real lynching's going to be done it will be done in the dark, Southern fashion; and when they come they'll bring their masks, and fetch a *man* along. Now *leave*—and take your half-a-man with you"—tossing his gun up across his left arm and cocking it when he says this.

The crowd washed back sudden, and then broke all apart and went tearing off every which way, and Buck Harkness he heeled it after them, looking tolerable cheap. I could 'a' stayed if I wanted to but I didn't want to.

TOPIC: GEOGRAPHY—United States Policy in the Caribbean
TIME: Two class periods
TIME PERIOD: During study of the Spanish–American War, the building of the Panama Canal, and similar United States involvement in the Caribbean in the 1890s and early 1900s

BACKGROUND

United States intervention in Latin America, and specifically in the Caribbean, began in the 1890s. Intervention became formally supported by Theodore Roosevelt in the Roosevelt Corollary to the Monroe Doctrine and by Taft with the policy of dollar diplomacy. Military intervention continued on and off throughout the century, with the United States occupation of the Dominican Republic from 1916 to 1924 and again in 1965 through1966, the unsuccessful anti-Castro invasion of Cuba in 1961, and the invasion of Panama in 1989. This teaching strategy furthers students' development of locational skills and understanding and encourages students to explore the connection between relative location and historical events.

MATERIALS

Copies of the map "United States Policy in the Caribbean"

SUGGESTED PROCEDURE

1. Write these headings on the chalkboard:

   Boundary Dispute Between Great Britain and the United States (1895)
   U.S.S. Maine Sent to Cuba (1898)
   Annexed by the United States (1898)
   Occupied by the United States (1898–1902)
   U.S.S. Nashville Sent to Support Rebels (1903)

2. Organize students into groups of three or four, and distribute a map to each student. Assign each group one of the topics, and tell them they are to write a one-paragraph lead for a newspaper article reporting on some aspect of the event they have been assigned. They are also to find where the event took place and label it on the map. The maps and one-paragraph leads will then work together to present a newspaper story. Before students begin writing, remind them that the first paragraph of a newspaper report answers the questions Who? What? Why? When? and Where? Have students follow the five-step procedure in writing their lead paragraphs.

   Step 1: Prewriting
   Have members of each group work together to identify their event, to locate it on the map, and to answer the five questions (Who? What? Why? When? Where?)
   Step 2: Writing a First Draft
   Ask groups to divide up the work so that some members work on the writing assignment while others label the map. (The students working on the map may want to color in the appropriate area and/or illustrate the event in some manner.)
   Step 3: Revising
   Have groups review the map work and the paragraph and critique them, suggesting improvements and checking to make sure that the five questions have been answered. Then ask students to revise their paragraphs.
   Step 4: Proofreading
   Have members of each group proofread for errors in spelling, punctuation, grammar, and word usage.
   Step 5: Writing a Final Copy
   Have students write a final copy of the paragraph on clean paper, and prepare a clean copy of the map. You may ask a volunteer from each group to read that group's paragraph. Paragraphs and maps may then be displayed in the classroom.

3. To conclude the activity, ask the class why the United States might become involved in the affairs of Caribbean and Latin American nations more than in the affairs of, for example, European nations. Have the class discuss how the proximity of the nations to the United States affects Americans' sense of responsibility.

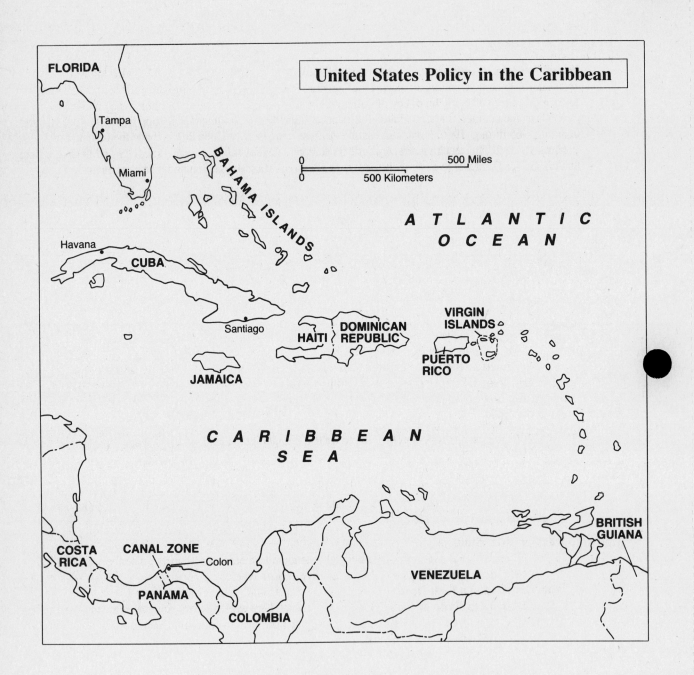

United States Policy in the Caribbean

TOPIC: Annexation of the Philippines—Conflicting Points of View
TIME: One class period
TIME PERIOD: During study of the annexation of the Philippines and other examples of American expansionism after the Spanish–American War

BACKGROUND

In 1898 and 1899 no issue was more fiercely debated than American expansionism. Expansionists argued from different positions, but all agreed that the United States had a right (if not an obligation) to extend its control over other nations in the world. Some expansionists argued that Americans, as representatives of the "Anglo-Saxon" race, had a mission to govern other peoples. Expansionists also argued along the lines of Social Darwinism, claiming that Americans, who were energetic, strong, and fit, seemed destined by the laws of nature to rule other peoples.

Expansionists met strong opposition from anti-imperialists on the issue of annexing the Philippines. Although many of the anti-imperialists had favored annexation of Hawaii and other territories, they thought that it was morally wrong to annex the Philippines. Emilio Aguinaldo and his rebels had helped the United States defeat Spain because they believed that they were fighting for their nation's independence. Anti-imperialists compared Aguinaldo to American colonists in 1776 and said that the United States had betrayed him and the people of the Philippines.

This teaching strategy encourages the development of historical empathy by asking students to enter into the spirit of the times. In addition, it asks students to examine national goals in light of ethical concerns and respect for human rights.

SUGGESTED PROCEDURE

1. Prior to the day you use this teaching strategy, assign students to watch a news program such as *The MacNeil-Lehrer News Hour* or *This Week with David Brinkley,* or show a videotape of such a program to the class. Ask them to make notes about the interviews that are done on the program. (On shows such as these, one or more interviewers ask questions of people who hold opposing points of view about a topic of current concern to Americans.)
2. Organize the class into small groups. Some groups should work to marshal arguments representing the expansionist point of view concerning annexation of the Philippines. Other groups should note arguments used by anti-expansionists, or anti-imperialists. Still others should infer the point of view of Emilio Aguinaldo, who led the fight for Philippine independence. The fourth group should write down questions an interviewer might ask of a representative from each of the other three groups.
3. After the groups have completed their work, ask for a volunteer from each of the four groups (the expansionists, the anti-expansionists, Aguinaldo, and the interviewers). Have the volunteer interviewer ask questions of the other three volunteers, in the manner of a news reporter on a TV program.
4. After the first interview has been completed, ask for four more volunteers and repeat the process as long as it seems valuable.
5. To conclude the activity, have the class discuss which seemed most compelling to them—the pro-expansionist point of view or the anti-expansionist point of view. Ask them to discuss the arguments presented by the representatives of the different points of view and then categorize them. Prompt students with the following questions:
   a. Which arguments had to do with a position that viewed non-Americans (or perhaps Asians) as somehow less capable than Americans? Were these arguments based on fact or emotion?
   b. Did some arguments suggest that "Might is right"?
   c. Which arguments had to do with morals—with right and wrong? Are moral arguments based on fact? On what are they based?

TOPIC: Mother Jones
TIME: Two class periods, with homework
TIME PERIOD: During study of the Progressive Era

BACKGROUND

The progressive movement, which rose in opposition to child labor, unsafe working conditions, slums, business abuses, and political corruption, was mainly a middle-class movement of both Democrats and Republicans. Women, who had joined reform movements since the early 1800s, were a driving force of progressivism. Industrialization, by providing canned foods, factory clothing, washing machines, and other labor-saving devices, had freed middle- and upper-class women from constant housework. Women began to look outside the home, joining women's organizations, entering the work force as secretaries, teachers, and sometimes doctors, banding together in support of women's suffrage, and beginning the settlement house movement of the 1890s.

Mary Harris "Mother" Jones was in many ways untypical of women who took part in the progressive movement. A socialist, Mother Jones carried on the work of her husband, a union leader, after he and their four children died of yellow fever in 1867. Called by her enemies "the most dangerous woman in America," Mother Jones crossed lines of militia, spent time in prison, and was castigated by politicians and employers. She helped to organize women garment workers, child textile workers, steel workers, women in the garment industry, and the group closest to her heart—coal miners.

In 1903, 100,000 textile workers joined in a strike in Philadelphia. Workers asked for a work week of 55 rather than 60 hours and were willing to accept a reduction in wages, which ranged from $2 a week for children to $13 a week for adults. Over 16,000 of the workers were children, many of them under 12 years of age. Although Pennsylvania outlawed labor by children under the age of 12, a child's age could be established if the parents swore to it. Many poor parents felt forced to lie about their children's ages.

When Mother Jones arrived in Philadelphia, she found child workers as young as 10 years of age, with stooped shoulders and missing hands and fingers. In response, she organized a march of child textile workers to Oyster Bay, Long Island (the site of Roosevelt's summer home), to convince the president to end child labor. About 300 men, women, and children were led by three children dressed as Revolutionary War soldiers. When Mother Jones and her army arrived in Coney Island, she was asked to speak. The result was the speech "The Wail of the Children," delivered on July 24, 1903.

This teaching strategy provides students with an opportunity to develop historical empathy and to further their understanding of the expanded role citizens expected government to play in dealing with the social and economic consequences of industrialization in the 1890s and early 1900s. It also asks students to examine the ethical implications of social and economic policies.

MATERIALS

Copies of the handout with the speech by Mother Jones

SUGGESTED PROCEDURE

1. Provide students with the background information. Then have students work with partners to read the excerpts from Mother Jones' speech. Discuss with students the following questions:
   a. Why was Mother Jones going to see President Roosevelt? (to protest child labor) What did she want him to do? (to recommend passage of a bill by Congress, protecting child workers)
   b. Why does she compare the child workers to black slaves? (Both groups were forced to labor without their consent.) Do you agree with her comparison? Why or why not?
   c. What point is Mother Jones making concerning the story about the man who could have been a United States senator "if he had stolen a railroad"? (Possible answer: The wealthy go unpunished for their huge crimes, whereas the poor are severely punished for minor crimes.)

2. Ask students to write a short speech that President Roosevelt might have given in reply to Mother Jones. Have students use their textbooks to review President Roosevelt's attitudes about progressives and workers. Then have students follow the following five-step procedure in writing their speeches:

Step 1: Prewriting

Have students work alone to list the points from Mother Jones' speech to which they want to respond. Then ask students to list their responses, or the points they will make as President Roosevelt.

Step 2: Writing a First Draft

Instruct students to write a first draft, incorporating the points and responses they listed in Step 1.

Step 3: Revising

Have students exchange their work with a partner, who will critique it and suggest improvements. Then have students revise.

Step 4: Proofreading

Ask students to proofread for errors in spelling, punctuation, grammar, and word usage.

Step 5: Writing a Final Copy

Have students write a final copy on clean paper. Then ask volunteers to read their speeches in front of the class.

The Wail of the Children

Speech by Mary Harris "Mother" Jones at Coney Island, Brooklyn, New York, during the march of the mill children, July 28, 1903; from *Mother Jones Speaks*, edited by Philip S. Foner

After a long and weary march, with more miles to travel, we are on our way to see President Roosevelt at Oyster Bay. We will ask him to recommend passage of a bill by Congress to protect children against the greed of the manufacturer. We want him to hear the wail of the children, who never have a chance to go to school, but work from ten to eleven hours a day in the textile mills of Philadelphia, weaving the carpets that he and you walk on, and the curtains and clothes of the people.

Fifty years ago, there was a cry against slavery, and the men of the North gave up their lives to stop the selling of black children on the block. To-day the white child is sold for $2 a week, and even by his parents, to the manufacturer.

Fifty years ago the black babies were sold C.O.D. To-day the white baby is sold to the manufacturer on the installment plan. He might die at his tasks and the manufacturer with the automobile and the yacht and the daughter who talks French to a poodle dog, as you can see any day at Twenty-third Street and Broadway when they roll by, could not afford to pay $2 a week for the child that might die, except on the present installment plan. What the President can do is to recommend a measure and send a message to Congress which will break the chains of the white children slaves.

He endorsed a bill for the expenditure of $45,000 to fill the stomach of a Prince who went galivanting about the country. We will ask in the name of the aching hearts of these little ones that they be emancipated. I will tell the President that I saw men in Madison Square last night sleeping on the benches and that the country can have not greatness while one unfortunate lies out at night without a bed to sleep on. I will tell him that the prosperity he boasts of is the prosperity of the rich wrung from the poor.

In Georgia where children work day and night in the cotton mills they have just passed a bill to protect song birds. What about the little children from whom all song is gone?

The trouble is that the fellers in Washington don't care. I saw them last Winter pass three railroad bills in one hour, and when labor cries for aid for the little ones they turn their backs and will not listen to her.

I asked a man in prison once how he happened to get there. He had stolen a pair of shoes. I told him that if he had stolen a railroad he could be a United States Senator. One hour of justice is worth an age of praying.

You are told that every American-born male citizen has a chance of being President. I tell you that the hungry man without a bed in the park would sell his chance for a good square meal, and these little toilers, deformed, dwarfed in body, soul, and morality, with nothing but toil before them and no chance for schooling, don't even have the dream that they might some day have a chance at the Presidential chair.

You see those monkeys in cages. They are trying to teach them to talk. The monkeys are too wise, for they fear that then the manufacturers might buy them for slaves for their factories. In 1860 the workingmen had the advantage in the percentage of the country's wealth. To-day statistics at Washington show that with billions of wealth the wage earners' share is but 10 per cent. We are going to tell the President of these things.

TOPIC: GEOGRAPHY—The Westward Movement and the Closing of the Frontier
TIME: One class period
TIME PERIOD: During study of the closing of the American frontier

BACKGROUND

By the 1890s the nation had been settled from coast to coast. Americans had settled the last frontier within the continental boundaries of the United States—the Great Plains. The land once described as "the great American desert" was now the "heartland," or food provider, for the nation. This teaching strategy offers students an opportunity to employ locational skills and understanding and furthers their understanding of patterns of human movement.

MATERIALS

Copies of the outline map of the continental United States

SUGGESTED PROCEDURE

1. Organize students into small groups, and distribute copies of the map to each student. Explain that the map is simply an outline map of the United States and that through their work they will create a map showing a history of the westward movement. Then write the following headings on the chalkboard:

   Settlers move through the Cumberland Gap.
   Pioneers travel west on the Oregon and Santa Fe Trails.
   Americans move into Texas and California.

   Ask the class to suggest other events in the history of the westward movement.
2. Have the groups use their textbooks as a resource. Students may discuss their maps in their group, but each student should create his or her own map. Students should draw on their maps the movement of different groups westward. Trails may be drawn with different colored pencils, in which case students should make a legend for the map. (If necessary, review with students the purpose of a map legend.)
3. Now have students color or shade in large areas in order of settlement. The Great Plains will appear as the last area to be settled.
4. Finally, have students draw two stars on their maps, with dates. The first should show the center of population in the United States in 1790. (It should appear slightly southeast of Baltimore, Maryland.) The second star should show the center of population in 1890. (It should appear southeast of Indianapolis, Indiana.) Ask the groups how these stars summarize the westward movement in the United States.
5. Display maps in the classroom, and have students examine and discuss the maps made by groups other than their own.

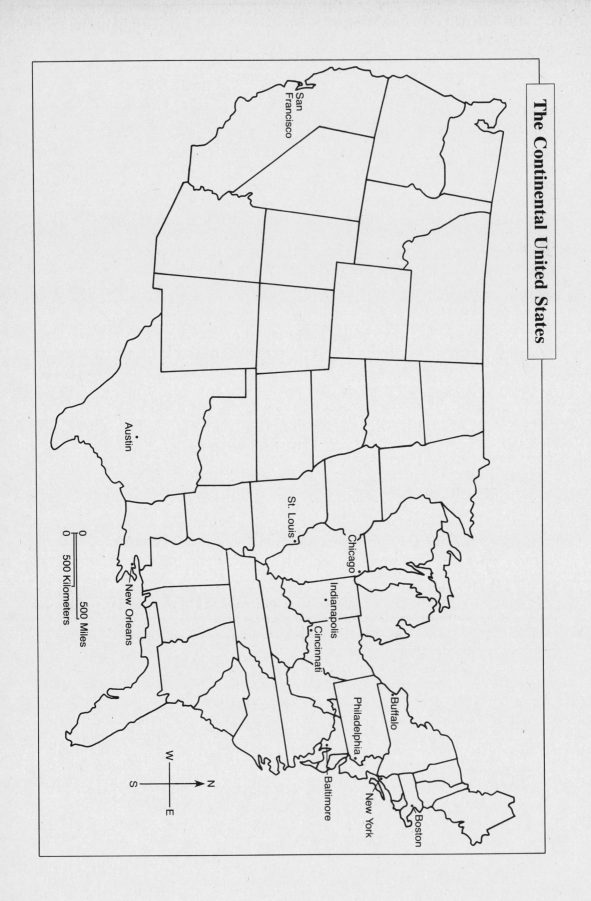

The Continental United States

San Francisco

Austin

St. Louis

Chicago

Indianapolis

Cincinnati

New Orleans

Philadelphia

Buffalo

Baltimore

New York

Boston

0
0
500 Miles
500 Kilometers

W
S
N
E

TOPIC: The Triangle Shirtwaist Factory Fire
TIME: Two class periods
TIME PERIOD: During study of the labor union movement during the late 1800s and early 1900s

BACKGROUND:

The Triangle Shirtwaist Company factory fire occurred in New York City at a time when experts had been warning city officials and state legislators about the impending disaster that awaited workers in buildings that failed to have even the most basic fire warning and prevention systems. As is often true when we speak of reform, it was too late in coming for the 146 workers, mostly young women, who perished in their attempts to escape the tragic fire that destroyed three upper floors of the Asch building on March 26, 1911.

Some of the workers burned to death; others died of smoke inhalation. Many died jumping from windows because they could not open doors onto stairways or use the fire escape. The owners of the factory, Max Blanc and Isaac Harris, were prosecuted for manslaughter due to willful negligence. They were acquitted after the defense charged that prosecution witnesses, many of whom were immigrants, had been coached in their testimony. The acquittal served only to further enrage already angry reformers and led to the passage of 35 new factory laws in New York State.

This teaching strategy provides an opportunity for students to engage in historical empathy by entering into the drama of the Triangle Fire. The strategy also furthers understanding of the relationship between a society and its laws by asking students to examine a specific example of a major social issue that was brought to the courts but was eventually resolved through legislation.

MATERIALS

1. Copies of the witness statements for the defense and the prosecution
2. Copies of the "Trial Procedures Guide"

SUGGESTED PROCEDURE

1. Provide students with the background information on the Triangle Fire, but do not tell them the verdict of the trial. Then explain to them that they will take part in a mock trial of the factory owners, Max Blanc and Isaac Harris, who were charged with manslaughter due to willful negligence. Discuss the charge with the class, making sure that students understand it.
2. Organize the class into four or six groups. Have groups draw slips of paper to determine whether their group will represent the prosecution or the defense. (When you prepare the slips of paper, make an equal number reading "Prosecution" and "Defense.") Then give the first witness statement sheet to the groups presenting the case for the prosecution and the second witness statement to the groups presenting the case for the defense. Distribute the "Trial Procedures Guide." Have students use the information in the handouts to prepare their case. Tell each group to choose one member as attorney and others as witnesses.
3. Before the first presentations begin, you may want to write the following statements on the chalkboard:

   Defendants: Owners of the Triangle Shirtwaist Factory, Max Blanc and Isaac Harris
   Charge: Manslaughter due to willful negligence
   Date and Location of Fire: March 26, 1911. The fire began on the eighth floor and traveled to the ninth and tenth floors of the Asch Building, Washington Place and Greene Street, New York City.

4. When students are prepared to argue their cases, select two groups at a time that represent opposing sides. Have students follow the procedures in the "Trial Procedures Guide." If you serve as judge, the jury (the class as a whole) may discuss and then vote on the verdict. Emphasize to the jury that the case must be decided on the basis of what the laws were in 1911.
5. To conclude, discuss with the class the relationship between law and social issues such as child labor, equal opportunity, safe housing, and so on. Have students discuss the government's role in ensuring safe working conditions. Then discuss the rights of individuals and businesspeople. Help the class examine the role of the government in providing a balance between what are sometimes conflicting interests.

Witnesses for the Prosecution

Excerpted

Newspaper reporter for *United Press*, Bill Shepherd, who saw the fire:

"I looked upon the heap of dead bodies and I remembered these girls were the shirtwaist makers. I remembered their great strike of last year in which these same girls had demanded more sanitary conditions and more safety precautions in the shops. These dead bodies were the answer."

P.J. McKeon, an expert on fire prevention from Columbia University, had inspected the building before the fire:

He discovered that the firm had never had a fire drill. He said that if workers were not instructed in how to handle themselves in an emergency, a fire would cause panic. He found the door to the Washington place staircase was "usually kept locked," and that the reason for this was that "it was difficult to keep track of so many girls." He recommended that the firm ask Mr. H.F.J. Porter, a fire prevention expert, to set up fire drill procedures for the company.

Bernstein, the manager, who looked for a hose:

He found the hose, but it did not work. "No pressure. No water," Bernstein said.

Anna Gullo, factory worker:

"I tried the [Washington Place stairway] door. The door was locked."

Mary Bucelli, factory worker:

"I tried to open the [Washington Place stairway] door but I couldn't."

Fire fighters:

The fire fighters found the fire escape's iron framework twisted and broken. It had come loose from the side of the building, its top story gooseneck ladder to the roof torn away from the side of the building. At each of the three Triangle floor levels, the iron window shutters were "sprung and warped." They had blocked the escape to life for many.

Newspaper reporter:

The fire on March 25 was not Triangle's first fire. In fact, the company was what insurance companies call a "repeater." They had filed seven claims since April 5, 1902.

Newspaper reporter:

There was evidence that Triangle was having serious financial problems.

Witnesses for the Defense

Excerpted

Joseph J. Asch, owner of the building:

"My building is fireproof. The architects claimed my building was ahead of any other building of its kind which had previously been constructed." He told news reporters, "I have obeyed the law to the letter. There was not one detail of the construction of my building that was not submitted to the Building and Fire Departments. Every detail was approved and the Fire Marshal congratulated me."

Fireman Edward F. O'Connor, who made an inspection of the Asch building about three months before the fire:

O'Connor reported that, according to existing codes, the fire escape was "good," the stairways were "good," and the building was "fireproof." He noted that an 8' x 10' foot tank on the roof could hold 5,000 gallons of water and that there were 259 water pails distributed over the building's ten floors for use in an emergency.

Fire Chief Croker:

"At the present time there is no law compelling the construction of such fire escapes [located on the front of the building]."

Albert G. Ludwig, Chief Inspector and Deputy Superintendent of the Building Department:

"Even the drop ladder at the bottom of the fire escape was in compliance with the law. The worst feature was that the escape ended in an enclosed court. There is nothing in the law to prevent this." Ludwig also said, "This building could be worse and come within the requirement of the law."

May Levantini, a factory worker:

She said that the key to the stairway door hung by a piece of colored string. "The door was locked. I turned the key that was in the lock and I opened the door."

The architect who designed the building:

"When the building was put up, there was an opening from the court in which the fire escape ended through an alley about 15 feet wide. Since then, the old buildings in that block have been torn down and new ones put up that have enclosed the court on all sides."

Trial Procedures Guide

1. The judge calls the court to order. One of the judge's assistants announces the business of the trial. The judge reminds the jury to take notes throughout the trial.

2. The prosecution gives its opening statement: what it intends to prove during the trial (that Blanc and Harris are guilty of manslaughter due to willful negligence) and how it intends to do it.

3. The defense gives its opening statement: what it intends to prove during the trial and how it intends to do it.

4. The prosecution calls its first witness. The prosecuting attorney asks the witness questions about what he or she knows about the facts of the case. If the defense thinks the question is unfair or the witness is not qualified to answer, the defense attorney may object to the question. It is then up to the judge to decide whether to allow the question.

5. The defense may choose to cross-examine the witness: to ask questions calling into doubt the accuracy of the witness's testimony. The defense may only cross-examine the witness on issues raised by his or her original testimony. The same rules of objection apply as in Step 4.

6. The prosecution calls its other witnesses in order, and the same procedure is followed as in Steps 4 and 5. When the prosecution has presented all its witnesses, the prosecuting attorney announces, "The prosecution rests."

7. The defense presents its witnesses. The defense attorney asks each witness questions about what he or she knows about the facts of the case. Then the prosecution gets a chance to cross-examine the witness. The same rules of cross-examination and objection as stated in Steps 4 and 5 apply here. When the defense has presented all its witnesses, the defense attorney announces, "The defense rests."

8. The judge calls on each side to present its closing statement; defense first, then prosecution. These statements review the cases that the defense and prosecution have presented and ask the jury to rule in favor of their particular side on the basis of the facts presented.

9. The jury deliberates, votes on the guilt or innocence of the accused, and announces its verdict.

10. The judge dismisses the jury. If the accused are found innocent, they are set free. If they are found guilty, the judge passes sentence.

TOPIC: Education During the Progressive Era
TIME: One class period
TIME PERIOD: During study of educational reform during the Progressive Era

BACKGROUND

Education was central to many of the issues raised during the Progressive Era. After the Civil War the United States had built schools at a rate greater than ever before, and most states had passed laws requiring school attendance. During the Progressive Era high school attendance reached new levels for a variety of reasons: child labor laws were enacted, and children no longer had to work long hours in factories; per capita income continued to rise; and the introduction of the typewriter and duplicator provided more white-collar jobs.

Debates over education in the Progressive Era focused mainly on its purpose. Liberal educators thought that schools were a force in building a larger community—the means by which more and more citizens could participate in government and economy. John Dewey, who advocated experiential learning, was an advocate of this point of view. Conservative educators, on the other hand, believed that schools were the means through which Americans could learn to improve efficiency and thus be able to manage and further industry. Schools, conservatives also believed, were responsible for inculcating American values, especially in children from immigrant families.

This teaching strategy provides an opportunity for students to examine school enrollment, particularly the spectacular increase in high school enrollment, during the Progressive Era. Students will explore the manner in which societal values are reflected in educational institutions.

MATERIALS

Graph paper, colored pencils, and rulers

SUGGESTED PROCEDURE

1. Have students explore increasing school enrollments during the Progressive Era by organizing the class into small groups and having each group create bar graphs. (If students are unsure of how to create a bar graph, direct them to a bar graph in their textbooks.) Some groups may graph enrollments for kindergarten through eighth grade while others graph high school enrollments. Provide the necessary statistics by writing these figures on the chalkboard:

K–8		High School	
1870	6,800,000	1870	80,000
1880	9,800,000	1880	110,000
1890	12,700,000	1890	200,000
1900	15,000,000	1900	500,000
1910	17,000,000	1910	900,000
1920	19,000,000	1920	2,000,000

2. After the groups have completed their bar graphs, discuss with the class the reasons for the dramatic increase in school enrollment. (less child labor, higher family income, more white-collar jobs) Ask how an increase in the number of high school graduates might have, in turn, affected the nation. (More educated people were entering the work force. They would obtain higher paying jobs and have more money to spend. Consumer and service industries would develop. People who were better educated would be able to particpate in government more fully.)
3. Provide students with the background information and have the class discuss the debates over education during the Progressive Era—debates that focused on the nature and purpose of schools. Then ask the class to describe the debates over education today. Have them give reasons that Americans become concerned if they think that students are not learning certain subjects. Encourage ideas by asking students to repeat

views expressed by adults they know, people on television, and so on. Then make a list on the chalkboard similar to this:

Americans want schools to:

> Prepare students so that the United States can compete economically with other nations.
> Teach students what is expected of people living in a democracy.
> Build an appreciation of America's heritage.
> Teach students to analyze problems and to think critically.
> Encourage healthy ways of life and good values.

4. Have the class categorize these goals. Ask students: Which goals are similar to the practical goals favored by the conservative educators of the Progressive Era? Which are more like those favored by the liberal educators of the Progressive Era? Are all of the goals important, or only some of them? Encourage debate and discussion.
5. Ask students to write down some of the goals that they hope to achieve as adults. Ask volunteers to share these goals with the class. Have the class discuss the role education will play in helping individuals reach their goals.

Creative Strategies for Teaching American History

The Twentieth Century
1914 to the Present

TOPIC: Neutrality and World War I
TIME: One to two class periods
TIME PERIOD: During study of Wilson's neutrality policy during World War I

BACKGROUND

When Americans opened their newspapers in 1914 to headlines of war in Europe, they were stunned. For many years government and business leaders had devoted much effort to developing international understanding and to promoting peace. The American people reacted to the European strife by withdrawing their interest in international affairs. As events unfolded across the Atlantic Ocean, the United States tried to steer a neutral course among the warring nations.

The American desire for neutrality, however, was not to be. Primarily the United States was caught in a triangle with Germany and Great Britain. Both countries were relying on the United States for trade. In order to remain neutral the United States had to deal fairly with both nations. But the policy of neutrality was easier proclaimed than enforced. Step by step the events of the war pushed the nation closer to involvement. Finally, in the spring of 1917, the United States entered the war on the side of the Allies.

Not all Americans were in favor of United States involvement in the war in Europe. After President Wilson delivered his war message to Congress, several congressmen spoke out against American involvement. One of these congressmen was Robert La Follette. His antiwar sentiments had earned him the title of leader of what Wilson called "a little group of willful men, representing no opinion but their own."

In this teaching strategy students will read and analyze excerpts from La Follette's speech to Congress. They will then read and discuss historian Melvin Small's ideas also concerning neutrality during World War I. Students will realize that neutrality is not a cut-and-dried issue. The readings will familiarize students with another point of view concerning the entry of the United States into the war.

MATERIALS

Copies of the handouts

SUGGESTED PROCEDURE

1. Review with students the events leading up to the involvement of the United States in World War I. Make sure students understand the concepts of *neutrality, contraband,* and *belligerent nations*. Remind them that until we entered the war on the side of the Allies, Great Britain was considered a belligerent nation.
2. Distribute the handout to each student. Call on students to read the first selection aloud. Then ask students the following questions:
   a. What did Thomas Jefferson say about neutrality? (If a neutral nation allows one warring nation to violate its rights, it must allow the enemy nation to violate the neutral's rights.)
   b. Does La Follette agree or disagree with Thomas Jefferon? Why? (La Follette agrees; he says that if a neutral nation is to have respect, it must treat warring nations in the same way.)
3. Tell students that the reading by Melvin Small will contain some information that might help explain La Follette's opinion on American neutrality. Call on students to read aloud the selection by Melvin Small. Remind students that the selection is one historian's theory and that it may not be shared by other historians. Explain to students that the selection ends before discussion of the sinking of the *Lusitania.*
4. Organize students into groups of four to debate the issue *Resolved:* The United States did not retain its policy of neutrality. Two students from each group should argue that America did retain its neutrality policy and two students should argue that it did not retain its neutrality policy. After 5 to 10 minutes of debate, bring the class back together. Tell students that they will each write a three-part essay on the question "Did the United States retain its policy of neutrality between 1914 and 1916?" Have students follow the five-step procedure in writing their essays:

Step 1: Prewriting

Students should make a list of reasons to support their opinions on the question of whether or not the United States maintained a policy of neutrality. Tell them to think about what they learned in their group debates. They may also refer to the readings.

Step 2: Writing a First Draft

Have students use their lists to write a first draft of their essays. Remind students that their three-part essays should have an introduction, a body, and a conclusion.

Step 3: Revising

Have students exchange their essays with a partner who will critique the essay for how well it defends the student's argument.

Step 4: Proofreading

Ask students to proofread their essays for errors in spelling, grammar, and punctuation.

Step 5: Writing a Final Copy

Have students write their essays on a clean sheet of paper.

5. To conclude the activity, ask volunteers to read their essays aloud to the rest of the class. Ask students from both sides of the argument to read their essays.

Speech to Congress by Robert La Follette, April 4, 1917

From the *Congressional Record*

Excerpted

Jefferson asserted that we could not permit one warring nation to curtail our neutral rights if we were not ready to allow her enemy the same privileges, and that any other course entailed the sacrifice of our neutrality.

That is the sensible, that is the logical position. No neutrality could ever have commanded respect if it was not based on that equitable and just proposition; and we from early in the war threw our neutrality to the winds by permitting England to make a mockery of it to her advantage against her chief enemy. Then we expect to say to that enemy, "You have got to respect my rights as a neutral." What is the answer? I say Germany has been patient with us. Standing strictly on her rights, her answer would be, "Maintain your neutrality; treat these other Governments warring against me as you treat me if you want your neutral rights respected."

I say again that when two nations are at war any neutral nation, in order to preserve its character as a neutral nation, must exact the same conduct from both warring nations; both must equally obey the principles of international law. If a neutral nation fails that, then its rights upon the high seas—to adopt the President's phrase—are relative and not absolute. There can be no greater violation of our neutrality than the requirement that one of two belligerents shall adhere to settled principles of law and that the other shall have the advantage of not doing so. The respect that German naval authorities were required to pay to the rights of our people upon the high seas would depend upon the question whether we had exacted the same rights from Germany's enemies. If we had not done so we lost our character as a neutral nation, and our people unfortunately had lost the protection that belongs to neutrals. Our responsibility was joint in the sense that we must exact the same conduct from both belligerents. . . .

Had the plain principle of international law announced by Jefferson been followed by us, we would not be called on to-day to declare war upon any of the belligerents. The failure to treat the belligerent nations of Europe alike, the failure to reject unlawful "war zones" of both Germany and Great Britain, is wholly accountable for our present dilemma. We should not seek to hide our blunder behind the smoke of battle, to inflame the mind of our people by half truths into the frenzy of war, in order that they may never appreciate the real cause of it until it is too late. I do not believe that our national honor is served by such a course. The right way is the honorable way.

Excerpts from *Was War Necessary?*

By Melvin Small; copyright 1980 by Sage Publications, Inc.

To define and maintain one's neutrality in 1914 was a messy business. . . . In few areas is international law as ambiguous as in neutrality law. . . .

In 1856, following the Crimean War, the major powers drew up a treaty redefining neutrality, contraband, and blockade. Between that time and 1914, sweeping changes in weaponry, transportation, and communication systems made a good portion of the mid-nineteenth century codes irrelevant and outmoded. In order to bring them up to date, most of the important nations met at London in 1909 to construct a new set of naval neutrality laws. The treaty they drafted was ultimately unacceptable to England since it was biased in favor of neutrals and belligerents with small navies. The London Treaty's definitions of contraband were so rigid and the freedom given to neutrals to trade with belligerents so liberal that the ruler of the seas could never have lived with the document, even thought it was ratified by other nations. In 1914, England, the number one sea power, was prepared to enforce its own historic neutrality laws. . . .

There were two very general ways in which neutrality could be defined. A neutral could try to maintain the strictest possible legal neutrality by using treaties, conferences, and precedents to establish a posture acceptable to its own international lawyers and, it hoped, to the international lawyers in the belligerent camps. . . .

On the other hand, a neutral could try to be fair to both sides by refraining from adopting a policy that upset the military balance. A neutral could act neutrally, in a legal sense, and in so doing ruin one of the belligerents. For example, in 1914, had Wilson demanded that the British behave themselves, and had the British refused, as was likely, he could have severed the Anglo-American trade link and the Germans might have won the war. In that case, Wilson would have been strictly neutral, but terribly unfair. Is a neutral responsible for the consequences of its neutral behavior?

Everything the United States did, whether in accordance with international law or not, had to affect the outcome of World War I to some degree. Perhaps prudent neutrals should call in their ships and stay out of the way of the belligerents until a war is over. This is what Thomas Jefferson did in 1807. Such behavior is not only economically unwise but also unneutral and unfair. When the war began, the British had every reason to expect to trade with the United States. Their naval and economic plans were predicated upon such a trade. Had we closed our ports and factories to them, we would have changed the rules in the middle of the game and thus would have been guilty of behaving unneutrally and unfairly.

Woodrow Wilson apparently tried to be both neutral and fair to both sides, or at least, to balance the two aspects of neutrality so that we did not influence unduly the belligerents' chances on the field of battle. There is a third element in neutral policy that may be the most important of all. It is possible that in its attempt to be neutral and fair, a nation might end up destroying its own security or economy. Faced with irritating nonlethal violations to neutrality but a prosperity dependent on an acceptance of those violations, what should a neutral do? . . . It seems sensible for a President to choose security and prosperity over neutrality—if the choice is ever that clear. Unfortunately, it never is, and so Wilson ended up declaring his absolute neutrality and then proceeded to bend international law to protect the economy.

In order to assess Wilson's definition of American neutrality, we have to ask several questions. Was he neutral, or more likely, was he as netural as possible? Was he as fair as possible? Did his neutrality policy affect our entry into the war?

As to the first . . . we must conclude that Wilson was generally neutral, at least in a legal sense. . . .

But were we fair to both belligerents and did the application of our netural policy help shape the outcome of the military battles on the continent? Clearly, the impact of our neutral policies was more damaging to the Germans than the British. For example, by accepting the mining of the North Sea as well as the British refusal to sign the London Treaty of 1909, we contributed to the establishment of British naval supremacy. One can imagine a German victory resulting from the following scenario. We insist on a revocation of the mining program and adherence to the London Treaty. The British refuse, and we counter with a severance of economic relations. Such an action coming in 1914 or 1915, when the British desperately needed our supplies, might have weakened the Allies sufficiently to insure their loss.

To look at things another way, we appeared to be hurting Germany by not hurting England. It was far easier for us to hurt England than Germany for Germany's main strength lay in her land forces, while England's lay in her navy. German activities on the European battlefields did not involve any violation of our neutrality, whereas everything that happened on the British-controlled seas was of vital importance to us. Had we made too many rulings against Britain, we could have caused her to lose the war. But by ruling against Germany's ancillary power *under* the Atlantic, we only made it more difficult for her to win. Thus, although Wilson was not as fair as he might have been, his activities did not upset the balance to a significant degree.

Wilson's neutrality and relative fairness does not tell the entire story. All through the war, he insisted that he maintained a scrupulous and impartial neutrality, even when it came to American interests. As we have seen in his early decisions, the Germans had every reason to suspect that he had been less than fair to them, or at least, more fair to England. His neutral policies, especially those involving the Atlantic link to Britain,

created an environment in which the Germans could not believe American protestations of good faith. Although their violations of our neutrality eventually led us into war against them, they felt they were merely righting the balance Wilson had tipped toward Britain from 1914 to 1917. . . .

Both the British and the Germans violated our rights. The former's disregard of international etiquette led to severe tension. The latter's led to war. On the surface, this situation seems unfair since the quantity of British violations greatly outnumbered the German. The respective quality of the two sorts of violations was quite another story.

The British assaulted neutral rights in many ways. First of all, they engaged in illegal searches and seizures. . . . According to our (and most neutrals') interpretation of the law, the British continually transcended the bounds of legitimate belligerent rights. For example, a belligerent warship was supposed to make its search for contraband on the high seas—it could not order a ship into port unless it had good reason to suspect that the ship carried contraband that could only be detected through the use of X-rays or other devices. The British did not think twice about forcing a neutral to England. . . .

The contraband question itself became a bitter issue of contention between America and Britain as the war progressed and the Admiralty's list grew longer and longer. By late 1915, just about everything the Germans might have wanted to buy from us was considered contraband and liable to British seizure. The prohibition of food shipments to the Central Powers was especially rankling. . . .

Furthermore, the British displayed American flags on some of their merchant vessels in order to deceive submarines. We were prepared to accept the limited use of this *ruse de guerre* as we had in the past, but the British overdid it and thus dangerously frustrated German submarine commanders who could not distinguish between a real and a bogus American ship. . . .

Had the British offended us in 1914 the way they finally offended us in 1916, we probably would have threatened to break relations with them unless they ceased and desisted. At that time, they relied upon our goods, especially foodstuffs, more than they did two years later when their empire took up the slack. Recognizing this factor in 1914, the British tread cautiously, violating our neturality in ways calculated to result in little more than verbal slaps on the wrist from Washington. By 1916, however, we needed them almost as much as they needed us. Their war trade had pulled us out of depression. Had we threatened to sever relations in 1916, they might have called our bluff, secure in their belief that at the last moment we would not have sacrificed our economy on the altar of Jeffersonian moral outrage.

Wilson did not take the British policy lying down. From the start, he and the State Department protested against each perceived violation of our rights. As the months passed, these protests increased in vigor and volume. It was said that Wilson had written so many protests that the White House had run out of stationery. . . . During the six months prior to the German declaration of unlimited submarine warfare on January 31, 1917, Wilson was far more worried about British behavior than German. . . .

At the same time, Wison had to worry about the Republicans; 1916 was an election year. . . . Had Wilson called for the British to halt their violations or else, and had they refused as they would have, we might have been thrown into a recession and Wilson would have been thrown out of office. Many more Americans would have been angry

about a depression than his failure to prosecute vigorously our legal case against the British. After all, none of the British actions cost one American life. . . .

The Germans never had the opportunity to violate our rights in the British manner. Although their navy was the second largest in the world, it was no match for the British. . . . From the German point of view, this waste of a spendid navy was a shame because the insular British were far more vulnerable to naval blockade and even starvation than were the autarchic Germans. The Kaiser did have some submarines. . . .

Unfortunately for the Germans, the submarine was not covered by existing maritime law. . . . With little to go on, Americans and other neutrals, as well as the gleeful British, had to adapt the rules for surface vessels to the submarine—and this was absurd. According to traditional practices, when a captain desired to search and maybe even destroy a contraband carrier, he hailed the offending ship, boarded her, and, before dispatching her to the bottom of the sea, adhered to a series of humanitarian rules that guaranteed the safety of crew and passengers. . . .

From the American point of view, when the submarine operated effectively—striking merchants by surprise—it operated immorally. When the Germans formally announced their submarine policy to the world in February of 1915, Wilson cautioned them that they would be held to "strict accountability" for violations of neutrality. He never used that phrase with the British.

TOPIC: The WPA's Federal Art Project
TIME: Two class periods
TIME PERIOD: During study of the New Deal

BACKGROUND

When Franklin Roosevelt took office in March of 1933, his motto was "Action, and action now." His first priority as president was to put people back to work. The greatest benefits of the New Deal program came from what was done about the unemployed and the poor.

Headed by Roosevelt's trusted aid, Henry Hopkins, the Works Progress Administration (WPA) was created in 1935 to provide jobs for the unemployed. Probably the most visible of all the New Deal agencies, the WPA hired workers to build and repair roads and to build schools, airports, and post offices. Besides providing jobs in construction, the WPA funded the Federal Theater Project and the Federal Writers' Project to create jobs for theatrical people and for writers, editors, and researchers.

The WPA's Federal Art Project was the first major attempt at government patronage of the visual arts. Hopkins chose Holger Cahill, a museum curator, to head the FAP. The FAP was essentially a work-relief program for artists. The project also developed an audience in the American people by taking art to regions where art and artists were almost unknown. The project established more than 100 community art centers and galleries across the country.

Most of the artists were employed from relief rolls. Each artist received a wage of $23.50 per week. In turn, the artist was expected to create an artwork within a specified time period, or to work a certain number of hours on a mural or sculpture. Artists of the 1930s wanted to document the look and feel of the country. The art movement of that time period became known as the "American Scene." Artists who worked under the WPA included Thomas Hart Benton, Ben Shahn, Jackson Pollack, Willem de Kooning, and William Groper. Some artists focused on social and cultural patterns; others focused on social progress.

Many of the mural artists were influenced by the Mexican mural movement, especially the work of artist Diego Rivera. The Mexican mural artists expressed the social ideals of the Mexican Revolution. American artists wanted to express what they saw as the social revolution our country was experiencing. The work of the mural artists can still be viewed in post offices and other public buildings all across the country.

In this teaching strategy students will gain an appreciation of the mural art that was produced during the 1930s. They will learn how mural art can be used for social commentary, and they will create their own murals to make social statements.

MATERIALS

1. Transparencies or copies of the photographs of WPA murals
2. Colored pencils, colored chalk, crayons, felt-tipped markers, or paints and brushes for each group
3. Butcher paper

SUGGESTED PROCEDURE

1. Review with students the agencies created by the New Deal and how the agencies aided various groups of people. Provide students with the background information on the WPA and the Federal Art Project.
2. Show the transparencies or distribute copies to students. Ask them to describe what is being depicted in each mural. Tell students that murals are one way of commenting on or reacting to a society.
3. Organize students into groups of four. Tell students that they are going to create murals that provide a social commentary of our time. Have groups decide on a social ideal or issue that they would like to illustrate. Tell the groups to make preliminary sketches of their murals. Distribute sheets of butcher paper and have each group hang its butcher paper on a designated wall or bulletin board. Give each group the art supplies and allow them at least one class period to work on their murals.
4. After the groups have completed the murals, have the class discuss the social commentary expressed by each group's mural. Discuss how murals can be a visual statement. Then ask each student to choose one mural and to write a paragraph explaining how the mural is a visual statement of our time.

TOPIC: The USO (United Service Organizations, Inc.)
TIME: Two class periods—one for library research and one for group presentations
TIME PERIOD: During study of WWI, the Korean War, and the Vietnam War

BACKGROUND

The USO (United Service Organizations) was founded on February 4, 1941, to provide social and recreational services for members of the United States armed forces. The organization was sponsored by public contributions and six private agencies: the YMCA, YWCA, Salvation Army, National Catholic Community Service, National Jewish Welfare Board, and the Travelers Aid Association of America. After World War II ended the organization faded out, but the advent of the Korean War in 1951 brought the organization back to life. Perhaps the most well-known service that the organization offered was Bob Hope's Christmas shows. The organization expanded in the 1960s during the conflict in Vietnam, and it began offering services such as counseling and drug abuse programs. The organization did much to help the morale of the armed forces through all three wars. Volunteers were able to help keep the men in touch with what was going on "at home."

The USO saw its heyday during World War II. Celebrities that were not fighting were entertaining the troops. Stars such as Dinah Shore, Jack Benny, and Frances Langford spent weeks touring the battle zones of Europe and the Pacific. The Hollywood Overseas Committee, a group of movie and talent agency executives, helped recruit stars for the shows. During the Vietnam war, however, the unpopularity of the war, coupled with the death of the president of the USO, made it harder for the USO to attract big-name stars. In this teaching strategy students will use the USO as a basis for learning about popular cultural trends in the United States. The strategy will provide an ideal opportunity to discuss social change, especially that produced by the freedom movement and the antiwar movement of the 1960s and 1970s.

MATERIALS

Copies of the "USO Show Worksheets"

SUGGESTED PROCEDURE

1. Provide students with the background information on the USO. Organize students into three groups. Assign each group one of the following wars: World War II, the Korean War, or the war in Vietnam. Distribute to each student the "USO Show Worksheet." Have the groups read the worksheets so that they have an idea of what they will be researching. Group members should divide up the topics for research. Allow students to use one class period in the school library to complete their research. Tell students that they may wish to perform songs, or they may find examples of popular recordings to use in their presentations. They may even wish to demonstrate the dances that were popular during the era. Encourage students to draw pictures of clothing from the time period, including the uniforms worn in each war, or they may bring in books that have appropriate illustrations. Each group member will be responsible for presenting at least one item in the "show." Group members will need to work together to decide the order in which to present their show.
2. On the day of the presentations, allow each group about 15 minutes to perform their "show." After all of the groups have presented, ask the class to discuss the effect of the USO volunteers on the members of the armed forces in each of the three wars.

USO Show Worksheet

Directions: You and your group are volunteers for the USO during the war in _____, which is taking place between 19___ and 19___. Your job is to make the members of the armed forces feel supported by the people at home. Each member of your group should choose one of the following topics. Research your topic and be prepared to present your information in front of the troops (the rest of the class). You may present you information through pictures, words, action, or music. Remember that you must research what was occurring during the time period of your assigned war.

1. What songs are popular back in the United States?

2. What movies are popular back in the United States?

3. What dances are popular back in the United States?

4. What hair styles are worn by women back in the United States? What hair styles are popular for men?

5. What style of clothes are worn by women back in the United States? What style of clothes are worn by men?

6. What are the soldiers wearing? What are the officers wearing?

7. What television shows are popular back in the United States?

8. What musicals are playing on Broadway?

9. What novels and magazines are read by people back in the United States?

TOPIC: The Montgomery, Alabama, Bus Boycott
TIME: One class period
TIME PERIOD: During study of the civil rights movement and the theory of nonviolent disobedience

BACKGROUND

Rosa Parks, a black woman, was arrested in 1955 for violating city segregation laws in Montgomery, Alabama. She refused to give up her bus seat to a white man and was arrested by city police. Park's arrest sparked a massive bus boycott that lasted more than a year. African American leaders asked the black community not to ride the buses and to either walk or carpool to work. The boycott was a success and forced the city to integrate its buses.

The reading in this teaching strategy is from *Stride Toward Freedom,* by Martin Luther King, Jr. King was 26 years old at the time of the bus boycott. His home was bombed or shot at three times during the boycott. Nine years later King would receive the Nobel Peace Prize. He donated the $54,600 award to the civil rights movement.

In this teaching strategy students will learn about the Montgomery bus boycott through the eyes of Martin Luther King, Jr. The reading also offers King's thoughts on Henry David Thoreau's essay on civil disobedience. Students will gain an appreciation for and an understanding of King's movement of massive noncooperation.

MATERIALS

1. Copies of the reading
2. Copies of the "Montgomery, Alabama, Bus Boycott" question sheet

SUGGESTED PROCEDURE

1. Write the following question on the chalkboard :

   Unjust laws exist: shall we be content to obey them, or shall we endeavor to amend them, and obey them until we have succeeded, or shall we transgress them at once?

   Tell students that the question was posed by Henry David Thoreau in his essay "Civil Disobedience." Ask students for their reactions to the question.
2. Explain to students the theory of civil disobedience (refusing to obey unjust laws). Tell students that civil disobedience is a special way of disobeying laws and that it follows these rules:
   a. Only an unjust rule or law may be disobeyed.
   b. The disobedience must be public, not secret, because the purpose of the disobedience is to show that the law is unjust.
   c. Even though the law is unjust, the person who practices civil disobedience must accept the penalty for disobeying it. For example, he or she must be willing to go to jail without a struggle. In this way, the protester shows that he or she understands and respects the general concept of law and order.
3. Explain to students that the primary goal of the civil rights movement was to overturn segregation laws. Through the efforts of leaders such as Martin Luther King, Jr., and through public demonstrations across the land, many civil rights laws were passed. The civil rights movement showed ways of protesting unjust laws without overturning the fundamental principles of law and order. The struggle for full civil rights continues to this day. The work will remain unfinished until all Americans are truly guaranteed "equal protection of the laws."
4. Provide students with the background information on Rosa Parks and Martin Luther King, Jr. Distribute copies of the reading to each student. Have students take turns reading aloud. When students have finished the reading, organize the class into groups of four and distribute the "Montgomery, Alabama, Bus

Boycott" question sheet. Tell students that they may discuss the questions with their groups, but each student must fill out his or her own question sheet.

5. To conclude the activity, ask students to write a paragraph explaining how Rosa Parks and the Montgomery bus boycott followed the rules of civil disobedience.

Answers to Question Sheet (Page 344)

1. She would not give up her bus seat to a white man; she wanted to preserve her dignity and self-respect.
2. The message would tell people that African Americans would no longer allow themselves to be treated unjustly and unfairly.
3. They were able to get the taxi companies to agree to transport people for the same cost as riding the bus.
4. He felt hope that new times were coming.
5. A black maid who could not read gave the boycott notice to her white employer. The employer then turned the notice over to the newspaper. This action helped the boycott by spreading the word to practically all the African American citizens in Montgomery.
6. They sprung up in response to the Supreme Court's decision in *Brown v. Board of Education of Topeka* that schools must be integrated. The Councils wanted to preserve segregation.
7. He asked himself if a boycott was unethical, unchristian, and negative.
8. He reasoned that the bus boycott would be in the cause of justice and freedom and that the White Citizens Councils' boycotts served to perpetrate injustice.
9. He realized that a man has a right and a duty to refuse to cooperate with an unjust and evil system.

Excerpts from *Stride Toward Freedom*
by Martin Luther King, Jr.

On December 1, 1955, an attractive Negro seamstress, Mrs. Rosa Parks, boarded the Cleveland Avenue bus in downtown Montgomery. She was returning home after her regular day's work in Montomery Fair—a leading department store. Tired from long hours on her feet, Mrs. Parks sat down in the first seat behind the section reserved for whites. Not long after she took her seat, the bus operator ordered her, along with three other Negro passengers, to move back in order to accommodate boarding white passengers. By this time every seat in the bus was taken. This meant that if Mrs. Parks followed the driver's command she would have to stand while a white male passenger, who had just boarded the bus, would sit. The other three Negro passengers immediately complied with the driver's request. But Mrs. Parks quietly refused. The result was her arrest.

There was to be much speculation about why Mrs. Parks did not obey the driver. Many people in the white community argued that she had been "planted" by the NAACP in order to lay the groundwork for a test case. . . .

But the accusation was totally unwarranted, as the testimony of both Mrs. Parks and the officials of the NAACP revealed. . . . Mrs. Parks' refusal to move back was her intrepid affirmation that she had had enough. It was an individual expression of a timeless longing for human dignity and freedom. She was not "planted" there by the NAACP, or any other organization; she was planted there by her personal sense of dignity and self-respect.

Only E.D. Nixon—the signer of Mrs. Park's bond—and one or two other persons were aware of the arrest when it occurred early Thursday evening. Later in the evening the word got around to a few influential women of the community, mostly members of the Women's Political Council. After a series of phone calls back and forth they agreed that the Negroes should boycott the buses. They immediately suggested the idea to Nixon, and he readily concurred. In his usual courageous manner he agreed to spearhead the idea.

Early Friday morning, December 2, Nixon called me. . . . I listened, deeply shocked, as he described the humiliating incident. "We have taken this type of thing too long already," Nixon concluded, his voice trembling. "I feel that the time has come to boycott the buses. Only through a boycott can we make it clear to the white folks that we will not accept this type of treatment any longer."

I agreed at once that some protest was necessary, and that the boycott method would be an effective one.

Just before calling me Nixon had discussed the idea with Rev. Ralph Abernathy, the young minister of Montgomery's First Baptist Church, who was to become one of the central figures in the protest, and one of my closest associates. Abernathy also felt a bus boycott was our best course of action. . . . Nixon suggested that we call a meeting of all the ministers and civic leaders the same evening in order to get their thinking on the proposal, and I offered my church as the meeting place. . . .

By early afternoon the arrest of Mrs. Parks was becoming public knowledge. Word of it had spread around the community like uncontrolled fire. Telephones began to ring in almost rhythmic succession. By two o'clock an enthusiastic group had mimeographed leaflets concerning the arrest and the proposed boycott, and by evening these had been widely circulated.

As the hour for the evening meeting arrived, I approached the doors of the church with some apprehension, wondering how many leaders would respond to our call. Fortunately, it was one of those pleasant winter nights of unseasonable warmth, and to our relief, almost everybody who had been invited was on hand. More than forty people, from every segment of Negro life, were crowded into the large church meeting room. I saw physicians, schoolteachers, lawyers, businessmen, postal workers, union leaders, and clergymen. Virtually every organization of the Negro community was represented. . . .

Bennett moved into action, explaining the purpose of the gathering. With excited gestures he reported on Mrs. Parks's resistance and her arrest. He presented the proposal that the Negro citizens of Montgomery should boycott the buses on Monday in protest. "Now is the time to move," he concluded. "This is not time to talk; it is time to act.". . .

Not once did anyone question the validity or desirability of the boycott itself. It seemed to be the unanimous sense of the group that the boycott should take place.

The ministers endorsed the plan with enthusiasm, and promised to go to their congregations on Sunday morning and drive home their approval of the projected one-day protest. . . . It was decided that we should hold a citywide mass meeting on Monday night, December 5, to determine how long we would abstain from riding the buses. . . .

The group agreed that additional leaflets should be distributed on Saturday, and the chairman appointed a committee, including myself, to prepare the statement. . . . It read as follows:

> Don't ride the bus to work, to town, to school, or any place Monday, December 5.
>
> Another Negro woman has been arrested and put in jail because she refused to give up her bus seat.
>
> Don't ride the buses to work, to town, to school, or anywhere on Monday. If you work, take a cab, or share a ride, or walk.
>
> Come to a mass meeting, Monday at 7:00 P.M., at the Holt Street Baptist Church for further instruction.

The final question before the meeting concerned transportation. It was agreed that we should try to get the Negro taxi companies of the city—eighteen in number, with approximately 210 taxis—to transport the people for the same price that they were currently paying on the bus.

With these responsibilities before us the meeting closed. We left with our hearts caught up in a great idea. The hours were moving fast. The clock on the wall read almost midnight, but the clock in our souls revealed that it was daybreak.

I was so excited that I slept very little that night, and early next morning I was on my way to the church to get the leaflets out. By nine o'clock the church secretary had finished mimeographing the 7,000 leaflets and by eleven o'clock an army of women and young people had taken them off to distribute by hand.

Those on the committee that was to contact the taxi companies got to work early Saturday afternoon. They worked assiduously, and by evening they had reached practically all of the companies, and triumphantly reported that every one of them so far had agreed to cooperate with the proposed boycott by transporting the passengers to and from work for the regular ten-cent bus fare.

Meanwhile our efforts to get the word across to the Negro community were abetted in an unexpected way. A maid who could not read very well came into possession of one of the unsigned appeals that had been distributed Friday afternoon. Apparently not knowing what the leaflet said, she gave it to her employer. As soon as the white employer received the notice she turned it over to the local newspaper, and the Montgomery *Advertiser* made the contents of the leaflet a front-page story on Saturday morning. It appears that the *Advertiser* printed the story in order to let the white community know what the Negroes were up to; but the whole thing turned out to the Negroes' advantage, since it served to bring the information to hundreds who had not previously heard of the plan. By Sunday afternoon word had spread to practically every Negro citizen of Montgomery. Only a few people who lived in remote areas had not heard of it.

After a heavy day of work, I went home late Sunday afternoon and sat down to read the morning paper. There was a long article on the proposed boycott. Implicit throughout the article, I noticed, was the idea that the Negroes were preparing to use the same approach to their problem as the White Citizens Councils used. This suggested parallel had some serious implications. The White Citizens Councils had had their birth in Mississippi a few months after the Supreme Court's school decision had come into being to preserve segregation. The Councils had multiplied rapidly throughout the South, purporting to achieve their ends by the legal maneuvers of "interposition" and "nullification." Unfortunately, however, the actions of some of these Councils extended far beyond the bounds of the law. Their methods were methods of open and covert terror, brutal intimidation, and threats of starvation to Negro men, women, and children. They took open economic reprisals against whites who dared to protest their defiance of the law, and the aim of their boycotts was not merely to impress their victims but to destroy them if possible.

Disturbed by the fact that our pending action was being equated with the boycott methods of the White Citizens Councils, I was forced for the first time to think seriously on the nature of the boycott. Up to this time I had uncritically accepted this method as our best course of action. Now certain doubts began to bother me. Were we following an ethical course of action? Is the boycott method basically unchristian? Isn't it a negative approach to the solution of a problem? Is it true that we would be following the course of some of the White Citizens Councils? Even if lasting practical results came from such a boycott, would immoral means justify moral ends? Each of these questions demanded honest answers.

I had to recognize that the boycott method could be used to unethical and unchristian ends. I had to concede, further, that this was the method used so often by the White Citizens Councils to deprive many Negroes, as well a white persons of good will, of the basic necessities of life. But . . . our purposes were altogether different. We would use this method to give birth to justice and freedom, and also to urge men to comply with the law of the land; the White Citizens Councils used it to perpetuate the reign of injustice and human servitude, and urged men to defy the law of the land. I reasoned, therefore, that the word "boycott" was really a misnomer for our proposed action. A boycott suggests an economic squeeze, leaving one bogged down in a negative. But we were concerned with the positive. Our concern would not be to put the bus company out of business, but to put justice in business.

As I thought further I came to see that what we were really doing was withdrawing our cooperation from an evil system, rather than merely withdrawing our economic support from the bus company. The bus company, being an external expression of the system, would naturally suffer, but the basic aim was to refuse to cooperate with evil. At this point I began to think about Thoreau's Essay on Civil Disobedience. I remembered how, as a college student, I had been moved when I first read this work. I became convinced that what we were preparing to do in Montgomery was related to what Thoreau had expressed. We were simply saying to the white community, "We can no longer lend our cooperation to an evil system."

Something began to say to me, "He who passively accepts evil is as much involved in it as he who helps to perpetrate it. He who accepts evil without protesting it is really cooperating with it." When oppressed people willingly accept their oppression they only serve to give the oppressor a convenient justification for his acts. Often the oppressor goes along unaware of the evil involved in his oppression so long as the oppressed accepts it. So in order to be true to one's conscience and true to God, a righteous man has no alternative but to refuse to cooperate with an evil system. This I felt was the nature of our action. From this moment on I conceived of our movement as an act of massive noncooperation.

The Montgomery, Alabama, Bus Boycott

Directions: Use the information in the reading to answer the following questions.

1. Why was Rosa Parks arrested? Why did she allow herself to be arrested?

_____

_____

2. What message did Nixon, King, and Abernathy think the bus boycott would deliver?

_____

_____

3. How did the leaders of the bus boycott solve the transportation problem for people in the black community?

_____

_____

4. Why do you think King says, "The clock on the wall read almost midnight, but the clock in our souls revealed that it was daybreak"?

_____

_____

_____

5. How did word of the boycott end up in the Montgomery *Advertiser?*

_____

_____

_____

6. What was the origin and purpose of the White Citizens Councils?

_____

_____

_____

7. Why did King begin to have doubts about the boycott?

_____

_____

8. How did King reason the difference between the bus boycott and the boycotts of the White Citizens Councils?

_____

_____

9. How did Thoreau's essay on civil disobedience lead King to the concept of massive noncooperation?

_____

_____

TOPIC: Protest Songs of the Twentieth Century
TIME: One class period
TIME PERIOD: During specific events of the twentieth century or at the end of study
of the twentieth century

BACKGROUND

Protest songs serve to strengthen the will of the protesters. The songs unify people and vocalize a common bond. They give people hope and make them realize that they are not alone—they are one of many.

The twentieth century urbanized the rural folksong and provided a multiplicity of issues and events to protest. In the 1920s labor union songs urged workers to struggle for better wages and working conditions. When the Depression hit after the stock market crash of 1929, Americans had plenty to protest. By 1934 one out of every six Americans was seeking government help. The drought of 1936 and 1937 created the Dust Bowl and forced thousands of midwest farming families to head west in hopes of finding work. The nonviolent civil rights movement used songs as a motivator of the people, and blacks and whites sang as they marched side by side. The divisiveness of the conflict in Vietnam prompted a multitude of antiwar songs.

In this teaching strategy students will discuss and analyze five twentieth-century protest songs. "Beans, Bacon, and Gravy," was a response to the Great Depression. "We Shall Overcome" was the unofficial theme song of the civil rights movement. Buffy Sainte-Marie's "Now That the Buffalo's Gone" brought attention to the continuing problem of the government's taking of Indian lands. "Where Have All the Flowers Gone?" was popular during the war in Vietnam. And finally, "Liberation, Now!" was the theme song of the women's feminist movement of the 1970s. Students will identify the events or movements associated with each song, and they will write a song or poem that protests a current issue about which they feel strongly.

MATERIALS

Copies of the five songs

SUGGESTED PROCEDURE

1. Explain to students that one way of expressing disagreement or unhappiness with an issue is through a protest song. Ask students if they are familiar with any protest songs. Ask if there are any current issues or events with which students disagree or about which they are unhappy.
2. Organize the class into groups of four, and distribute the five protest songs. Have group members work together to read and discuss the songs. Write the following questions on the chalkboard and have the groups answer the questions. Explain that every question can be applied to each song, so the groups should end up with five answers to each question. A recorder from each group should write the group's answers on a sheet of paper.
   a. What issue or event is this song protesting? How can you tell?
   b. How does the songwriter use repetition and rhyme?
   c. Summarize in two or three sentences the song's message.
3. After the groups have answered the questions, discuss the questions and answers as a class.
4. Ask students to work in their groups again. Now they will write a poem or a song protesting a current issue or event about which the group feels strongly. Group members will have to agree on an event or an issue. Encourage students to study the formats of the protest songs to pick up ideas for their own songs or poems. Have volunteers from each group read or sing their group's song or poem to the rest of the class.

Beans, Bacon, and Gravy

author unknown

1. I was born long ago
   In eighteen ninety four,
   And I've seen many a panic, I will own.
   I've been hungry, I've been cold,
   And now I'm growing old,
   But the worst I've seen is nineteen thirty-one.

   CHORUS
   Oh, those beans, bacon, and gravy,
   They almost drive me crazy.
   I eat them till I see them in my dreams
   (in my dreams).
   When I wake up in the morning
   And another day is dawning,
   Yes, I know I'll have another mess of beans.

2. We congregate each morning
   At the country barn at dawning,
   And everyone is happy, so it seems.
   But when our work is done,
   We file by one by one
   And thank the Lord for one more mess of beans.

3. We have Hooverized on butter,
   For milk we've only water,
   And I haven't seen a steak in many a day.
   As for pies, cakes, and jellies,
   We substitute sow bellies,
   For which we work the country road each day.

4. If there ever comes a time
   When I have more than a dime,
   They will have to put me under lock and key,
   For I've been broke so long
   I can only sing this song
   Of the workers and their misery.

We Shall Overcome

New words and new music arrangement by Zilphia Horton, Frank Hamilton, Guy
Carawan, and Pete Seeger

We shall overcome, we shall overcome,
    We shall overcome someday.
    Oh, deep in my heart, I do believe,
    We shall overcome someday.

We are not afraid, we are not afraid,
    We are not afraid today.
    Oh, deep in my heart, I do believe,
    We shall overcome someday.

We are not alone, we are not alone,
    We are not alone today.
    Oh, deep in my heart, I do believe,
    We are not alone today.

The truth will make us free, the truth will make us free,
    The truth will make us free someday.
    Oh, deep in my heart, I do believe,
    We shall overcome someday

We'll walk hand in hand, we'll walk hand in hand,
    We'll walk hand in hand someday.
    Oh, deep in my heart, I do believe,
    We shall overcome someday.

The Lord will see us through, the Lord will see us through,
    The Lord will see us through someday.
    Oh, deep in my heart, I do believe,
    We shall overcome someday.

Black and white together, black and white together,
    Black and white together now.
    Oh, deep in my heart, I do believe,
    We shall overcome someday.

We shall all be free, we shall all be free,
    We shall all be free someday.
    Oh, deep in my heart, I do believe,
    We shall overcome someday.

Now That the Buffalo's Gone

By Buffy Sainte-Marie

1. Can you remember the times
   That you have held your head high
   And told all your friends of your Indian claim,
   Proud, good lady, and proud, good man?
   Your great, great grandfather from Indian blood sprang
   And you feel in your heart for these ones.

2. Oh, it's written in books and in songs
   That we've been mistreated and wronged.
   Well, over and over I hear the same words
   From you good lady, and you, good man.
   Well, listen to me if you care where we stand,
   And you feel you're a part of these ones.

3. When a war between nations is lost,
   The loser we know pays the cost,
   But even when Germany fell to your hands,
   Consider, dear lady, consider dear man,
   You left them their pride and you left them their land,
   And what have you done to these ones?

4. Has a change come about Uncle Sam,
   Or are you still taking our lands?
   A treaty forever George Washington signed,
   He did, dear lady, he did, dear man,
   And the treaty's being broken by Kinzua Dam,
   And what will you do for these ones?

5. Oh, it's all in the past, you can say,
   But it's still going on here today.
   The government, now, wants the Iroquois land,
   That of the Seneca and the Cheyenne.
   It's here and it's now you must help us, dear man,
   Now that the buffalo's gone.

Where Have All the Flowers Gone?

By Pete Seeger; verses 4 and 5 by Joe Hickson

1. Where have all the flowers gone?
   Long time passing.
   Where have all the flowers gone?
   Long time ago.
   Where have all the flowers gone?
   The girls have picked them, ev'ry one.
   Oh, when will you ever learn?
   Oh, when will you ever learn?

2. Where have all the young girls gone?
   Long time passing.
   Where have all the young girls gone?
   Long time ago.
   Where have all the young girls gone?
   They've taken husbands, ev'ry one.
   Oh, when will you ever learn?
   Oh, when will you ever learn?

3. Where have all the young men gone?
   Long time passing.
   Where have all the young men gone?
   Long time ago.
   Where have all the young men gone?
   They're all in uniform.
   Oh, when will we ever learn?
   Oh, when will we ever learn?

4. Where have all the soldiers gone?
   Long time passing.
   Where have all the soldiers gone?
   Long time ago.
   Where have all the soldiers gone?
   They've gone to graveyards, ev'ry one.
   Oh, when will they ever learn?
   Oh, when will they ever learn?

5. Where have all the graveyards gone?
   Long time passing.
   Where have all the graveyards gone?
   Long time ago.
   Where have all the graveyards gone?
   They're covered with flowers, ev'ry one.
   Oh, when will they ever learn?
   Oh, when will they ever learn?

6. [*Repeat verse 1.*]

Liberation, Now!

Words by Betty Friedan and Jacquelyn Reinach;
music by Jacquelyn Reinach and Jo Rene

Liberation, now. Liberation, now.
We're breaking out of our cage of ruffles and rage.
Liberation, now. Liberation now.

Femininity, what's femininity?
Masculinity, what's masculinity?
It's humanity that we both share.

Liberation now, liberation now.
It's time to spell our own names,
We're people, not "dames,"
Liberation, now.

Opportunity, opportunity,
And equality, full equality,
Are the property of everyone.

Liberation now, liberation now.
We're more than mothers and wives
With second-hand lives,
Liberation now.

When a woman's free, when a woman's free,
Then a man is free, and the world is free
To make love not war.

Liberation, now, liberation now.
It's time for woman and man
To walk hand in hand,
Liberation now, liberation now!

TOPIC: Watergate and Executive Privilege
TIME: One class period
TIME PERIOD: During study of the Watergate affair

BACKGROUND

The Watergate scandal during the years 1972 to 1974 caused Americans to become disillusioned that a president could be involved in a massive criminal cover-up. More importantly, the scandal caused a constitutional tug of war between the executive branch and the judicial branch. The separation of powers set forth in the Constitution was being threatened. The Supreme Court's decision in 1974 that executive privilege is limited was crucial in preserving a balance and a separation of powers of our federal government.

In this teaching strategy students will read and discuss a case study of *United States v. Nixon*. They will understand the concepts of absolute and limited executive power, and they will discover how the Supreme Court goes about weighing information when it makes a decision. Students will gain an appreciation of how the separation of powers in the Constitution protects the national interest of the people. (For more case studies such as this one, see *The Constitution: Past, Present, and Future*.)

MATERIALS

Copies of the case study *United States v. Nixon*

SUGGESTED PROCEDURE

1. Organize the class into groups of five. Distribute the case studies to the groups and have group members take turns reading aloud the first section, "What Was This Case About." While students are reading the first section of the case study, write the following questions on the chalkboard (the answers in parentheses are for your convenience):
   a. What was the conflict between the president and the judicial branch? (The judicial branch asked Nixon to turn over some tapes, but Nixon refused.)
   b. From what you have read, what do you think is the nature of executive privilege? (Possible answer: an understood power of the president to refuse to disclose information)
   c. What were President Nixon's two arguments for refusing to turn over the tapes? (If the branches are totally independent, then the president does not have to obey court orders to release evidence; presidential communications with advisers need to be confidential.) Do you agree with his arguments?
2. Have the groups discuss and write answers to the three questions. Then tell them to take turns reading aloud the second and third sections of the case study. While students are reading, write the following questions on the chalkboard:
   a. How did the Supreme Court rule in this case? (that Nixon had to turn over the tapes)
   b. How did the chief justice respond to Nixon's two arguments? (He rejected the first argument, saying that if the president did not turn over the evidence, then the courts could not do their job; he said that the second argument had merit, but that the need for confidentiality would have to be judged on a case-by-case basis.)
   c. What did the chief justice think was the need that was competing with confidentiality? (finding the truth in a criminal court case)
   d. Why did this need outweigh President Nixon's request for confidentiality? (If the courts did not have the evidence, they could not do their duty; the tapes did not contain diplomatic or military secrets.)
3. Have the groups discuss and write answers to the four questions. Then have them take turns reading aloud the last section. While students are reading, write the following questions on the chalkboard:
   a. Which branch of government has enforcement power? (the executive branch) Which branch is the final judge on the meaning of the Constitution? (the judicial branch)
   b. What would happen if a president defied the courts? (then the president would be the final judge of his or her own actions and decisions)

c. What two principles did the Supreme Court put forth? (The need for confidentiality must be weighed against other needs, such as the needs of the criminal justice system; the weighing will be done by the federal courts.)

4. As a class, discuss the groups' answers to the questions. Ask students: Do you agree or disagree with the Supreme Court's decision? Then ask: Under what circumstances do you think the president should be allowed to ask for executive privilege?

UNITED STATES V. NIXON (1974)

WHAT WAS THIS CASE ABOUT?

The story. It was late at night on June 17, 1972. In most of the nation's capital people were sleeping. In the Watergate Hotel five burglars were breaking into the headquarters of the Democratic National Committee. Their criminal mission was to photograph the Democratic party's plans for the upcoming presidential campaign and to install "bugs" for listening in on the Democratic party's telephone conversations. The burglars were caught in the act. One of them turned out to be an employee of President Richard Nixon's campaign organization, called the Committee to Re-elect the President. Investigation showed that two other Republican campaign officials were also involved.

When the president denied that anyone at the White House had known about the burglary, most people believed him. After his reelection, however, investigators uncovered additional information. Important members of the Nixon administration *had* known about the burglary after all. In a massive cover-up, they had even destroyed evidence! Most shocking of all, the president's lawyer, John Dean, testified before the Senate that the president had helped plan the cover-up from the beginning.

Could this be true? When Nixon denied it, investigators were stumped. But then another witness revealed that Nixon had secretly tape-recorded every conversation that had ever taken place in his office. The tapes would show whether or not Nixon was telling the truth.

By April 1974 criminal charges had been filed against seven members of the Nixon administration. Although Nixon was not charged, he was listed in the case as one of the people involved in the conspiracy. The special prosecutor in charge of the case at the time, Leon Jaworski, asked Nixon to let him hear the tapes. Nixon had already ordered a previous special prosecutor fired for asking the same thing, and to no one's surpise, Nixon refused again. Jaworski, however,

persisted. He asked the federal district court for help. When the judge ordered Nixon to release the tapes to the court for secret examination, Nixon disobeyed.

Refusing the special prosecutor's request caused a scandal, but disobeying the judge's order caused much more than a scandal. It caused a constitutional crisis—a tug of war between the two branches of government. Could a president defy a federal judge?

Nixon claimed that he could. As president, he said, he had an executive privilege of keeping presidential communications confidential. He also said that the privilege was absolute, which meant that nobody could override it for any reason. Because of the urgency of the case, the United States Supreme Court agreed to skip over the Court of Appeals in order to settle the case right away.

The question. Does the Constitution give the president an absolute executive privilege?

The issues. President Nixon gave two arguments for his position. His first argument was that the principle of separation of powers requires that the executive and judicial branches be totally independent of each other. If presidents had to obey judges who ordered them to release evidence, this independence would be destroyed.

His second argument was that the secrecy of communications between a president and his advisers is necessary for the president to be able to look after the public good. Nixon said that if a president's advisers knew that anything they said could be repeated to the public, they might worry too much about what people would think, and they would not give him good advice. Nixon said that if a president did not receive good advice, it would be harder for him or her to carry out the presidency as spelled out in the Constitution.

HOW WAS THE CASE DECIDED?

In a decision written by Chief Justice Warren Burger, the Court ruled that executive privilege is not absolute and that Nixon had to turn over the tapes as he had been ordered.

WHAT DID THE COURT SAY ABOUT GOVERNMENTAL POWERS?

The Court examined each of the president's two arguments in turn. One, you remember, was that preservation of the separation of powers requires the executive and judicial branches to be totally independent. Total independence means that the president does not have to obey court orders to release evidence. The chief justice rejected this claim. The Constitution is based on separation of powers, but under this separation it gives each power or branch a job of its own to do. If the president could withhold evidence from the courts, the courts could not do the job the Constitution gave them. "The powers," concluded the chief justice, "were not intended to operate with absolute independence."

Nixon's second argument was that communications between the president and his advisers need to be confidential for the sake of the public good. Chief Justice Burger admitted that sometimes confidentiality, or secretiveness, is important. But it only applies in specific instances. When communications are about diplomatic or military secrets, confidentiality is of the utmost importance. On the other hand, when communications concern other subjects, confidentiality might not be important at all. The chief justice concluded that in presidential claims of executive privilege, the need for confidentiality must be balanced against competing needs on a case-by-case basis.

Now, how does this idea help settle the case at hand? With what other need or needs did confidentiality compete in *United States v. Nixon?* It competed with the need to find out the truth in a criminal trial. The purpose of criminal justice, said Chief Justice Burger, "is that guilt shall not escape or innocence suffer." But finding out the truth in a criminal trial requires that courts have all the evidence they need, even if it includes presidential communications. In this case the courts needed the information on the tapes to carry out their duty. When the need to find out the truth in the Watergate trial was weighed against President Nixon's need for confidentiality, confidentiality lost. Confidentiality might have won had the tapes been about diplomatic or military secrets or had they not contained crucial evidence. Moreover, the district court had not even planned to make the complete tapes public. Only the parts that were necessary for the trial would be used in open court.

WHAT IMPLICATIONS DOES THIS CASE HAVE FOR THE FUTURE?

If the president had defied the Supreme Court as he had defied the district court, it would have been an important sign for the future. One reason is that the courts have no enforcement powers of their own. They depend on the executive branch to enforce their orders. If the executive branch defies a court order, the courts have no recourse. Another reason is that successful defiance of the Supreme Court would call the entire area of judicial review into question. The judicial branch is the final judge of the meaning of the Constitution. Defiance by the president would be like saying that the executive branch is its own final judge.

Nixon did not defy the Supreme Court. He obeyed, not out of respect for judicial review, but out of self-interest. He feared that unless he gave in, the Senate would remove him from office. Even so, the evidence of the tapes turned out to be so damaging that Nixon thought he had to resign or the House would start impeachment proceedings. The tapes showed that he had been part of the cover-up.

What principles emerge from this case? The Court did not say whether or not such as thing as executive privilege exists. It clearly stated, however, that there is no such thing as an *absolute* executive privilege. Executive privilege is limited. The Court put forth the following principles:

• The president's need for confidentiality must be weighed against competing needs, such as the needs of the criminal justice system.

• In disputed cases this weighing must be done by the federal courts.

Conflicts over executive privilege will probably continue to arise. Presidents have claimed executive privilege over 50 times just since 1952. In most of these cases they claimed the privilege in order to avoid giving Congress information it had requested. So long as the two principles listed above are accepted by all parties, these conflicts have much less chance of hurting the nation. The final decision is made by the judicial branch.

TOPIC: Community Awareness
TIME: Two class periods, with homework
TIME PERIOD: During study of current issues

BACKGROUND

Within a few years students will be voting, working, attending colleges and vocational schools, and living in a community. With all of the problems that students experience or hear about, including drugs, crime, homelessness, poverty, and unemployment, it is important to instill in students a sense of community awareness and pride. Many neighborhoods are fighting back against crime, drugs, and decay. In order for students to become involved in helping their communities, they must first know their communities. In this teaching strategy students will work in groups to complete a community survey. They will discover what kinds of services are offered by their town or city. Students will have the opportunity to talk with members of the community. They will learn about the history, politics, and economics of their community. If students live in a large city, you will need to use your own discretion in limiting the activity in some way. For example, you could limit the survey area to a five-mile radius around the school. Whether students live in a rural town or an inner-city neighborhood, they will benefit from becoming knowledgeable about their own communities.

MATERIALS

Copies of the "Community Awareness" surveys. Separate the sections after you copy them.

SUGGESTED PROCEDURE

1. Ask students to define the following words: *town, city, neighborhood,* and *community.* Ask students how they would classify the area in which they live and go to school.

2. Explain to students that they will be working in groups to complete a community survey. After the groups have completed their research, they will report back to the class. In this way students will become familiar with all aspects of their community. Organize the class into six groups. Assign to each group one of the survey topics: Politics, Parks and Recreation, Transportation and Planning, Services, Business, and Education. Have the groups look over the survey sheets. Tell them that they will have one week to answer the questions on the survey. They will be expected to use after-school hours to complete their investigations. Allow the groups the rest of the class period to divide up jobs and to decide the best way in which to go about obtaining the information for the questions.

3. On the day of the presentations, allow each group five minutes to present their information. Encourage the rest of the class to take notes. After all groups have made their presentations, discuss with the class any ideas they might have about improving their communities. Have them suggest ways in which they could become involved in helping their communities.

Community Awareness: Politics

Directions: Your group is responsible for finding the answers to the following questions about your community. Resources you will find helpful include the telephone book, the public library, and the League of Women Voters. Make telephone calls. Talk to people.

1. Who is your mayor? Where is his or her office located? How many people are employed by the mayor's office? When will the next mayoral election take place?

2. Is there a city council or some type of governing board for your community? How many people are on it? When and where do they meet? Are members elected or appointed? Do members receive a salary? If possible, attend a meeting and take notes on what occurs.

3. How many registered voters are there in your town or city? How many people voted in the last local election? When is the next local election?

4. Is there a particular issue about which citizens in your community are most concerned?

5. Who are your representatives to the United States House of Representatives?

Community Awareness: Parks and Recreation

Directions: Your group is responsible for finding the answers to the following questions about your community. Resources you will find helpful include the telephone book, the Parks and Recreation Department, and the public library. Make telephone calls. Talk to people. Visit your community's parks and recreation facilities.

1. How many public parks are there in your town, city, or community? Who uses the parks? What other kinds of recreation facilities does your town or city offer? Are there baseball diamonds? soccer fields? swimming pools? basketball courts?

2. Are there any community centers? Where are they? What services do they offer?

3. Where is the public library? Are there any other branches? Where are they? What are the library hours? How can a person obtain a library card?

4. Does your town, city, or community put on any annual festivals, races, or parades? For what reasons? Where and when do the events take place?

5. Is there a theater where residents can go to see plays or to hear musical events? Where is it? Is anything being performed there now?

6. What kind of services does your community provide for senior citizens?

Community Awareness: Transportation and Planning

Directions: Your group is responsible for finding the answers to the following questions about your community. Resources you will find helpful include the telephone book, the Transportation Department, and the public library. Make telephone calls. Talk to people.

1. Does your town or city have public transportation? What kind? How much does it cost? Does it offer a lower rate to senior citizens? How often does it run? Where does it run?

2. Take a poll among 10 of your neighbors. How many of them drive to work? How many ride the bus or other public transportation? How many walk or ride a bicycle? How far does each person travel to his or her job?

3. Is there a traffic problem in your community? Between what hours is traffic the heaviest? If there is a traffic problem, what can be done to solve it?

4. Are the neighborhood streets safe for children and pets?

5. Are the streets of your town or city laid out in an organized manner? Are streets organized by name or number? Could a visitor to your community easily find his or her way around?

6. Draw a map of your town or city's downtown area. Label the streets. Does the downtown area use traffic lights or stop signs to direct traffic? Is parking a problem in the downtown area?

Community Awareness: Services

Directions: Your group is responsible for finding the answers to the following questions about your community. Resources you will find helpful include the telephone book, the police and fire departments, the water and waste collection departments, and the public library. Make telephone calls. Talk to people.

1. Does your community provide a garbage-collection service? Where do the garbage-collection trucks take the refuse? How close to capacity is the dump or collection point? How is the refuse treated?

2. What is your community's source of water? How much water does an average resident use per day? What happens to the water you use in your home? Who monitors the water quality in your community?

3. Does your community have a recycling program? Does it provide a curb-side pickup? What items does the program recycle? Is there a place in your community where you can take aluminum cans? How much money is a pound of aluminum worth today?

4. How many police officers does your community have? How many firefighters? How many police and fire stations are in your community? Are most people in your community satisfied with the number of police and fire personnel?

5. Is pollution a problem in your community? Who monitors air pollution?

6. Are there community hospitals in your area? How many?

Community Awareness: Business

Directions: Your group is responsible for finding the answers to the following questions about your community. Resources you will find helpful include the telephone book, businesspeople, shopowners, and the public library. Make telephone calls. Talk to people.

1. What are the biggest businesses in your community? What kinds of businesses are they? How many people do they employ?

2. Are there any shopping malls in your community?

3. Are there many small businesses or shops in your community? What kinds of goods and services do they offer?

4. How many banks or financial institutions are there in your community?

5. How many supermarkets are there in your community? how many neighborhood grocery stores?

6. How many movie theaters are there in your community? video stores? pizza parlors? fast-food restaurants?

7. How many newspapers does your community offer? how many local television stations?

Community Awareness: Education

Directions: Your group is responsible for finding the answers to the following questions about your community. Resources you will find helpful include the telephone book, your school's district office, and the public library. Make telephone calls. Talk to people.

1. How many students attend your school? How many teachers work at your school? What is the attendence rate for students?

2. How many schools are there in your school district? Is there more than one school district serving your town or city? What is the dropout rate of your school district's high school students? Is it more or less than last year?

3. How many members are on the school board for your school district? Where and how often do they meet? If possible, attend a school-board meeting and take notes on what occurs.

4. Are there any community colleges in your area? How old do you have to be to attend a community college? What are the requirements for attending a community college?

5. Are there any four-year colleges or universities in your area? If so, how many students are enrolled?

6. Are night courses offered anywhere in your community? Is so, where? What kinds of classes are offered?